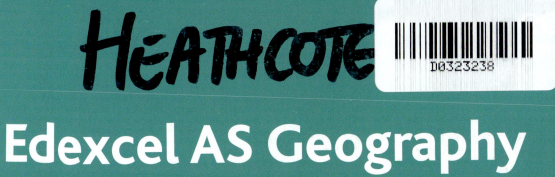

g learning, changing lives

Edexcel AS Geography

Peter Byrne   Viv Pointon   Steph Warren   Nigel Yates

STUDENT BOOK

We are grateful to the following for permission to reproduce copyright material:

Barcelona Field Studies Centre for the figure "Longshore Drift" published on http://geographyfieldwork.com/LongshoreDrift.htm, reproduced with permission; The BBC for an extract from London Olympics 'could make profit' www.news.bbc.co.uk 1 November 2002 copyright © The BBC; Boeing Management Company for the figure "Capacity Growth Within Regions" representing growth in air passenger numbers from 2006 to 2026 from Boeing Current Market Outlook 2007 www.boeing.com copyright © Boeing Management Company; Climatic Research Unit for a figure from the paper "Hemispheric and large-scale surface air temperature variations: An extensive revision and an update to 2001". J.Climate 16, 206-223 by P.D. Jones and A. Moberg, 2003 by European Environment Agency, reproduced with permission; Cohn and Wolfe for a map adapted from "The wealthy as a proportion of the total population" copyright © Cohn and Wolfe; Communities and Local Government for the figure and data "The Index of Multiple Deprivation data for Benwell in Newcastle's West End (2007)" http://www.imd.communities.gov.uk © Crown copyright 2007; Department for Environment Food and Rural Affairs for the figure "The Combined Densities Map: Sparsity" from The New Definition of Rural Areas of England and Wales and its Application to the 2001 Census www.statistics.gov.uk © Crown Copyright 2001; Department of Tourism and Commerce Marketing for an adapted map of Dubai, www.dubaitourism.ae reproduced with permission; EM-DAT for the graphs "The number of natural disasters reported, 1900–2006"; "The frequency of the major types of natural hazard reported over the twentieth century"; "The diminishing reported death toll due to natural hazards, 1900–2006"; and "The estimated costs (in $US billions) of damage due to natural hazards, 1900–2006", reproduced with permission of EM-DAT: The OFDA/CRED International Disaster Database – www.emdat.be, Université Catholique de Louvain, Brussels (Belgium); Environment Agency for the figure "1953 Surge Levels" published on http://www.environment-agency.gov.uk copyright © Environment Agency. All Rights reserved; Eurostat for data from "The Social Situation in the European Union 2004" copyright © Eurostat; Floridians for a Sustainable Population, Inc for the figure "Florida Population 1950-2030" published on www.flsuspop.org, reproduced with permission; The Free Press, a Division of Simon & Schuster Adult Publishing Group for 2 figures adapted from Marketing Places: Attracting Investment, Industry, and Tourism to Cities, States and Nations by Philip Kotler, Donald H Haider, and Irving Rein copyright © 1993 by Philip Kotler, Donald H Haider, Irving Rein. All rights reserved; Government Office for London for the map 'Index of Deprivation' from the Borough of Hackney 2004, Crown copyright 2004; Greater London Authority for extracts from The London Plan, Spatial Development Strategy for Greater London, Consolidated with Alterations since 2004, issued February 2008 reproduced with permission; Guardian News & Media Ltd for extracts adapted from "Lots of chic as well as lots of sheep is new message from Lakes tourist bosses" by Terry Macalister and Nigel Burnham published in The Guardian 14 May 2007; "Welcome to Katine" by Sarah Boseley published in The Guardian 20 October 2007 and "North–south divide widens in health map of England" by John Carvel published in The Guardian 23 October 2007 copyright © Guardian 2007; HM Revenue & Customs for table 3.13 "East Midlands taxpayers mean and median" © Crown copyright 2008; HM Treasury for the figure "Falling Transport and Communication Costs 1930-2000" www.hm-treasury.gov.uk © Crown copyright 2000; Hodder Education for an extract and figure from Introducing Social Geographies by Rachel Pain et al copyright © 2001 Rachel Pain, Michael Barke, Duncan Fuller, Jamie Gough, Robert MacFarlene & Graham Mowl reproduced by permission of Edward Arnold (Publishers) Ltd; Hodder & Stoughton Ltd for the figure "The Demographic Transition Model" from Tomorrow's Geography for Edexcel GCSE: Revision Guide: Specification A by Steph Warren and Mike Harcourt copyright © 2003. Reproduced by permission of Hodder & Stoughton Ltd; The Home Office for the graphs "Where the post-accession migrants settled in the UK" and "Where the post-accession migrants came from" 2006, www.homeoffice.gov.uk © Crown copyright 2008; Intergovernmental Panel on Climate Change for a map from page 11, a table from page 8, a figure from page 5 and text extracts from "Climate Change 2007: The Physical Science Basis", contribution of WG1 to the Fourth Assessment Report of the IPCC, www.ipcc.ch copyright © IPCC, reproduced with permission; John Wiley & Sons Limited for a table from "International retirement migration in Europe" by Russell King, Anthony M. Warnes, Allan M. Williams; and 2 tables from "European retirees on the Costa del Sol: A cross-national comparison" by Vicente Rodríguez, Gloria Fernández-Mayoralas, Fermina Rojo both published in International Journal of Population Geography Vol 4, Issue 2, June 1998 copyright © 1998 John Wiley & Sons Limited. Reproduced with permission; The Jurassic Coast Trust for a map of the Jurassic Coast copyright © Jurassic Coast, World Heritage Site, reproduced with permission; Manila Observatory & Department of Environment and Natural Resources, Philippines for the figures "Combined Risk to Climate Disasters" source: Joint Typhoon Warning Center (Typhoon Data), The Intergovernmental Panel on Climate Change Data Distribution Centre (Rainfall Data), Hadley Centre for Climate Prediction and Research (Projected Rainfall Data), Australia's Commonwealth and Scientific Research Organization (Projected Temperature Data), National Statistics Office (Population Density 2000), UNDP (Human Development Index 2000) and -NAMRIA (Base Map); and "Combined Risk to Geophysical Disasters" source: The Philippine Institute of Volcanology and Seismology (PHIVOLCS) National Geophysical Data Center (Earthquake Data), Environmental and Natural Resources ATLAS of the Philippines, Center of the Philippines Foundation (ECPF), 1998; 2003, Philippine Statistical Yearbook (Population Density 2000), UNDP (Human Development Index 2000) and NAMRIA (Base Map) from the Sectoral Paper Climate/Weather-Related and Geophysical Risk http://www.observatory.ph/, copyright © Manila Observatory & Department of Environment and Natural Resources, Philippines; McDonalds for text, figures and diagrams about McDonalds, reproduced with permission; The Met Office for the Synoptic Chart for 1 October 2004 © Crown Copyright 2004 and figure 'Characteristics of the six main types of air mass' © Crown Copyright 2007, reproduced with permission of the Met Office; Migration Policy Institute (MPI) and Rainer Muenz for the map "foreign-born populations" by Rainer Muenz published on www.migrationinformation.org, originally published by Migration Information Source, www.migrationinformation.org, the online journal of the Migration Policy Institute, June 2006, reproduced with permission; Donnie Morrison, Work Global for an extract from www.connectedcommunities.co.uk copyright © Work Global, Outer Hebrides; The National Bureau of Statistics of the People's Republic of China for the data "Consumer durable ownership in China 1990–2002" quoted from the web site of the National Bureau of Statistics of the People's Republic of China www.stats.gov.cn; National Centre for Health Outcomes Development for the table "Percentage employment by social class 2001" www.nchod.nhs.uk © Crown copyright 2001; Natural Resources Canada for the figure "Effects of climate change on forests and forestry" http://adaptation.nrcan.gc.ca/posters/on/on_07_e.php reproduced with the permission of Natural Resources Canada 2008, courtesy of the Earth Sciences Sector; National Statistics for the figures "Social class of residents of Hackney Borough and Penwith District in Cornwall, compared with England overall" and "The population structure of Cornwall" based upon the 2001 Census in England and Wales; "Attainment of five or more GCSE grades A* to C: by parental NS-SEC, 2002, England & Wales" from Education Exam results differ by social status, 2004; "Percentage of households with consumer durables: Great Britain, 1972 to 2002" from A summary of changes over time; "Age distribution of the UK population over 50"; "Older people in the UK in 2002 who live alone, in selected age groups"; "London's age distribution in 2005 compared with the UK as a whole" "Long term unemployment and health services in South West Cornwall, 2006" adapted from the National Statistics thematic mapper; the table "House price and household income ratios by UK region in 2005" and data adapted from Long term unemployment and health services in south west Cornwall, 2006 and Population pyramids for Reading, Christchurch (Dorset), East Lindsey and Cornwall and the Isles of Scilly, www.statistics.gov.uk © Crown copyright 2008; NOAA/National Weather Service for the figures "Integrating Research and Education: Hurricane Katrina", "Map of perceived temperatures in Europe on 8 August 2003", "Victims of the hot summer of 2003 in Europe" and "The pathway predictions for Hurricane Floyd" published on www.nhc.noaa.gov and www.cpc.ncep.noaa.gov; Nova/WGBH Educational Foundation for the figure 'The locations of the world's volcanoes' copyright © 2002 WGBH/Boston; Stephen B. Olsen Director Coastal Resources Center for the figure "Operating the process of Integrated Coastal Zone Management" from Coastal Management Report #2211. University of Rhode Island by Olsen, Lowry & Tobey, 1989; The Open University for the figure "There are many forms of renewable energy, both above and below the surface of the earth" published on www.openlearn.open.ac.uk, reproduced with permission; Pearson Education Ltd for the figure "Cliff morphology and geological structure" from Geomorphology and Hydrology by Small, Price & Taylor copyright © Pearson Education 1989; The Pew Center on Global Climate Change for the figure "The increasing frequency of North Atlantic tropical storms" published on www.pewclimate.org/global-warming-basics/facts_and_figures/impacts/storms.cfm, reproduced with permission; The Policy Press for figure 4 'Households living in poverty in 2001' from People and places: A 2001 Census Atlas of the UK by Daniel Dorling and Bethan Thomas, 2004 copyright © The Policy Press, reproduced with permission of The Policy Press; The authors at Red Door Associates for an extract about 'Sociograms' adapted from Open Hearts, Open Minds – A Social inclusion Self-Assessment Handbook. The handbook is full of resources and exercises for people who want to learn more about supporting members of the public who face different forms of disadvantage and exclusion in society. Printed copies can be obtained from its publishers Exeter Community Initiatives on +44 (0)1392 205800 and downloads can be found at www.openheartsopenminds.org.uk/products.php. Reproduced with permission; Risk Management Solutions for the figure "Hurricane Katrina: Profile of a Super Cat" published on www.rms.com, reproduced with permission; David Ross, Britain Express for the figure "Thomas Hardy's Dorset" published on www.britainexpress.com, reproduced with permission; South East Coastal Group for a figure from South East Coastal Annual Report 2004, reproduced with permission; South West Observatory for the map "Index of Multiple Deprivation 2004 by Super Output Area – National Quartiles" with the permission of Ordnance Survey on behalf of the Controller of Her Majesty's Stationery Office © Crown Copyright; Steve Smith for an extract about Detroit published on www.buildingsrus.co.uk, reproduced with permission; Stroud Community Agriculture for an extract about Stroud Community Agriculture published on http ://transitiontowns.org/Stroud/Food, reproduced with permission; Sustain: the alliance for better food and farming for a figure and extract from www.sustainweb.org, reproduced with permission; Taylor & Francis for the figure "The Dutch Polders" from Fundamentals of Physical Geography by David Briggs and Pete Smithson copyright © 1985. Reproduced by permission of Taylor & Francis Books UK; UK Parliament for the table "Numbers of students (under 21) enrolled on full-time higher education courses 1987-2006" www.parliament.uk © Parliamentary copyright 2006; United Nations Department of Economic and Social Affairs for the figure "Global urbanisation percentages 2000, 2030" by United Nations Department of Economic and Social Affairs, Population Division; United Nations Environment Programme/GRID-Arendal for the figure "The costs of weather-related extreme events" cartographer Emmanuelle Bournay, UNEP/GRID-Arendal published on http://maps.grida.no/go/graphic/global_costs_of_extreme_weather_events Munich Re, 2004, reproduced with permission; United Nations Framework Convention on Climate Change for the figure "Change in GHG emissions/removals from 1990 to 2005 %" from Emissions Summary for United Kingdom of Great Britain and Northern Ireland published on http://unfccc.int; University of Strathclyde for the figure "The location of the proposed Severn barrage" copyright © Strathclyde University, reproduced with permission; The U.S. Census Bureau for the Population pyramid for the United Kingdom in 2000 and map and facts of Detroit published on www.census.gov; The Wikipedia Foundation for extracts concerning New Orleans Levee System and Detroit Population; World Bank for the figures "High Mortality Risk hotspots in relation to the different types of natural hazards" and "High Total Economic Loss hotspots in relation to the different types of natural hazards" published in Natural Disaster Hotspots: A Global Risk Analysis by Dilley copyright © World Bank; and Worldmapper Team for the map "People living in absolute poverty" copyright © 2006 SASI Group (University of Sheffield) and Mark Newman (University of Michigan) http://www.worldmapper.org.

In some instances we have been unable to trace the owners of copyright material and we would appreciate any information that would enable us to do so.

CONTENTS

Unit 1 Global challenges

Unit 2 Geographical investigations

ABOUT THIS BOOK

Written by a team of experts, including experienced examiners and teachers, this Edexcel AS Geography Student Book and CD-ROM provides all of the content, tools and exam guidance you need to study for Edexcel's Advanced Subsidiary GCE in Geography.

Divided into two units – Global Challenges and Global Investigations – the Student Book contains a number of features that are designed to help your learning and exam preparation.

The Student Book

Learning objectives

At the beginning of each chapter, these provide a clear overview of what you need to learn in the chapter.

> **Learning objectives**
>
> After studying this chapter, you will be able to discuss these ideas and concepts and provide located examples of them:
> * The definitions of inequality and poverty at different scales and in contrasting areas.
> * The social and economic causes of inequalities and the processes that lead to uneven levels of environmental quality, social opportunity, wealth and the quality of life.
> * The spatial impact of varying opportunity which means that some areas thrive while others struggle and may decline.

Key terms

At the beginning of each chapter, these list the important terms and concepts that are explored in the chapter. Some key terms are defined in margin boxes when they first appear in the text.

> **Key terms**
>
> Drought
> Forecast
> Hard engineering
> Management
> Prediction
> Soft engineering

Case study

Real-life case studies feature throughout the Student Book, allowing you to apply the theory to actual events. Compulsory case studies are highlighted with this icon **Compulsory case study**.

> **Case study: Hackney, inner London**
>
> Hackney was named the 'Worst place to live in the UK' on a Channel 4 programme in 2006. Here are ten facts about Hackney that may explain why:
> * It has a higher proportion of lone-parent households than London as a whole or England and Wales.
> * 28% of its households (housing 35% of the population) are described as 'overcrowded' – the third highest in England and Wales.
> * The number of schoolchildren receiving free school meals is three times the national average.
> * 40% of the residents are from non-white ethnic backgrounds, compared to 8% of the UK population.
> * Its employment rate is some 14% lower than the wider London rate and 19% lower than the national average (2006).
> * The area had the highest unemployment rate in England and Wales in 2001.
> * Higher than average numbers of the residents have a long-term illness or are permanently sick or disabled.
> * The number of people infected with HIV in the borough was five-and-a-half times the average for England in 2001.
> * The crime rate was 42 per 1,000 population in 2005–06 compared to a national figure of 26 per 1,000.
> * Education results are poor; only 51% of students achieved five or more A* to C grade GCSEs in 2006, although this had improved from 31% 4 years earlier.
>
> ▲ Figure 2: The location of, and main districts and railway stations in, the London Borough of Hackney.

Taking it further

Provides stretch and challenge content and activities for further study beyond the Student Book. Some of these are found on the page while others take you to your Student CD-ROM.

> **Taking it further**
>
> To learn more about the distribution of earthquakes read 'Shockingly unexpected' on your Student CD-ROM.

Examiners' tips

Benefit from reading top tips from the examiners for added exam success.

Fieldwork

Interesting fieldwork and research ideas for Unit 2.

Fieldwork

Aim:

To investigate ways of managing and responding to extreme weather events and show how some strategies are more acceptable than others to the general public.

1. Decide which extreme weather events pose a risk to your local environment.
2. Using local records from newspapers, try to calculate the frequency of these events and their recurrence intervals.
3. Examine ways in which these risks have been managed, by conducting interviews with the local authority and using the internet to look at risk-assessment research that they might have conducted.
4. Design and distribute a questionnaire to the public to examine whether there is awareness of both the risks and the policies in place to deal with them.

Risk assessment

This is a low-risk activity, although questionnaires involve some contact and not everyone is willing to answer questions. It is strongly advised that these be conducted by at least two students working together.

Health and safety

Make sure that a responsible adult knows where you are and when you are going to conduct your fieldwork.

Data presentation

A number of statistical tools can be used to assess the level of concern and awareness about potential threats, and also awareness about the policies in place to deal with them. It might also be possible to show differences in awareness according to age, length of time living in the area, geographic proximity to the 'risk' area and other socio-economic variables. These could be shown in tables or graphs.

Conclusion

It is probable that you'll find that awareness is very different from reality. In some cases risks might be exaggerated and in others, they may be underestimated. There will be significant variations according to length of residence.

Evaluation

Think about how you might extend your investigation by looking at other areas of higher (or lower) risk, and assess whether these areas show significant differences in public awareness of risk and in judgement of the management schemes in place.

Summary

Having studied this chapter you are now in a position to answer questions about the processes and principals involved in urban and rural rebranding. You will be able to recognise how these strategies differ in scale and in purpose, and you will be able to discuss these ideas and concepts and provide located examples of them:

- The strategies and people involved in the rebranding process.
- The variety of ways by which rural areas have been rebranded and how to research these ideas.
- The variety of ways by which urban areas have been rebranded and how to research these ideas.

Summary

An end-of-chapter summary reviews the main concepts and learning points.

Exam practice

At the end of each chapter or topic, practice what you've learnt with Edexcel exam-style questions.

Exam practice

Study the diagrams below which compare the impact of six major hazard types over a 30-year period.

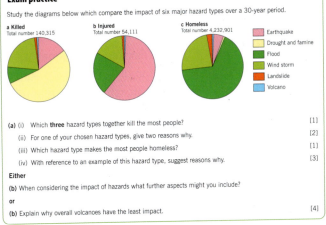

a Killed
Total number 140,315

b Injured
Total number 54,111

c Homeless
Total number 4,232,901

- Earthquake
- Drought and famine
- Flood
- Wind storm
- Landslide
- Volcano

(a) (i) Which **three** hazard types together kill the most people? [1]

(ii) For one of your chosen hazard types, give two reasons why. [2]

(iii) Which hazard type makes the most people homeless? [1]

(iv) With reference to an example of this hazard type, suggest reasons why. [3]

Either

(b) When considering the impact of hazards what further aspects might you include?

or

(b) Explain why overall volcanoes have the least impact. [4]

The CD-ROM

Study and revision skills Advice and guidance on how to get the most out of your study and revision to ensure exam success.

Geographical skills Advice on how to carry out fieldwork and research, and guidance on how to develop your statistical and graphical techniques.

MCQ Test your learning and monitor your progress with the interactive Multiple-Choice Question function. With any incorrect answers, you will be directed back to the relevant section of the Student Book for further revision.

Taking it Further Ideas for further study to challenge the concepts and ideas explored in the Student Book.

Glossary Full definitions of useful geographical terms and concepts.

CHAPTER 1 What are the main types of physical risk facing the world and how big a threat are they?

Key terms

Anthropogenic
Avalanche
Capacity
Chronic and context hazards
Convection current
Crust
Cyclone
Disaster
Drought
Earthquake
Flood
Geophysical hazard
Global warming
Greenhouse gas
Hydro-meteorological hazard
Kyoto Protocol
Lithosphere
Landslide
Lava
Low pressure system
Magma
Mantle
Natural hazard
Physical risk
Risk equation
Tectonic plate
Volcanoes
Vulnerability

Learning objectives

After studying this chapter, you will be able to discuss these ideas and concepts and provide located examples of them:
- Disasters result when hydro-meteorological hazards and geophysical hazards threaten the life and property of increasing numbers of the world's people.
- Examples of hydro-meteorological hazards include cyclones, droughts and floods, and examples of geophysical hazards include earthquakes, volcanoes, and landslides/avalanches.
- The risk of disaster grows as global hazards and people's vulnerability increases, while their capacity to cope decreases.
- The risk of disaster may be calculated using a 'disaster risk equation'.
- Global warming – arguably the greatest hazard we currently face – is a chronic hazard. It has widespread impacts, raises issues of injustice (polluters and vulnerable victims) and has complex solutions.

Physical risks can be defined as natural phenomena that threaten life or property. More commonly, physical risks are referred to as 'natural hazards'. There are many types of natural hazards, a number of which will be explored in this chapter. The devastating effect of natural hazards can be severe in the short term, with massive loss of life. There can also be longer-term effects on the economic and social fabric of communities, which can take many years, or even decades, to recover. Physical risks (natural hazards) can be broken into two broad categories: hydro-meteorological hazards and geophysical hazards.

▶ **Figure 1:** A cyclone, as seen from space. Notice the circulation of winds (as shown by the cloud patterns) around the centre or 'eye' of the cyclone.

Hydro-meteorological hazards

Hydro-meteorological hazards are defined as the natural hazards that are caused by water, the weather, or a combination of both. Cyclones, droughts and floods are examples of hydro-meteorological hazards.

Cyclones

The term 'cyclone' can be applied to any area of low atmospheric pressure that is created when air rises from the surface of the earth (Figure 2). As the air rises into the atmosphere, it is cooled and condensation occurs. This may result in the formation of clouds and eventually precipitation, both of which often characterise low pressure systems. As the rising air is relatively unstable (when compared to falling air that exists within high pressure systems), cyclones can also bring windy conditions and are often associated with storms. Tropical cyclones, also commonly known as hurricanes and typhoons, are fuelled and formed by warm ocean water. Temperate cyclones are formed when air of different characteristics converges and rises, drawn upwards by an accelerating jet-stream.

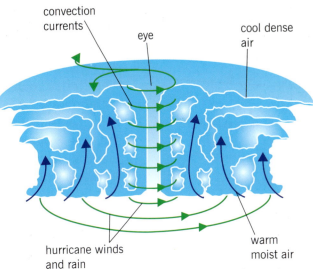

▲ **Figure 2:** Cross-section of a tropical cyclone (northern hemisphere).

The word 'cyclone' often conjures up images of violent storms, heavy rainfall and destructive winds. These violent cyclonic storms are the deep low pressure systems that can wreak havoc in coastal areas. The most intense cyclones are those that develop over the warm waters of the earth's tropics. Here, the warmth of the tropical ocean rapidly heats the air lying just above its surface. As the air rises into the atmosphere, condensation is rapid and cloud formation occurs quickly. The tropical cyclones that result from this process are often very large, and their behaviour can be extremely hard to predict. Tropical cyclones that begin life in the Atlantic Ocean are often referred to as 'hurricanes'. Those that begin in the Pacific Ocean are sometimes called 'typhoons' (by people who live in Asia) or 'cyclones' (by those who live nearer Australia).

Tropical cyclones can continue to grow in size and strength while they remain over a warm ocean. Usually, the point at which a cyclone crosses a coastline will be the point of greatest destruction. For those living in small island communities, such as those found throughout Polynesia in the Pacific Ocean, a tropical cyclone can spell potential devastation for an entire island. Once cyclones cross from sea to land, they tend to lose their strength rapidly, as they are no longer fed by the warmth and moisture of the oceans. Often, they end up as much less violent 'rain-bearing depressions', which can bring large amounts of much-needed rainfall to relatively dry inland areas.

You can explore these ideas further in Chapter 15.

Drought

A drought is an extended period of lower-than-average precipitation which causes water shortage. Droughts can extend for as little as one year, during which the rainfall that is received is noticeably lower than in average years. More often, however, a drought is a dry period that extends over two or more growing seasons or years. Droughts can be localised, occurring in relatively small regions (approximately the size of a country or state), or they can be much larger, affecting, at their worst, entire continents. Some parts of the world are more drought-prone than others, due to the variability of rainfall from one season to the next. This includes large parts of Northern Africa, Central Asia and most of Australia.

Reduced levels of rainfall in just one or two seasons can often be coped with because of the existing supplies of water that are held in storages such as rivers, lakes, dams and reservoirs. The careful rationing of water use will usually help a community manage its water needs until the rains come again. However, when surface water storages are not recharged and replenished for a number of consecutive seasons, the situation can become desperate. In these circumstances, all non-essential uses of water tend to be the first to be completely restricted (in the more developed parts of the world this might include watering gardens and washing cars). After this, the situation becomes extremely serious indeed, because it may no longer be possible to irrigate crops and water animals, as dwindling water supplies are prioritised for human use. At this point, the ability of a community to feed itself is placed under threat. Eventually, and in the worst case, a severely drought-affected community may not be able to meet its own water needs for purposes such as drinking and sanitation. This can lead to the rapid spread of both dehydration and disease, resulting in widespread death.

Case study: Drought in the Sahel, Africa

The effects of drought are also felt in the physical environment. A prolonged dry period can lead to the loss of the vegetation that usually holds soils in place. Soils are then exposed to the wind. If nutrient-rich topsoils are lost to the winds, the community's ability to recover from the drought (if and when the rains return) is also placed at risk. Severe erosion can occur and, in some circumstances, desertification of an area can result. In the Sahelian region, in western Africa, such drought is a recurring experience. One of the worst droughts in the Sahel lasted more than a decade, from 1972 to 1984. During this time, more than 100,000 people lost their lives and millions were dependent on food aid.

You can explore these ideas further by looking at the material in Chapters 15 to 18.

▲ **Figure 3:** The Sahel, in western Africa, experiences regular and persistent droughts.

Floods

A flood occurs when land that is usually dry becomes inundated. In most cases, floods occur after a prolonged period of rainfall, which causes water courses to burst their banks and overflow. Sometimes, floods occur because the systems that have been designed to cope with average levels of rainfall, such as stormwater drains and levee banks, simply fail to work properly because of a blockage or a structural weakness. Floods can even occur in regions that have experienced no recent rainfall themselves. This is especially true in regions that lie downstream of regions with heavy rainfall or vast amounts of meltwater.

Some areas are more prone to flooding than others. For example, the relatively low-lying nation of Bangladesh is regularly inundated by meltwaters that originate in the mountainous regions of its neighbours India and Nepal. The Egyptians, on the other hand, have seemingly mastered the annual flood of the Nile River and used it to their advantage for centuries. In fact, it could be argued that it was the flooding of this river that was actually the foundation for this great civilisation.

Case study: The flooding of New Orleans

▲ Figure 4: Large sections of New Orleans were flooded by Hurricane Katrina in August 2005.

Even in places where floods are regularly expected, the best planning and infrastructure can be challenged by nature. The city of New Orleans, in the southern United States, serves as an excellent example. Constructed in a virtual 'bowl', and lying at an average depth of 2 metres below sea level, New Orleans is completely dependent on its system of levees to keep out the waters that surround it – including Lake Pontchartrain, the Mississippi River, and the Gulf of Mexico. However, in late August 2005, the flood defences of the city were breached during the onslaught of Hurricane Katrina. The Category 5 hurricane proved to be too powerful for the levee system and simply overwhelmed it. In the remarkable days that followed, virtually half of the city was flooded. The death toll from the hurricane and its effects grew to more than 1,300, with at least 60,000 left homeless in its wake.

Geophysical hazards

Geophysical hazards are defined as the natural hazards caused by the physical processes that act upon, above, or within the earth. Earthquakes, volcanoes, and landslides and avalanches are examples of geophysical hazards.

Earthquakes

We experience earthquakes as a series of vibrations at the surface of the earth. These can vary from very slight vibrations or tremors which only the most sensitive earthquake-monitoring devices can detect, right through to catastrophic events that can level entire cities. Earthquakes are caused by movements of rock within the earth's lithosphere.

Key terms

Lithosphere: The 'crust' that comprises the thin, outer layer of the planet.

Much like the fragmented shell of a cracked hard-boiled egg, the crust of the earth is broken into segments or sections that are known as tectonic plates (Figure 5). The tectonic plates in effect 'float' on the layer of semi-molten rock, or mantle, that lies underneath them. Heat generated by the earth's core causes movements within the mantle, known as 'convection currents'. The tectonic plates respond to the movement of these convection currents and move with them. Most of this movement is imperceptible to humans, but, over time, it has resulted in the movement of whole continents, as first proposed in a theory known as 'continental drift'. As the tectonic plates move, they can collide, drift apart, or slide past each other. The force of the processes involved in this movement is responsible for the vibrations that we detect as earthquakes.

▼ Figure 5: The earth's tectonic plates and their direction of movement.

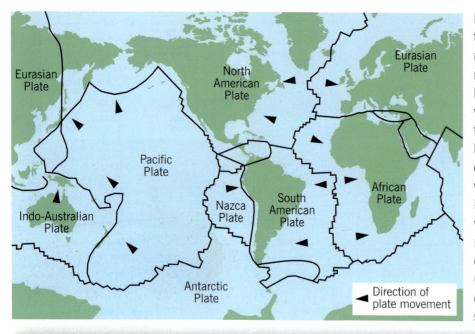

Most of the injuries and deaths that occur in an earthquake are a result of people being hit by falling roofs or being trapped in collapsed buildings. In the more developed world, and especially those parts that are prone to earthquakes, buildings may be designed and engineered to withstand the vibrations of an earthquake. Sadly, in less developed parts of the world, where buildings may be less rigidly constructed or made from cheaper, readily available materials (including mud, brick or stone), the death toll from earthquakes can be significantly higher.

Case study: Earthquake zones

Earthquakes are one of the few natural hazards that occur within particular zones. Most often, but not always, earthquakes occur within the most tectonically active areas of the earth – at the boundaries of the tectonic plates (Figure 6). In countries that are in close proximity to the plate boundaries, such as Japan, people grow accustomed to the almost regular, small-scale tremors of the earth. Large quakes are relatively rare, but people who live in earthquake-prone areas often practise procedures that are designed to keep them safe in the event of a major quake. This is especially true in Japan, where the government regularly conducts 'Disaster Preparedness Days'.

Taking it further

To learn more about the distribution of earthquakes read 'Shockingly unexpected' on your Student CD-ROM.

Volcanoes

A volcano is defined as an opening within the earth's crust, from which material from below the earth's surface is, or has been, ejected. The materials ejected from volcanoes can include magma (molten rock, which when exposed above ground is referred to as 'lava'), volcanic gases (such as hydrogen sulphide), ash and dust. An 'active' volcano is one which is in the process of erupting or showing signs that an eruption is imminent.

Like earthquakes, volcanoes are a result of tectonic activity, and just like earthquakes, they tend to be located in zones on plate boundaries (Figure 6). The chain of volcanoes that is located on the boundaries of the Pacific Ocean is known as the 'Rim of Fire', and represents one of the world's most tectonically active zones.

The rocks that are extruded from volcanoes tend to be rich in minerals and nutrients, and are highly sought after by miners and farmers alike. This in part explains why – throughout history – so many settlements have been built next to or near volcanoes. Even in this modern age, this trend continues. Around the Bay of Naples in Italy, 3 million people live within a 20 km radius of Vesuvius, one of Europe's most notorious volcanoes. It is also important to bear in mind that lava flows actually help to create new land. The small island of Iceland, in the Northern Atlantic, was created by volcanic activity, and continues to grow in size as the years pass. Today, Iceland is home to almost 300,000 people, who live alongside the island's volcanoes.

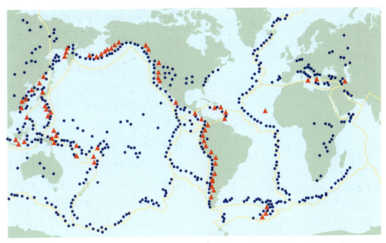

▲ **Figure 6:** The locations of the world's volcanoes (red triangles) and major earthquakes (blue dots). Plate boundaries are shown in yellow.

Case study: Other types of volcano

Volcanoes tend to be difficult to categorise – and difficult to predict. Some volcanoes are said to be 'dormant', which is often equated to 'sleeping'. Dormant volcanoes are not expected to erupt any time soon, though that is not to say that they can't burst into life at any moment. There are other volcanoes that are not expected to erupt again, and these are referred to as being 'extinct'. The Fourpeaked Volcano, in Alaska, which was thought to be extinct, suddenly came back to life on 17 September 2006. Vesuvius had long been thought of as extinct because it had not erupted for centuries when, in AD 79, it suddenly erupted, burying the town of Pompeii.

▲ **Figure 7:** Pompeii today, showing the close proximity of the ancient city to the infamous Mount Vesuvius.

Landslides and avalanches

A landslide is exactly what it sounds like – the sliding of a large amount of rock or soil down a slope, under the force of gravity. An 'avalanche' usually refers to a sudden downward movement of snow or ice in mountainous regions (though the word may sometimes be used for other materials). Whilst the areas likely to be affected by earthquakes or volcanoes can be roughly predicted, landslides can occur almost anywhere – and often do so, without warning.

Landslides and avalanches are usually triggered by a specific event. This event will cause or exacerbate a structural weakness within a body of soil, rock or snow, which in turn can lead to the complete loss of structure that we call a landslide or avalanche. Examples of events that can trigger landslides include heavy rainfall or earthquakes. Change to a slope that causes an increase in its steepness (such as a road cutting or certain types of earthworks) could also trigger a landslide.

Most often, we associate landslides with high-rainfall areas such as those located within the earth's tropics. Here, where hurricanes and monsoons can dump large amounts of rainfall in a matter of hours, soil can very quickly become saturated. Human activity, such as the ill-considered clearing of vegetation from hillsides, can increase the likelihood of a landslide occurring.

Key terms

A chronic hazard is one which is long-term and persistent, such as El Niño (see Chapter 2) or global warming; possibly drought in some parts of the world, such as the Sahel. Global warming and El Niño are both context hazards because they have potentially global impacts and could also lead to more of some other types of hazard, such as flooding or hurricanes.

The disaster risk equation

If you had to face one of the hazards that you have read about so far, which one would you prefer to be facing? Most likely, your choice will not be based on the type of hazard alone. You will subconsciously factor in other variables to this equation, including how vulnerable your location is to the different types of hazard, and the capacity of your community to recover from a particular natural hazard. These variables help determine if a hazard event will result in a diasaster – a catastrophe which affects people and/or infrastructure severely.

The factors outlined above and those that contributed to your choice of hazard to face, can be summed up rather neatly in the 'disaster risk equation'. This equation helps us to analyse the risk to a community from a natural hazard. The risk (R) can be expressed as:

$$R = \frac{H \times V}{C}$$ where:
H = Type of hazard
V = Vulnerability to hazard
C = Capacity to cope/recover

We can begin to understand the risk equation by first recognising that not all natural hazards (H) are equally devastating. Certainly, the impact that earthquakes have on buildings results in more deaths (worldwide, per year) than the effects of either cyclones or floods. Landslides and avalanches are fast-acting hazards that tend to happen without warning, unlike cyclones, which can be monitored and to some extent predicted and planned for.

Investigating the risk equation further, it is apparent that not all of the earth's inhabitants are at equal risk from natural hazards. For example, whilst theoretically it is possible for nearly any location on earth to experience an earthquake, they are likely to be far more powerful in places that are located at or near the boundaries of the tectonic plates. The chances are that people who live along plate boundaries would be far more likely to experience an earthquake of a large magnitude than those who do not. In effect, this makes these people and their communities more vulnerable (V) to earthquakes.

The concept of vulnerability is quite easy to extend to other hazards: if you do not live in close proximity to a volcano, then you are not likely to be threatened by lava flows. However, that is not to say that your location may not be affected by clouds of volcanic ash, which can significantly alter the climate of places many miles, even continents, away from their point of origin. It is important to note that vulnerability can also be increased by other factors such as poverty.

Capacity (C) refers to the ability of a community to absorb, and ultimately recover from, the effects of a natural hazard. We have already noted that people in Japan increase their capacity to cope with the effects of an earthquake by regularly practising how to respond to a major quake. In theory, this will mean that their community will have a better chance of coping with a large earthquake than if they had not practised these procedures. Compare this to the capacity to cope that currently exists in a sprawling slum in the less developed world, where dwellings have been hastily constructed from poor quality materials, and where there is neither the time nor resources to commit to a large-scale community training programme. The effect of their lower capacity increases the risk that this community faces from these hazards.

As our knowledge of natural hazards has steadily grown, so too has our preparedness for these events and our ability to cope with, and recover from, them. That said, the risk equation shows us that millions of people are still at the mercy of the natural environment, and that their ability to survive is largely determined by factors that are beyond their control.

Global warming

Since the Industrial Revolution of the late eighteenth century, human economic and social activity has resulted in the production of thousands of tonnes of 'greenhouse gases'. The emission of these gases has led to the phenomenon of global warming. It has become clear that the threat that human activities pose to the health and well-being of the planet is a chronic hazard with the potential to impact globally.

As a consequence of the rise in average global temperatures, climates around the world have begun to change. Melting ice caps, rising sea levels and changes in the migratory patterns of wildlife are indicators of how the environment has already responded to the extra warmth in the planetary system. Worse still are the predictions of the changes that are yet to occur (see Chapters 4 to 7). The effects of climate change will be felt differently across the earth. Recent research has shown that people living in the more marginal areas of the planet, which are usually found in the less-developed parts of the world, will be most vulnerable to climate change. These people also have the lowest capacity to cope with change.

Case study: Greenhouse gases

Greenhouse gases are those that trap the sun's heat in the earth's atmosphere. Water vapour is the most important greenhouse gas although the best known greenhouse gas is carbon dioxide (CO_2). Atmospheric concentrations of CO_2 are estimated to have increased by 35% as compared to levels in pre-industrial times. Other important greenhouse gases are methane (CH_4) and nitrous oxide (N_2O). Although estimates vary, climatic studies indicate that in the last hundred years, average global temperatures have increased by between 0.5 and 1.0 °C. A predicted rise in global average temperature of between 1.8 and 4.0 °C is expected by the end of this century.

Since the global warming phenomenon was first recognised by the scientific community in the 1970s, there has been much debate about the extent to which anthropogenic (human) activities are responsible for the evident warming trend. Throughout the 1980s and 1990s it seemed that for every scientist that recognised and validated the contribution that humans were making to global warming, there was another scientist who was willing to cast doubt on the accuracy of this theory. The World Meteorological Organization (WMO) and the United Nations Environment Programme (UNEP) created the Intergovernmental Panel on Climate Change (IPCC) in 1988, to help debate and clarify the issue. An 'Earth Summit' was held in Rio de Janeiro in 1992, in the hope of beginning a constructive political dialogue on the issue.

Key terms

Global warming: the observable increase in the average temperature of the earth, caused by the enhanced Greenhouse Effect.

Taking it further

To learn more about our individual impact on climate change read 'Test Yourself' on your Student CD-ROM.

Key terms

Anthropogenic: caused by human activity.

Taking it further

To learn more about the arguments surrounding climate change read 'Us? – it wasn't us' on your Student CD-ROM.

▲ Figure 8: The film *An Inconvenient Truth* did much to open the eyes of people to the realities of global warming.

Interestingly, a documentary film called *An Inconvenient Truth* (2006), narrated by former US Vice-President, Al Gore, helped to crystallise global public opinion about the need to take action on climate change. Our shared stewardship of the planet appears to have finally been recognised, and it is apparent that the solution to this global problem requires a united effort.

The reduction in emissions of greenhouse gases must be thought of, in the first instance, in terms of the overall global amount. This planetary approach ignores international boundaries, and regards us all as citizens of the globe. After this, a system of quotas can be applied to allow the global community to set and meet emissions targets at the scale of individual nations, with a view to ensuring the right of any nation to seek out a better standard of living for its inhabitants, whilst still managing its greenhouse gas emissions in an environmentally responsible way. However, the reality is that the nations of the world are a long way from being ready to help one another in terms of development or living standards. The moral and ethical will for change exists, but must now be matched by the political will of national governments.

Case study: Issues of injustice

The world's more developed nations have grown accustomed to providing monetary and medical aid to those people (especially in the less developed world) who are affected by natural disasters. However, global warming cannot be solved by the actions of the developed world alone. It requires the immediate reduction in the emission of greenhouse gases on a global scale. This has, however, raised interesting issues of injustice. The developed nations of the world grew rich on the back of industrialisation and the greenhouse gas emissions that it generated. With a better understanding of the mechanism of global warming comes the realisation that the development of the wealthiest nations of the world has had serious consequences for the health of the planet.

Taking it further

To learn more about the ethics of controlling climate change read 'Blaming the poor?' on your Student CD-ROM.

The challenge ahead

The most serious political attempt to limit global emissions has been the Kyoto Protocol, which came into effect in 2005. The Protocol was the first international agreement that set emission targets, which, for the more developed nations of the world, was a commitment to reduce their emissions by 5%, relative to 1990 levels, by 2012. Many nations have made good progress towards this goal. However, some nations, such as the USA (a significant greenhouse gas emitter), are not signatories to this agreement, and others, like Australia, have only recently ratified it. This has somewhat limited the effectiveness of the Kyoto Protocol as an international agreement to address climate change, but it has been a good start.

The issue of global warming and climate change is arguably the greatest hazard facing humanity. Unlike natural hazards, which tend to strike deep at the heart of localised communities, global warming is a truly global problem. Chillingly, the exact effect of climate change on the frequency and magnitude of hydro-meteorological hazards such as cyclones, floods and landslides, is yet to be fully determined. There is, however, little doubt that in the future we will live in a more hazardous world, and that global warming has far-reaching ramifications for all of us.

Summary

Having studied this chapter, you should be able to discuss these ideas and concepts and to provide located examples of them:

• Disasters result when hydro-meteorological hazards and geophysical hazards threaten the life and property of increasing numbers of the world's people.

• Examples of hydro-meteorological hazards include cyclones, droughts and floods, and examples of geophysical hazards include earthquakes, volcanoes, and landslides/avalanches.

• The risk of disaster grows as global hazards and people's vulnerability increases, while their capacity to cope decreases.

• The risk of disaster may be calculated using a 'disaster risk equation'.

• Global warming – arguably the greatest hazard we currently face – is a chronic hazard. It has widespread impacts, raises issues of injustice (polluters and vulnerable victims) and has complex solutions.

MCQ

Exam practice

Study the diagrams below which compare the impact of six major hazard types over a 30-year period.

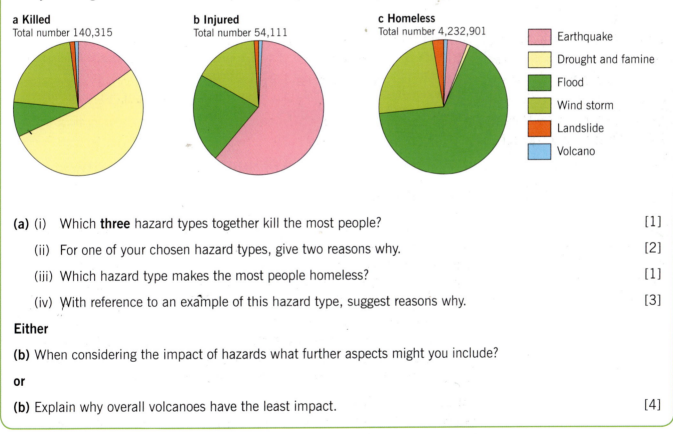

a Killed
Total number 140,315

b Injured
Total number 54,111

c Homeless
Total number 4,232,901

- Earthquake
- Drought and famine
- Flood
- Wind storm
- Landslide
- Volcano

(a) (i)   Which **three** hazard types together kill the most people? [1]

(ii)   For one of your chosen hazard types, give two reasons why. [2]

(iii) Which hazard type makes the most people homeless? [1]

(iv) With reference to an example of this hazard type, suggest reasons why. [3]

Either

(b) When considering the impact of hazards what further aspects might you include?

or

(b) Explain why overall volcanoes have the least impact. [4]

CHAPTER 2 How and why are natural hazards now becoming seen as an increasing global threat?

Key terms

Ageing population
Centre for Research on the Epidemiology of Disasters (CRED)
Community memory
Delta
El Niño
El Niño Southern Oscillation (ENSO)
Emergency Disasters Database (EM-DAT)
Frequency
Infrastructure
La Niña
Magnitude
Megadelta
Natural disaster
Social-demographic
Urbanisation

Learning objectives

After studying this chapter, you will be able to discuss these ideas and concepts and provide located examples of them:

• Some types of hazards are increasing in magnitude and frequency, and are having greater impacts upon people and their lives.
• Natural disasters are increasing because of a combination of physical and human factors.
• The unpredictability of global warming and El Niño events leads to increasing natural hazards.
• The increasing exploitation of resources (e.g. deforestation), world poverty, and rapid population growth and urbanisation contribute to the frequency of natural disasters.
• Trends show that the number of people killed by natural hazards is falling, whereas the number affected and the economic losses are escalating.
• Natural disasters are increasingly being seen as a growing threat to humankind and its associated infrastructure.

Disasters – increasing in magnitude and frequency

It is clear that the number of reported natural disasters is increasing with each passing year. Some argue that this is due to improvements in technology that allow even the smaller-scale and more isolated disasters to be recorded. Others suggest that with international monitoring agencies like the Belgium-based Centre for Research on the Epidemiology of Disasters (CRED) in operation, people are encouraged to report the occurrence of natural hazards more than in the past thus the numbers go up because of better recording rather than any other trend.

◀ **Figure 1:** Volcanoes are one of the most spectacular natural hazards which confront humankind.

Whilst these arguments have merit, when the data is considered (Figure 2), it is apparent that the increase in natural disasters over the last century could not be due to technological factors alone. Data collected by the Emergency Disasters Database (EM-DAT) shows that in the early 1900s, on average, fewer than 10 natural disasters were reported annually. After 1940, there seems to have been a gradual rise in the reporting of natural disasters, climbing towards an annual average of 50 cases over the course of the subsequent 2 decades. The creation of the international disaster data collection agencies in the 1960s and 1970s did contribute to a sharp increase in the number of disasters that were reported. Through the 1980s, the average number of disasters reported annually grew to more than 200. This upwards trend continued following the creation of EM-DAT in 1988, and by the early 2000s, more than 400 natural disasters were being reported each year.

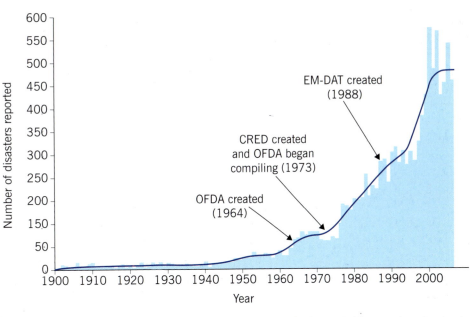

Figure 2: The number of natural disasters reported, 1900–2006.
Source: EM-DAT: The OFDA/CRED International Disaster Database, www.em-dat.net

It would appear then that the increase in the number of disasters is not simply due to better monitoring and reporting of disasters. There has also been a closer analysis of the available data, and of the types of disaster that have constituted this increase. Six major types of natural hazard affect humankind and they equate to those outlined in Chapter 1:

Hydro-meteorological hazards

- Cyclones (or 'windstorms')

- Drought

- Flood

Geophysical hazards

- Avalanches/landslides

- Earthquakes

- Volcanoes

Usefully, EM-DAT collects information on the frequency of each of these natural hazards.

It is apparent that since the mid-1970s general increases occurred in the reported number of all natural hazards. The increases in the number of avalanches and landslides, droughts and earthquakes reported have been comparatively small. However, the increase in the reported occurrence of floods, windstorms and volcanic activity appear to be more significant. It is, of course, not possible to attribute increasing volcanic or earthquake activity to anything other than natural causes.

Decreasing numbers of deaths

What is interesting about the increase in the reported number of natural disasters is the fact that there has been a decrease in the number of reported deaths due to these disasters (Figure 3). During the period from 1900 to 1940, approximately 500,000 people were reported to have been killed by natural disasters each year. After 1940, however, this annual death toll rapidly decreased, to the point where in the early part of this century, the number of people killed by natural disasters each year is less than 50,000.

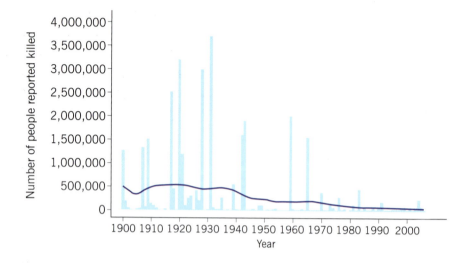

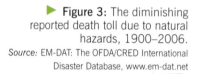

▶ **Figure 3:** The diminishing reported death toll due to natural hazards, 1900–2006.
Source: EM-DAT: The OFDA/CRED International Disaster Database, www.em-dat.net

This falling death toll due to natural hazards reflects the ability of humankind to understand natural disasters better, including improvements in our ability to predict their occurrence and to take the appropriate precautions (such as evacuation). For those living in the developed world, this knowledge also encourages the construction of houses that are more likely to withstand the effects of most natural disasters. Sadly, this is not always the case in the less developed world.

Increasing numbers of people affected and economic costs

While fewer people die each year as a result of natural hazards, these events are *affecting* more people than ever before. At the same time, they are taking a greater economic toll than in the past (Figure 4). Since 1980, the average annual economic cost of natural hazards has risen from less than $20 bn to more than $160 bn. In the same period, the number of people reported as being affected has risen from an annual average of 100 million to more than 200 million.

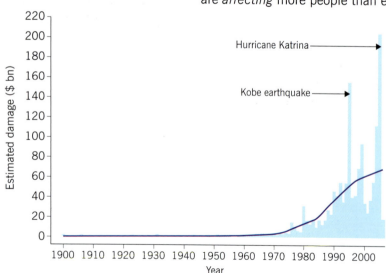

◀ **Figure 4:** The estimated costs (in $ bn) of damage due to natural hazards, 1900–2006. The increasing economic cost of natural hazards is revealed – note the standout events of the years 1995 (Kobe earthquake) and 2005 (Hurricane Katrina).
Source: EM-DAT: The OFDA/CRED International Disaster Database, www.em-dat.net

Case study: The cost of a mini-drought

In 2003, parts of Europe experienced a heat wave that lasted from June until the middle of August. During this time, average summer temperatures increased by 3 to 5 °C over Central and Southern Europe. The situation was exacerbated by the fact that 2003 was also a very dry year in this region, with rainfall deficits of 300 mm in some parts. The result was a 'mini-drought', which is estimated to have cost more than €13 bn in terms of lost agricultural opportunities and increased production costs.

The heatwave and associated drought also had a range of other, far-reaching effects. During the summer of 2003, tinder-dry vegetation was highly susceptible to wildfire, and approximately 650,000 hectares of forest was burnt. Portugal lost 5% of its total forest area (twice as much as the previous record), with an economic cost estimated to be €1 bn. There were also the inevitable water supply problems across the continent, which combined with power shortages to create some interesting situations. In France, 25 to 30% of the cold-storage facilities in food-related outlets were found to be below standard. Clothing sales decreased in the heat (by 9%), but happily, sales of ice-cream and bottled water increased (by 14% and 18%, respectively).

This case study and others can be followed by exploring Chapters 15 to 19.

The year 2005, in which Hurricane Katrina struck the Gulf Coast of the USA, was clearly an 'above average' year (Figure 4). In 2005, the number of people who were reported to be affected by natural disasters was more than 650 million.

Capacity

There is an increase in our capacity to cope with disaster. Logic would say that in modern times we should be less at risk from natural hazards, because we have increased our capacity to understand and manage the effects of disasters. Disaster-warning systems and emergency responses are better now than at any stage in human history. The preparedness of governments to respond appropriately in the face of crises has improved dramatically in the last few decades, with the global community being able to provide relief within hours. Scientists and engineers have provided us with the latest in disaster-proof building materials and governments have increasingly strengthened building regulations through appropriate codes of construction in disaster-prone areas.

Vulnerability

We are experiencing a simultaneous increase in our vulnerability to natural hazards. While there have been improvements in our capacity, in the latter half of the twentieth century, we have significantly increased our vulnerability to natural hazards through a combination of economic, social-demographic and technological factors. These factors far outweigh the gains made in terms of capacity.

Taking it further

Is the fact that an increasing number of people are affected by natural disasters due to an increase in the frequency and/or magnitude of natural hazards, or is it because we are becoming more vulnerable to disasters?
For a full discussion of this, in the context of hydro-meteorological hazards, go to Chapter 17.

Examiners' tip

Make sure you know and can use the disaster risk equation (see page 12) for the exam.

Economic factors of vulnerability: exploitation of natural resources

As we continue to degrade our environment by exploiting natural resources in pursuit of economic progress, we are making ourselves more vulnerable to natural hazards. Changes that humans make to the physical environment remove many of the natural buffers that exist between our communities and natural hazards. Clearing of vegetation from hillsides or sloping land, in order to allow for development, is a well-recognised example. Although this practice is known to increase the risk of landslides, it continues to be carried out in a variety of global settings to create more useable land for agriculture or in the pursuit of profits from forestry. In a similar way, the draining and filling of wetlands to create land for housing or industry is equally risky. This practice can significantly alter drainage patterns within the natural environment and expose the new development to flooding.

Case study: Multiple stresses on the Mekong River

The risks posed by climate change, which include an increase in the magnitude and frequency of natural hazards, become frightening when combined with the other changes that are occurring to the environment due to human activity. The Mekong River is a prime example. The Mekong begins in the highlands of China and then winds its way through Myanmar, Thailand, Laos, Cambodia and Vietnam. More than 60 million people live within its basin, two-thirds of whom are dependent on the river, in some way, for their livelihood.

Climate change is likely to affect the flow of the river significantly. Shifting patterns of rainfall, combined with the changed nature of snow melts and the likelihood of sea-level rise will have a major impact. When anthropogenic activities such as continued urbanisation, increased clearing, soil erosion and over-fishing are factored in, the complexities of the interrelationships become apparent. The recent IPCC *Fourth Assessment Report* summed up the situation this way:

'The sustainability of megadeltas in Asia in a warmer climate will rest heavily on policies and programmes that promote integrated and co-ordinated development of the megadeltas and upstream areas, balanced use and development of megadeltas for production and conservation goals, and comprehensive protection against erosion . . . that combines structural with human and institutional capability-building measures.'

Source: 'IPCC Climate Change 2007: Impacts, adaptations and vulnerability', contribution of Working Group II to the *Fourth Assessment Report* of the IPCC.

Socio-demographic factors of vulnerability: population growth and urbanisation

The rapid growth of the human population has meant that there are more people on the planet, and therefore a greater number of people at potential risk from natural hazards. Urbanisation has also continued at a great pace. More of us now live in urban areas than ever before. Additionally, most urban centres are located in coastal areas, and these are the parts of the world which are most exposed to the hydro-meteorological hazards such as cyclones and floods.

The net result of urbanisation is the concentration of people and infrastructure. Even though natural hazards have a low probability of occurring, when they strike in highly urbanised areas, they do so with a high cost. The greatest economic cost of a natural disaster clearly lies in replacing lost infrastructure. The hidden costs of a disaster can also include the cost of taxpayer-funded disaster relief programmes, tax breaks to assist communities to rebuild, and the inevitable increase in the price of goods and services as businesses re-establish themselves after a disaster.

As the need for more land for urban centres has continued to grow, the opening up of marginal areas which are at higher risk of natural hazards such as floods has occurred. Insurers have responded by charging higher premiums to those who occupy these areas. Whilst this seems appropriate in the developed world, there are no such guarantees of coverage in the less developed parts of the world.

Case study: Deltas – the world's vulnerability 'hotspots'

Deltas are the sedimentary deposits that are formed at the mouth of river systems. A recent survey of 40 deltas, which included all of the world's largest 'megadeltas', found that these areas have been subject to a high degree of urbanisation. Nearly 300 million people were found to be living on these 40 deltas. The average population density of the deltas studied was an incredible 500 people per km^2 – which perhaps reflects the 'desirability' of delta locations. By 2050, sea-level rise, combined with the natural subsidence of these deltas over time, will affect more than a million people who live in the world's three largest megadeltas – the Nile, the Mekong (see Figure 6) and the Ganges-Brahmaputra (Bangladesh). Tens of thousands more will be affected in smaller deltas across the globe, with the largest areas of concern again occurring in the less developed world, most notably in Africa and Asia.

▲ **Figure 5:** Vietnam's 'nine-tailed dragon', the Mekong Delta, as seen from space.

An ageing population

In a demographic sense, the ageing population of the developed world has, in effect, made our communities more susceptible to natural hazards. Older people (those in the 65+ age bracket) are the least mobile in a community and have less capacity to take action either before or after a natural disaster. In an interesting contrast, it is the mobility of the rest of the population – who are now freer to move between locations for work or family reasons than at any other stage in human history – that has broken down what demographers refer to as our 'community memory'. In the past, when people were less mobile, communities built up a strong local knowledge about natural hazards and their likely effect on local places. This was an effective reminder to people about the places that were worst affected by natural hazards and helped to prevent, or at least discourage, development in the riskier parts of the local environment. Sadly, with our increased mobility during our working lifetimes, this community memory has diminished.

Case study: The susceptibility of older people to natural hazards

In the European heatwaves of the summer of 2003, thousands of deaths occurred. People aged 70 years or older were the hardest hit, with women being found to be more at risk than men. Many of these deaths were triggered by the heat, which induced strokes or failures in the renal, respiratory and cardiovascular systems of the elderly. These problems are more likely in people aged 65+, so they are pre-disposed to be more at risk during hazard events such as this.

Follow this up by reading Chapter 16.

Technological factors of vulnerability: dependence on technology

How has development been allowed to take place in areas that are in effect more exposed to the risks associated with natural hazards?

Our belief that we are able to predict and control the natural environment and its processes is partly responsible. This belief has led us to develop areas for human habitation which previously may not have been considered safe or viable. We have developed a reliance on technology for our salvation from the hazards of the natural world. This includes the early warning detection systems that allow us to prepare for the onset of a natural hazard, such as a cyclone, flood, tsunami or earthquake. It also includes physical barriers, such as levee banks and flood-control systems that help to contain or divert floodwaters away from major urban centres. A floodcontrol network is used on the River Thames to protect London. This has helped the city to expand and develop to a tremendous size, despite the fact that much of it rests on the flood plain of one of Britain's main rivers.

We are more dependent now on our systems of water, power, communication and transport than ever before. When these systems collapse under the onslaught of a natural hazard, we are unable to fend for ourselves. Many of us would struggle to cope with a power cut for a few hours, let alone for the days or weeks that might follow a severe natural disaster. Even the infrastructure designed to protect us from natural hazards can in effect make us more vulnerable, especially if it ages and is not replaced. Worse still, it may not be designed to withstand the intensity of the hazard that we might experience. Of course, this will not be evident until it is too late, as when Hurricane Katrina struck New Orleans in 2005.

Case study: When technology fails – Hurricane Katrina

The city of New Orleans is built on the delta of the Mississippi River. Not only is the city built on low-lying ground on the flood plain of the river, but it is located on land that subsides, on average, between 6 and 15 mm a year. Generally, the city was well protected from the regular flood events of the Mississippi and the surging sea water of the Gulf of Mexico by a series of embankments and levees. However, over time, as the population of the city increased to half a million, development took place in areas that were more vulnerable to flooding.

As Hurricane Katrina approached the Mississippi coast towards the end of August 2005, it brought with it a storm surge that was 5 metres above normal sea levels. With the city's levee banks constructed to withstand a storm surge of only 4.5 metres, disaster quickly loomed. More than half of New Orleans's homes were flooded by water that averaged a depth of 1.2 metres, while in some parts of the city the water was up to 6 metres deep. The cost of the flooding of these homes, alone, was $8 to 10 bn. In a tragic twist, approximately 35,000 of these dwellings were not insured against floods because, with the dependence on the technology of the flood protection system, they supposedly existed outside the area that was designated as a 'flood risk zone'.

Follow this up by reading the material in Chapter 16 about 'Katrina'.

Climate change

We have seen that human activity is making people more vulnerable to natural hazards. Changes that are occurring within the earth's physical environment are also increasing our vulnerability. With a changing climate due to anthropogenic global warming, it stands to reason that the frequency and magnitude of hydro-meteorological hazards such as cyclones, floods and drought may also change – and possibly for the worse.

The Intergovernmental Panel on Climate Change (IPCC) released its *Fourth Assessment Report* on climate change in 2007. This report gives projections of how global warming will affect the magnitude and frequency of what it refers to as 'extreme events' (natural hazards). It concludes that a warming of 2 °C above 1990–2000 temperatures will increase the likelihood of events such as floods, droughts, heatwaves and wildfires. Any further increases of temperature are likely to increase the risks to an even greater extent.

Perhaps the most obvious change in climate due to global warming will be an increase in the number of hot days and nights. This will have some very obvious impacts for humans in terms of their comfort and their health. A 'heatwave' of unseasonably warm summer temperatures resulted in nearly 2000 deaths in the Netherlands and Belgium during July 2006. Accompanying the warming trend will be an increased demand for water, which will be exacerbated by the rise in evaporation rates.

Global warming is expected to cause changes in the rainfall patterns of the earth. More rain is expected to fall in high-latitude areas. Where rainfall increases, it is expected to be more intense, leading to an increase in the risk of both flash flooding and large-area floods. It is possible that these problems could be exacerbated by an earlier seasonal melting of snow packs.

Some areas of the globe are likely to receive either similar or lower levels of rainfall than at present. These areas can expect an increase in the frequency and intensity of droughts. This will be particularly apparent in the Mediterranean climates of the mid-latitudes, and also within the continental interiors of the mid-latitudes. Millions of people will be affected by the water stress associated with drought, which, in turn, will enhance existing problems of dehydration and disease in less-developed parts of the world.

There is some debate about how climate change will affect the magnitude and frequency of cyclones. As sea surface temperatures rise as a result of global warming, there is little doubt that the intensity of tropical cyclones will increase. It is likely that there will be more Category 4 and Category 5 storms, the formation of which will be fuelled by the warm temperatures of the ocean. However, there is some debate within the scientific community about whether the frequency of cyclones will change. Despite this, it is clear that cyclones of a larger intensity will pose serious challenges to the design criteria of existing infrastructures. This has the potential to result in thousands of deaths and costs of billions of dollars in economic aid and reconstruction.

The IPCC's *Fourth Assessment Report* indicates that, in the future, the effects of natural hazards will have varying impacts across the globe. This is because climate change models show that the vulnerability of some communities will be relatively high whilst their capacity will be relatively low. Those nations expected to be most at risk are the less-developed countries of the low latitudes. Even within these nations, the level of risk will vary, with those people living in coastal areas or on river flood plains at the greatest level of risk from natural hazards such as cyclones and floods.

The impact of climate change on earth processes – El Niño

Just as there is debate on how climate change will affect natural hazards, there is also debate on how it will impact on other earth processes. El Niño, one such process, is a natural phenomenon which sailors have known about for many years, but which scientists have only recently come to understand. The name 'El Niño' refers to a warm ocean current that appears off the western coast of South America intermittently – usually every few years. It replaces the cool ocean current that is normally found in these waters. The term 'El Niño' was originally coined by Peruvian sailors and in Spanish means 'Christ child'. The warm ocean current was referred to this way because it usually appeared after Christmas.

Today, the term 'El Niño' is used to describe a prolonged period of warmer-than-average conditions that occurs as a result of the warmer ocean waters of the Eastern Pacific. Scientists have now established that El Niño occurs for periods on average of between 12 and 18 months, and that El Niño events occur at intervals of between 2 and 7 years. The opposite effect is a period of cooler weather, which is known as 'La Niña'. The conditions that exist under La Niña could be considered as the prevailing conditions, because they are more usual.

The movement of the weather between El Niño and La Niña conditions is known as the El Niño Southern Oscillation (ENSO). The oscillation is based on the differences in air pressure that occur between the western and eastern sides of the Pacific Ocean.

El Niño events are characterised by an increase in the number of natural hazards. Most commonly, El Niño is accompanied by a change in rainfall patterns in countries on either side of the Pacific Ocean. When an El Niño event is in full swing, it translates to drought conditions in places lying to the west of the Pacific Ocean, including parts of South East Asia, southern Africa and eastern Australia. Yet at the same time, floods are found to occur in places lying to the east of the Pacific, most notably Peru and Ecuador. La Niña events tend to bring the opposite conditions – floods in regions to the west of the Pacific Ocean and droughts in areas to the east, although it must be said that La Niña conditions tend to be less intense than El Niño ones.

With scientists having come to terms with the ENSO only recently, it remains to be seen how climate change will impact on this important process.

Case study: Peru and Ecuador, 1997

Tragically, some of the areas affected by the ENSO are among the world's poorest regions. This includes the coastal and inland areas of southern Africa, South-East Asia and western South America. As we have already seen, the large concentration of population in the coastal parts of these regions increases their vulnerability to the type of natural hazards that are associated with the ENSO. Additionally, the vulnerability of these communities is further increased by the poor construction of dwellings, made from cheap and readily available materials. To top it off, many of these communities exist in marginal areas where the buffers within the physical environment to natural hazards may be few. For example, the severity of the 1997 El Niño events brought ten times the average level of rainfall to Ecuador. Large-scale flooding led to problems with water supply and sewerage, landslides and erosion resulted, with the accompanying tragic loss of lives and homes. Direct damage to infrastructure was estimated at $123.3 m, whilst economic losses due to events associated with El Niño were estimated to be $1,291.9 m.

Summary

Having studied this chapter, you should be able to discuss these ideas and concepts and provide located examples of them:

- Some types of hazards are increasing in magnitude and frequency, and are having greater impacts upon people and their lives.
- Natural disasters are increasing because of a combination of physical and human factors.
- The unpredictability of global warming and El Niño events leads to increasing natural hazards.
- There is an increasing exploitation of resources (e.g. deforestation), world poverty, and rapid population growth and urbanisation, which contribute to the frequency of natural disasters.
- Trends show that the number of people killed is falling, whereas the number affected and the economic losses are escalating.
   - Natural disasters are increasingly being seen as a growing threat to humankind and its associated infrastructure.

MCQ

Exam practice

Study the diagram which compares the profiles of a drought (a hydro-meteorological hazard) and an earthquake (a geophysical hazard).

(a) (i) Describe the main features of the profile of a drought. [3]

(ii) Explain **two** ways in which the profile of the earthquake is different from that of a drought. [4]

(b) Suggest reasons why, globally, the number of earthquakes shows a fluctuating trend and is only rising slightly, whereas the **frequency** of droughts is increasing considerably. [5]

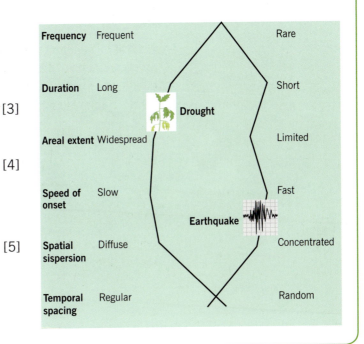

Chapter 3 Why are some places more hazardous and disaster-prone than others?

Key terms

Direct loss
Duration
Economic loss
Gross Domestic Product
Hotspots
Indirect loss
Location
Loss/Recovery Cycle
Mortality
Office for the Coordination
   of Humanitarian Affairs
   (OCHA)
World Bank

Learning objectives

After studying this chapter, you will be able to discuss these ideas and concepts and provide located examples of them:

- The real or potential natural hazard risks in your local area, based on evidence about past or likely future events and their impact on people, property and the environment.
- The global distribution of the world's major hydro-meteorological hazards and geophysical hazards, with maps and reports.
- The causes and impacts of natural hazards in disaster hotspots.
- Comparisons of how multiple disasters affect developed and less developed regions, using case studies.
- How multiple hazards are managed on the California coast, and in the Philippines, a vulnerable location.

The year 2005 was a memorable one for natural hazards. Following on from the Tsunami of 26 December 2004, which claimed 300,000 lives and left 1.5 million people homeless, 2005 saw the advent of 360 separate natural disasters. These events claimed 90,000 lives, affected 150 million people and left a damage bill of $159 bn.

▲ **Figure 1:** People who have been left homeless by flooding in the Indian province of Gujarat escape with the help of soldiers.

Identifying disaster hotspots

The World Bank recently published a report entitled *'Natural Disaster Hotspots: A Global Risk Analysis'*. The aim of this initiative was to reduce the losses that occur as a result of natural disasters. The report identified those areas that were most vulnerable to natural hazards and considered the elements that are at risk. These risks were calculated at the local level, rather than on national scales, allowing for the better comparison of relative risks between various locations.

The World Bank report uses the term 'hotspots' to describe those nations that are most vulnerable to disasters caused by natural hazards. Amazingly, in 160 countries, at least 25% of the population live in areas where the risk of mortality due to a natural hazard is considered high.

Case study: Armenia – a disaster-prone nation

Armenia is one of the world's most disaster-prone nations. Within its relatively small borders (Armenia is a country with an area of just 29,800 km^2) the nation is exposed to the risk of earthquakes, landslides, hailstorms, droughts, windstorms and floods. With its mountainous landscape, landslides are one of the mostly common natural hazards, and it is estimated that 15% of Armenians live in areas prone to landslides. Landslides are also perhaps the costliest hazards to beset the nation, resulting in an annual damage bill of $10 m. Amazingly, more than 300 of Armenia's largest landslide areas are considered to be in the 'active' stage, which means that a significant landslide event could occur at any time. When you consider that 1,500 km of Armenia's 8,000 km of transport corridors lie within landslide zones, then it is clear how here – as in many of the world's disaster hotspots – the threat posed by natural hazards can simply become part of everyday life.

Assessing the characteristics of natural hazards

It is important to note that the 'hotspots' are *not* necessarily the most likely to be hit by natural hazards – but one where natural disaster is likely to result from the hazard. Natural disasters result from a combination of factors, one of which is the natural hazard itself. The characteristics of the natural hazard which have some bearing on whether a disaster results include its:

- Magnitude
- Duration
- Location
- Timing.

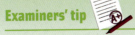

There have been instances where natural hazards of particularly large magnitude and duration have struck and caused relatively low levels of damage. Sometimes, this can be explained by their location. When large hazards strike in remote, isolated or unpopulated areas their effects may not lead to a natural disaster. However, it is equally true that natural hazards of relatively small magnitude or short duration can cause immense amounts of damage, and result in large-scale disasters. Obviously, there are additional factors at play in relation to how a disaster is caused.

Assessing the elements at risk

There are other factors that help to determine whether the occurrence of a natural hazard will result in disaster. These factors relate to the characteristics of the 'elements' that are exposed to the hazard, and include:

- People
- Infrastructure
- Economically important or environmentally important land uses.

Whether or not a disaster occurs following a particular hazard event will depend on the extent to which these elements are damaged or destroyed by the hazard, yet not all of these elements are at the same level of risk from the different types of major hazards. Consider infrastructure such as a bridge. During an earthquake, a bridge will face stress from shaking, which could endanger its structure. There may be a relatively high chance that the bridge will be damaged or destroyed. However, during drought conditions, the main stresses in the environment relate to moisture reduction. Less moisture in the soil is not likely to threaten the structure of the bridge. Conversely, in a flood, when stress to the environment comes from the inundation of the land, the bridge may in fact be threatened.

The location of the world's disaster hotspots

The idea that disasters result from a combination of factors, and not just the hazard event, is important to help us understand how the groundwork of disasters is laid. It also helps us to identify the places in the world that are at highest risk of disaster. These are the world's disaster hotspots.

The World Bank's analysis found that more than half of the world's population live in an area that could be 'significantly impacted' by at least one natural hazard. But there are places that are at an even greater risk. There are 35 countries in which at least 5% of people live with a high risk of mortality from three or more natural hazards. Of these nations, Taiwan is arguably one of the riskiest places. In Taiwan, 73% of the population live in areas that are exposed to three or more hazards. Other high-ranking countries with at least 90% of their population exposed to two or more natural hazards, include Bangladesh, Nepal, Burundi, Haiti, Malawi, El Salvador and Honduras.

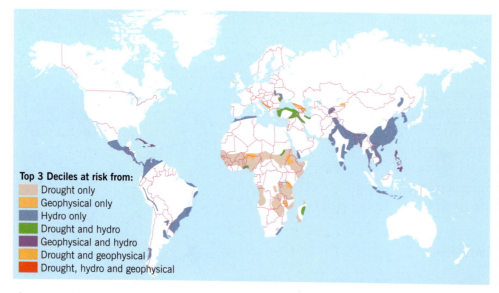

Top 3 Deciles at risk from:
- Drought only
- Geophysical only
- Hydro only
- Drought and hydro
- Geophysical and hydro
- Drought and geophysical
- Drought, hydro and geophysical

▲ **Figure 2:** The 'High Mortality Risk' hotspots in relation to the different types of natural hazards (the areas most at risk from these hazards).
Source: World Bank, *Natural Disaster Hotspots: A Global Risk Analysis – Synthesis Report*, p. 22

Through its *Natural Disaster Hotspots: A Global Risk Analysis*, the World Bank was able to produce, through maps, a global picture of those places at greatest risk from natural hazards. The first of these maps shows the risk that is posed to human life (Figure 2). What emerges is a clear indication that people living in large tracts of the less developed world are doing so with the high risk of mortality due to natural hazards.

The hotspots for the hydro-meteorological hazards (cyclones, floods and droughts) exist in Southern, Eastern and South East Asia, in addition to Central America and eastern parts of South America. An interesting feature of the results is how the African continent is broadly affected by drought – across vast swathes of Central and Southern Africa.

As Figure 2 reveals, the hotspots for
the geophysical hazards (earthquakes,
landslides/avalanches and volcanoes) tend
to be located in areas exposed to hydro-
meteorological risks as well. The Himalayan
region, Japan, and parts of the Middle East
and Southern Europe are examples of places
that are exposed to multiple hazards.

The World Bank's analysis has also
produced a different version of the disaster
hotspots, and one that paints a very different
view. This map portrays hotspots as the
places that face the greatest economic risk
from the various types of natural hazards (Figure 3).

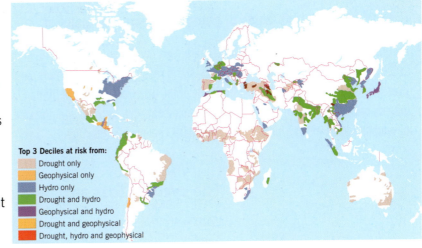

Top 3 Deciles at risk from:
- Drought only
- Geophysical only
- Hydro only
- Drought and hydro
- Geophysical and hydro
- Drought and geophysical
- Drought, hydro and geophysical

▲ **Figure 3:** The 'High Total
Economic Loss' hotspots in relation to
the different types of natural hazards
(the areas most at risk from these
hazards).

Source: World Bank, *Natural Disaster
Hotspots: A Global Risk Analysis – Synthesis
Report*, p. 22

The key difference between Figure 2 and Figure 3 is just how much more of
the world stands to be affected by economic losses as opposed to the risk of
mortality. Much of the developed world, with its highly urbanised populations and
concentrated infrastructure, is now brought into the calculations.

The impact of disaster

Whilst the lives lost in disaster situations can never be replaced, it is the job of
organisations such as the World Bank to help facilitate the reconstruction of areas
that have experienced disaster. These agencies must consider the two types of loss
that emerge from natural disasters:

- Direct losses – these result from the loss of assets, such as homes, buildings
  and factories, due to the natural hazard.
- Indirect losses – these continue to mount up as long as assets that were
  damaged in the hazard remain destroyed or in a state of disrepair. For example,
  the direct loss of a factory will have indirect losses in terms of lost business, lost
  wages and perhaps lost jobs.

The disproportionate effect of disasters in the less developed world

The less developed and developing nations of the world are at the greatest risk
from natural disasters. It is estimated that 95% of all of the deaths caused by
natural hazards actually occur outside of the developed world. Total financial
losses due to natural disasters, when considered as a percentage of GDP, are 20
times greater in the less developed world than in the developed world.

There is an explanation for the disproportionate effect that natural hazards can
have within the less developed parts of the world. One argument claims that some
of the poorer areas of the world are less developed because of their climates, their
exposure to extreme weather events or their unstable geology. In effect, these
characteristics have made these places harder to develop than other places. When
developmental gains are made in the less developed regions of the earth, they
are often more difficult to secure and hold on to. As a result, the area is more
vulnerable to the impact of severe hazards and has less capacity to plan for and
manage these events.

Case study: The high costs of being vulnerable to disaster

Natural disasters bring about great loss of life. This can be greatly amplified in poorer and less developed parts of the world. In 1999, a Venezuelan landslide and a French storm resulted in approximately similar damage bills – close to $3 bn in each nation. However, the key difference was in the scale of the disaster in terms of human lives claimed. In the developed nation of France, with its hazard management plans and enhanced capacity to cope with disaster, the death toll was just 123. However, in the less developed nation of Venezuela, more than 50,000 people lost their lives.

The cycle of loss and recovery

With high levels of poverty, disease and conflict which so often characterise the nations of the less developed world, the priority given to disaster risk reduction is much lower than in more developed nations. In the less developed world, economic progress and the hard work undertaken to achieve it can easily be erased by the occurrence of a natural disaster.

Some nations, especially those in areas exposed to multiple natural hazards, can become trapped in a cycle of loss and recovery. Much physical effort is placed into rebuilding and repair following a natural disaster. For poorer nations, this can consume much of the national income. Worse still, these efforts can be completely undermined by a subsequent disaster. Countries that are trapped in this type of cycle have very little chance of reaching a point where they are economically self-sustaining. The cycle thus threatens their ability to become further developed.

Case study: Honduras – a nation caught in the loss and recovery cycle

In 1955, the tiny nation of Honduras had just 2,500 km of roads. The lack of transport routes proved to be a major barrier to development. In 1958 the World Bank began to fund a programme of highway building. By the mid-1990s, the World Bank had funded seven road-building projects in Honduras, with a combined value of $120 m. By 1998, the Bank had funded the construction of 1,270 km of road, with the total road network having now grown to 10,000 km. But the occurrence of Hurricane Mitch in 1998 destroyed 6,000 km of the road network, and damaged 163 bridges. The total damage bill for the road network alone was $454 m. What had taken decades to build, with the help of the international community, was completely wiped out in a matter of days.

▲ **Figure 4:** Mudslides in the wake of Hurricane Mitch did great damage to roads and infrastructure in Honduras.

Measuring the costs of disaster hotspots

The World Bank report has demonstrated that countries with a high proportion of their population, productive resources or industries located in hotspot areas are the nations that are most likely to plunge into the cycle of loss and recovery that is associated with repeated natural disasters.

This is evidenced by the figures for the aid given by the international community. During the period 1992 to 2003, the United Nations Office for the Co-ordination of Humanitarian Affairs (OCHA) contributed $2.5 bn to disaster relief programmes. Of this total, approximately $2 bn was consumed by relief efforts in just 20 countries. World Bank figures tell a similar story. From 1980 to 2003, the World Bank contributed $14.4 bn in 'Disaster Reconstruction Loans' to those nations recovering from natural disasters. Again, an incredible $12 bn of this amount was consumed by just 20 countries, even though disasters occurred in many more nations than this.

Case study: The Boxing Day Tsunami, 2004

Not all places within a nation are affected equally by a natural disaster. The impact of the Boxing Day Tsunami of 2004 upon the Indonesian archipelago makes an interesting study. The tsunami effectively reduced the growth in Indonesia's national GDP by between 0.1% and 0.4%. However, in the province of Aceh, a relatively poor and underdeveloped area of the archipelago, the effects were much greater. This area suffered great loss of life, combined with losses of infrastructure and productive capacity. In fact, Aceh's losses in capital stock alone were equivalent to 97% of the province's GDP.

Compulsory case study

California – a vulnerable coastline in the developed world

California, on the western coast of the USA, is another of the world's most recognisable natural hazard hotspots. The state is located on the boundary of two of the earth's largest tectonic plates – the North American Plate and the Pacific Plate. The San Andreas Fault, a fracture within the crust of the earth, forms the boundary between the two plates. The fault is characterised by the movement of rock on either side. It traverses nearly the entire length of the Californian coast, and is one of the prime drivers of the geophysical hazards that exist in this region.

Some of California's best-known cities lie to the west of the San Andreas Fault. These cities, which include San Diego, Los Angeles and Santa Barbara, are located on the Pacific Plate. This plate is moving in a north-west direction relative to the North American Plate, on which the eastern parts of California are located. San Francisco, in northern California, however, is right on the boundary between the plates – on the San Andreas Fault.

Each year, approximately 50 mm of movement occurs at the boundary of the plates along the San Andreas Fault. The San Andreas Fault is just one of the thousands of fault lines that exist throughout California. This makes the region prone to frequent seismic activity. It is estimated that annually, California experiences between 100 and 150 earthquakes that are large enough to be felt by humans. Of these, perhaps three or four are large enough to cause moderate levels of damage.

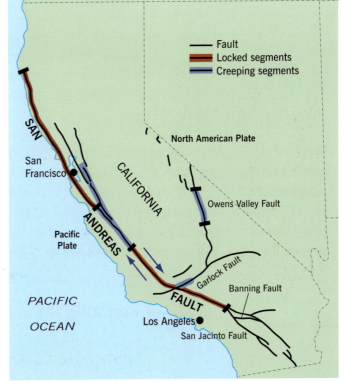

▲ **Figure 5:** The San Andreas Fault in California marks the boundary between two of the world's great tectonic plates.

Major earthquakes are experienced in California perhaps once in 10 years. In recent times, California's largest earthquakes have been in the magnitude of 7.1 to 7.4. When these occur in densely populated areas, they can cause major damage. Events of a larger magnitude, between 7.7 and 7.9, are rare but cause widespread damage over a much larger area. The San Francisco earthquake of 1906 (magnitude 7.8) was an example of this. California has not experienced what is known as a 'great earthquake' (magnitude greater than 8) in the last 300 years, but a quake of this magnitude could be expected to do extensive damage to a very large area of the state.

California has earned the title of natural disaster hotspot because it faces a range of natural hazards. One of the other ever-present risks in California is the threat of landslides. California is a hilly region, with many slopes in excess of 15 degrees. Many of these slopes are covered in a layer of sandy soil, increasing the likelihood of landslides. In the last 25 years, more than 100 Californians have lost their lives to landslides.

Landslide events are usually triggered by the saturation of hillside soils following intense rainfall. Since 1905, northern California has experienced landslides in at least 14 of its rainy seasons. In January 1982, heavy rainfall in the area of San Francisco Bay triggered thousands of small, localised landslides. These landslides resulted in 14 deaths and caused damage to many structures, including hundreds of homes.

Other triggers for landslides in the state of California include the frequent occurrence of seismic activity and the prevalence of wildfires. Wildfires tend to leave the slopes covered in a layer of ash. Without the protective cover of vegetation, this ash, and the soil over which it lies, can be easily loosened by rainfall. In the first year that follows a wildfire, sediment yields in streams that drain burnt-out areas can increase to as much as 35 times normal levels.

Case study: Volcanoes in California

Being located on the Pacific rim also exposes California to hazards from volcanic activity. The state has a number of volcanic craters, including the Long Valley Caldera, in eastern California. It is estimated that in the past 1,000 years there have been 12 volcanic eruptions in this area, which have helped to form a chain of craters through the Long Valley Caldera. Although the caldera itself was formed by a massive volcanic eruption some 760,000 years ago, recent earthquake activity in the area and ground deformation are considered to be signs that the area is still volcanically active. However, the likelihood of a volcanic eruption occurring in any given year remains small (less than a 1% chance).

Reducing the vulnerability of hotspots

Now that natural disaster hotspots have been identified, work can begin on reducing the vulnerability of these areas to natural hazards. The first phase in this process will be to conduct localised assessments of disaster, as not all places are at equal risk. This is exactly what has occurred in the Philippines, which is one of the world's most hazardous locations.

The Philippines – a vulnerable location

The group of islands that make up the Philippines in the Pacific Ocean is located in a natural disaster hotspot, characterised by a high vulnerability to natural hazards. The Philippines are regularly exposed to tropical cyclones – on average, 19 to 21 cyclones every year. One windstorm, in November 1995, is estimated to have affected more than 33 million Filipinos. Cyclonic activity not only exposes the nation to intense rainfall and strong winds, it also heightens the risk of localised flooding and landslides.

The Philippines are also exposed to a range of other hazards. The region is subject to the El Niño Southern Oscillation that exists within the Pacific Ocean and which causes cyclical drought and flood. The Philippines are also located on the Pacific 'Rim of Fire' and experience considerable seismic and volcanic activity. The relatively recent eruptions of Mount Pinatubo (1991) and Mount Mayon (2000 and 2001) led to many thousands of people being evacuated from their homes. In combination, the natural hazards to which the Philippines are exposed have the potential to cause many deaths and cost the nation millions of dollars in lost infrastructure and production.

There is little doubt that, as a nation, the Philippines has earned its title as a natural disaster hotspot. In a bid to produce more localised information about vulnerability to natural hazards, a team at the Manila Observatory recently undertook a project entitled 'Mapping Philippine vulnerability to environmental disasters'. It was hoped that through this project the various provinces of the Philippines could begin to plan for and manage the various natural hazards to which they are exposed.

One of the most useful pieces of information to emerge from the project was the map that showed 'Combined risk to climate disaster' (Figure 6). This map dealt with the Philippines on a province-by-province basis. It was produced by considering the sum of normalised risks in each province for the following climatic events:

- Typhoons (cyclones)
- Drought
- Projected rainfall changes
- Projected temperature changes.

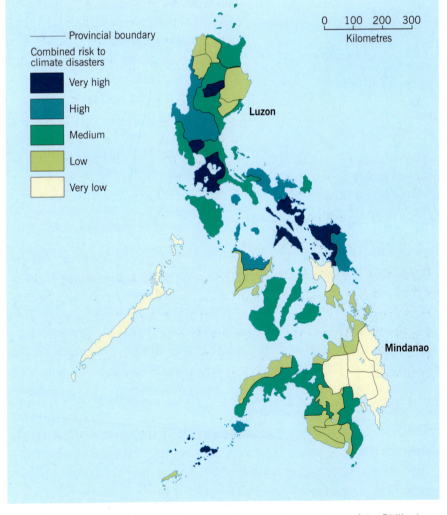

▲ **Figure 6:** Combined risk to climate disasters in the provinces of the Philippines.
Source: Manila Observatory www.observatory.ph/vm/findings.html

In a similar way, a 'Geophysical disaster risk' map was compiled (Figure 7). This map was produced by considering the sum of normalised risks in each province for the following geophysical hazards:

- Earthquakes
- Landslides
- Tsunamis
- Volcanoes.

Manila Observatory has since confirmed that the provincial areas of Central Luzon and Eastern Mindanao are at a 'high' to 'very high' level of risk from both hydro-meteorological and geophysical hazards. The study suggests taking this research a step further, by conducting localised studies that will help to identify the areas of highest priority within each province.

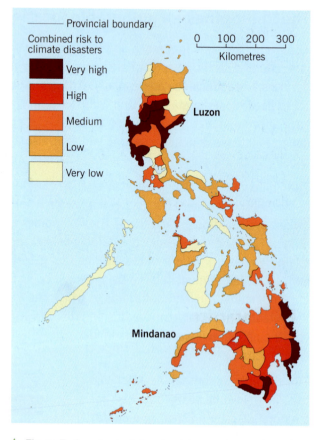

▲ **Figure 7:** Geophysical disaster risk map, for provinces in the Philippines.
Source: Manila Observatory /www.observatory.ph/vm/findings.html

Taking it further

What is the degree of correlation between geophysical risks and the risks posed by climate hazards in the Philippines?

What has occurred through the 'Mapping Philippine vulnerability to environmental disasters' project is a good example of the work that needs to be done if disaster hotspots are to be made less vulnerable to natural hazards.

Case study: Colombia – working to reduce its vulnerability

In 2006, the World Bank approved a $260 m loan to Colombia through its 'Natural disaster vulnerability reduction project'. The aim of this 5-year project is to help the Colombian nation to manage the risks posed to its financial stability through natural hazards. This is very important, given that Colombia's location incorporates the Andes mountains and borders on the Pacific Ocean's 'Rim of Fire'. As such, Colombia regularly experiences hazards such as earthquakes, volcanic activity, torrential rain, landslides and flooding. In the period between 1980 and 2005, Colombia experienced six significant earthquakes, three volcanic eruptions and a number of landslide and flood events.

The Colombian 'Vulnerability reduction project' has the stated aim of better managing the risks posed by natural hazards within 'high-risk places' as well as 'high national income areas'. This reflects the fact that the direct and indirect costs of hazards upon the Colombian economy have been crippling in the past. With high-risk areas being highly urbanised and containing much of the nation's industry, and in the face of uncertainties about climate change, the time to better manage the risks is now.

Summary

Having studied this chapter, you should be able to discuss these ideas and concepts and provide located examples of them:

- The real or potential natural hazard risks in your local area, based on evidence about past or likely future events and their impact on people, property and the environment.
- The global distribution of the world's major hydro-meteorological hazards and geophysical hazards, with maps and reports.
- The causes and impacts of natural hazards in disaster hotspots.
- Comparisons of how multiple disasters affect developed and less developed regions, using case studies.
- How multiple hazards are managed on the California coast, and in the Philippines, a vulnerable location.

MCQ

Exam practice

Study the map which shows areas at high risk from major natural hazards.

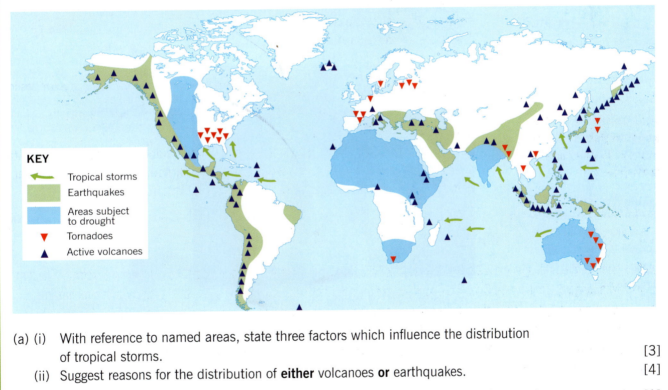

KEY

← Tropical storms

Earthquakes

Areas subject to drought

▼ Tornadoes

▲ Active volcanoes

(a) (i)   With reference to named areas, state three factors which influence the distribution of tropical storms. [3]

   (ii) Suggest reasons for the distribution of **either** volcanoes **or** earthquakes. [4]

(b) (i)   Annotate the map to identify one multi-hazard zone using your own knowledge and the map. [1]

   (ii) Justify your choice. [4]

Chapter 4 Is global warming a recent short-term phenomenon or should it be seen as part of longer-term climate change?

Key terms

Biophysical
Carbon dioxide
Climate modelling
Fossil fuels
Ice cores
Insolation
Methane
Nitrous oxide
Palaeoclimatic
Parts per million (ppm)
Parts per billion (ppb)
Radiative forcing
Third Assessment Report
United Nations Framework
  Convention on Climate
  Change (UNFCCC)

Taking it further

To learn more about the debate surrounding climate change read 'Consensus, what consensus?' on your Student CD-ROM.

Learning objectives

After studying this chapter, you will be able to discuss these ideas and concepts and provide located examples of them:

• The current phenomenon of global warming should be set in the context of longer-term, medium-term and short-term climate change.
• A range of evidence from ecology, historical records and climate change is available to help set global warming in context.
• The causes of climate change may be both natural and anthropogenic (human).
• Recent climate change (global warming) is unprecedented in historical terms and scientists now argue that human causes may be more to blame.
• Global warming might be a natural trend in longer-term climate variations.

◀ **Figure 1:** Since the dawn of the Industrial Revolution, the temperature of the globe has risen. The evidence of the effects of a warmer planet are starkly apparent in the polar regions of the earth.

The world is warming, and this trend is expected to continue. However, there are some variations in the estimates of how much the earth will warm in the next 100 years as climate change can be difficult to predict. Current research estimates that average global temperatures will increase by between 1.8 and 4.0 °C in the next 100 years. We should note that even the minimum estimates of temperature increase represent a climate that is warming more rapidly than any 100-year climate trend that has occurred in the last 10,000 years.

Until relatively recently, some scientists have argued that the current warming trend is part of a naturally occurring cycle. However, there is now a range of evidence to suggest that human activities are the most likely cause of the present global warming phenomenon. This point has recently been acknowledged and accepted by most of the world's governments, with the release of the *Fourth Assessment Report* from the Intergovernmental Panel on Climate Change (IPCC).

Evidence of a changing world

Warmer global temperatures have led to an increase in evaporation rates, which has been felt differently in various regions of the world. In the tropics, which are some of the wetter parts of the earth, increased evaporation has led to an increase in rainfall. The effect in the drier parts of the globe has been the opposite. Increased evaporation has made water scarcer. The worst affected regions are those of the Sahel, in Africa. In the catchment basins of Niger, Lake Chad and Senegal, there has been a 40 to 60% reduction in the total amount of water that is available. Reduced amounts of rainfall have had the effect of lowering soil moisture and making the existing problems of drought and desertification much worse. The Mediterranean region and parts of southern Asia have been affected in a similar way.

Whilst rainfall is declining in some regions, the frequency of heavy rainfall events has increased in many parts of the world. This has been most noticeable in North and South America, northern Europe and northern and central Asia. Increased rates of evaporation will result in more water vapour being present in the atmosphere. At the same time, warmer oceans are expected to give rise to an increased intensity of tropical cyclones. This trend has been evident in the North Atlantic since the 1970s (the absence of satellite imagery before then makes it difficult to track this trend further back in time).

The decline of winter

With a warming world, the season of 'winter' seems to be entering into decline. This has been most noticeable in the polar regions, where the effects of global warming are more easily apparent. During the past 100 years, the Arctic region has experienced a warming trend twice the rate of the remainder of the world. Ice sheets and snow cover have melted. Collectively, the northern hemisphere has had a 10% reduction in the amount of snow cover in its mid- to high latitude regions since the 1960s. As glaciers have retreated, the amount of water contained in glacial lakes has increased. It is estimated that Switzerland lost two-thirds of the volume of its glaciers during the twentieth century.

The loss of snow and ice from the polar regions has also impacted on sea level. Meltwater from Greenland and Antarctica has been one of the main contributors to the rapid rise in sea level that has occurred in recent decades. Between 1961 and 2003, the average global rise in sea level was 1.8 mm per year. However, from 1993 to 2003, the annual rate of increase was much faster at 3.1 mm per year.

Changes in the natural world

There have also been changes in the natural world that reveal the impacts of global warming. A recent publication by the *United Nations Framework Convention on Climate Change* (UNFCCC) estimated that climate change is now thought to be responsible for altering at least 420 physical processes or biological communities across the globe.

Case study: Biophysical changes in the Alps

The effects of climate change upon the natural world have shown up in interesting ways. In the Alps, for example, there are some plant species that have been forced into higher regions of the mountains, as increasing temperatures have caused their habitats to disappear from areas lower down the slopes. For some species of plant, this 'retreat' has occurred at the rate of 1 to 4 metres per decade. At the same time, some plant species have not been able to cope with the warming climate, and have completely disappeared from mountain slopes. There are species of moth, butterfly, beetle and dragonfly that are now found at higher altitudes than ever before, because the increase in temperature has allowed them to prosper further up the mountain.

▲ **Figure 2:** Unique alpine plants such as *Arenaria tetraquetra* could be threatened by the warming climate.

Summarising the changes

There is now much evidence that the climate of the earth is changing. These changes have been observed in local areas, and on a global scale. The direct changes that have been observed include:

- Increases in global average air temperatures
- Increases in global average sea temperatures
- Melting of snow and ice
- Rising global average sea level.

All of these changes point to a warming planet. The phenomenon of global warming will also bring a range of indirect changes, including:

- Changes in rainfall patterns
- Changes in wind regimes
- Changes in the nature of extreme weather events (droughts, floods, cyclones)
- Changes in the biophysical world.

Climate change in context

Equally important work lies in understanding the climate of the past. By studying the evidence contained in the earth's 'palaeoclimatic record', it is possible for scientists to make inferences about the climatic regimes that have existed in the past.

Since the release of the IPCC's *Third Assessment Report* in 2001, there have been efforts to improve the reliability of our estimates of the earth's climatic history. Scientists have begun to analyse multiple indicators of past climates (such as ice cores, tree rings, fossil pollen), looking for similarities in the climatic evidence across a range of indicators and a range of locations. As a result, the most recent interpretations of palaeoclimatic data are considered to be sounder than previously.

Case study: Studying the climate of the past

Much palaeoclimatic evidence is to be found in ice cores, which are columns of ice that are 'drilled' out from deep within ice sheets in the polar regions. The samples contain molecules of 'ancient air' that were trapped within the ice when it formed. Scientists can study these molecules to obtain data on the composition of gases within the atmosphere at the time the ice was formed. With their knowledge of atmospheric processes, scientists can use this information to infer what the climate of the earth must have been like at these times. In effect, the ice core samples are 'time capsules' of the earth's past, which will better enable us to predict its future.

Natural cycles of warming and cooling

Natural cycles of warming and cooling are evident in the earth's climatic record. By studying the palaeoclimatic record of the earth, scientists have found that over time, the earth has experienced periods that were either warmer or colder than the present.

The findings are of great importance because they allow us to put the current phenomenon of global warming into context. This allows us to make judgements as to whether present-day global warming is part of a natural cycle or fluctuation, or whether it is occurring because of anthropogenic influences.

There are a number of well-known physical causes of climate change that certainly explain most of the earth's climate history and obviously contribute in various degrees to current changes.

Variations in the Earth's orbit

The Serbian engineer Milankovitch developed a theory that tried to explain climate change, especially the episodes of glaciation in 'recent' Earth history. He studied the variations in the Earth's orbit including its mildly eccentric orbit around the sun, its tendency to 'wobble' on its axis and variations in the tilt of the axis. These changes operate in different time frames but all of them have an impact on temperature especially since they create differences between summer and winter conditions, making them either more or less extreme. When the troughs and peaks of all three cycles coincide, then they exert the greatest influence. Until recently Milankovitch's calculations have been interesting but without any real support from past climate history. However, recent technological breakthroughs allow us to measure temperatures using ice core samples from both Greenland and Antarctica and these provide much support for his theory.

Variations in solar output

Historically, the output of the sun was regarded as being constant, hence measurement of the amount of energy arriving at the edge of the atmosphere is known as the 'solar constant'. Once again better technology has allowed us re-valuate this. For example, in an 18-month period in the late 1980s satellite measurements recorded a drop of 0.1% in solar output. If that trend was to continue it could certainly influence global climate. Models suggest that a 1% fall in solar output would reduce temperatures by about 1 °C on average. Scientists have long tried to link climate change to sunspot activity; when sunspots are active the surface of the sun cools by 6 °C (not much it is true given that surface temperatures are around 5,000 °C).

However, there is not much supportive data; on the contrary, during the little Ice Age (1650-1750) there was very little sunspot activity.

Volcanic eruptions

In the 1960s and 1970s the consensus view was that the earth was getting cooler. Some of the fiercest voices supporting the anthropogenic view of global warming today were, in their relative youth, keen advocates of the global cooling 'party'. Some of the blame for this was attributed to volcanic eruptions.

The theory here is much more straightforward and there is much more evidence out there to support the idea that volcanic eruptions do cause climate to cool. The coldest year in the past 2 centuries occurred in 1815 following the Tambora eruption. It used to be thought that the culprit was volcanic dust blocking incoming solar radiation but it is now widely agreed to the result of sulphur dioxide remaining in the atmosphere for up to three years after an eruption reacting with water vapour to form a dense optically opaque 'haze' in the upper atmosphere. Recent eruption by El Chichon in Mexico (1982) and Pinatubo in the Philippines (1991) caused a drop in global temperature of between 0.8 °C and 1.1 °C. This type of 'global dimming' affect can also be caused by man emitting sulphur dioxide in a large number of industrial processes, most notably the burning of fossil fuels.

The present rate of global warming is unprecedented

Whilst the phenomenon of global warming is not unusual in the earth's climatic history, the real cause for concern is the rate at which it is occurring. The *Fourth Assessment Report* reveals that global average land temperatures have increased across all of the earth's continental areas in the last hundred years (Figure 3).

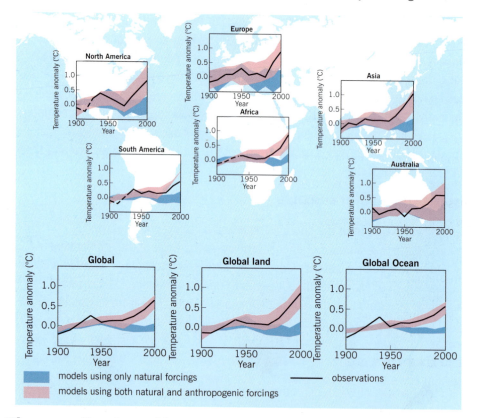

▶ Figure 3: Global temperature change by continent in the twentieth century. Note the correspondence between the observed increases in temperature (black lines) and the results obtained in computer models that used both natural and anthropogenic forcing of climate (pink shading), as opposed to these that considered natural forcing alone.
Source: 'Climate Change 2007: The Physical Science Basis', contribution of Working Group I to the *Fourth Assessment Report* of the IPCC, p.11.

The contribution of humankind to global warming

Evidence is now available that the current phenomenon of global warming is largely due to the actions of humans. The *Fourth Assessment Report* makes the following statement:

'Most of the observed increase in global average temperatures since the mid-twentieth century is very likely due to the observed increase in anthropogenic greenhouse gas concentrations.'
Source: 'Climate Change 2007: The Physical Science Basis', contribution of Working Group I to the *Fourth Assessment Report* of the IPCC

These findings are backed by climate modelling. Present day conditions (in terms of global land and sea temperatures) can only be simulated in the computer models when significant anthropogenic contributions to the climate are included. In other words, the warming trend of today's world is not the result of natural changes within the planetary system in isolation. Humans have had an involvement – though we have yet to determine how much.

The impact of greenhouse gases

The earth's climatic system is a balancing act among the factors of insolation, the atmosphere and the surface of the planet. Whilst the presence of greenhouse gases in the atmosphere is vital in making the earth warm enough to support life, it is now clear that humans have significantly altered the balance of the earth's climatic system through anthropogenic changes to the atmosphere and the land surface of the earth.

The atmospheric concentration of greenhouse gases has increased dramatically since 1750. The biggest increases have occurred in the concentrations of carbon dioxide (CO_2), methane (CH_4) and nitrous oxide (N_2O) gases. There is now a raft of atmospheric data to show that humankind is responsible for emitting these gases in ever-increasing quantities since the Industrial Revolution.

CO_2 is often referred to as the 'prime' greenhouse gas. In pre-industrial times, its concentration in the atmosphere was just 280 parts per million (ppm). By 2005, this figure had increased to 379 ppm. The increase in the concentration of CO_2 is directly attributable to the burning of fossil fuels, such as coal, oil and gas. During the 1990s, the average annual CO_2 emissions from burning fossil fuels was equivalent to 6.4 gigatonnes of carbon. Worryingly, in the first 5 years of the new millennium, this figure increased to 7.2 gigatonnes of carbon.

Land use changes also contribute to a higher concentration of CO_2 in the atmosphere. Development activities that involve the clearing of vegetation (especially forests) to allow for the establishment of new land uses, such as agriculture, industry or housing, effectively reduce the number of plants that can act as CO_2 filters. The contribution of CO_2 from land use changes is much smaller, on an annual scale, than that which arises from the burning of fossil fuels. During the 1990s, the average annual contribution resulting from land use changes was 1.6 gigatonnes of carbon. Although smaller, this figure is still significant in the overall picture of the increasing atmospheric concentration of CO_2.

Radiative forcing

Scientists now talk of changes to the energy balance of the climate system in terms of 'radiative forcing'. This concept describes the way in which various factors are able to change the net irradiance of the climate system.

Radiative forcing is measured in units of Watts per square metre (W/m^2). It can be expressed as either a positive or negative amount. Positive forcing enhances the warming trend of the atmosphere, whilst negative forcing promotes cooling.

The concept of radiative forcing allows us to compare the influences of natural cycles and anthropogenic activities on the climate. It can be used to quantify the effect of greenhouse gas emissions on the climate system.

Key terms

Insolation: incoming solar radiation.

Key terms

Radiative forcing: a measure of the relative contributions of anthropogenic activities and natural cycles to the changing climate.

Taking it further

To learn more about CO_2 in the atmosphere read 'The historical record on CO_2' on your Student CD-ROM.

The combined contribution of three of the best known greenhouse gases, namely carbon dioxide, methane and nitrous oxide, is +2.30 W/m^2, representing the fact they have led to an increase in global temperatures. Radiative forcing can also be used to compare anthropogenic impacts with the changes that have occurred in natural systems and processes. The only change in a natural system that has been identified as making a contribution is an increase in solar irradiance since pre-industrial times. This means that the energy received by the earth from the sun has in fact increased since the 1700s. However, this increase has had a relatively small impact on the climate system, with a radiative forcing contribution of just +0.12 W/m^2.

Clearly, the impact of anthropogenic activities upon the climate system is much greater than that of changes in natural processes. In a 'net' sense, the radiative forcing resulting from human activities is 1.6 W/m^2.

Climate change phenomena and trends

The IPCC's *Fourth Assessment Report* paints a very vivid picture of the specific climatic phenomena and trends that our planet experienced during the twentieth century (Figure 4). It also sets out the likelihood that these trends are due to anthropogenic contributions.

Phenomenon and direction of trend	Likelihood that trend occurred in late twentieth century (typically post-1960)	Likelihood of a human contribution to observed trend	Likelihood of future trends based on projections for twenty-first century using SRES scenarios
Warmer and fewer cold days and nights over most land areas	Very likely (a)	Likely (b)	Virtually certain (b)
Warmer and more frequent hot days and nights over most land areas	Very likely (c)	Likely (nights) (b)	Virtually certain (b)
Warm spells/heat waves. Frequency increases over most land areas	Likely	More likely than not (d)	Very likely
Heavy precipitation events. Frequency (or proportion of total rainfall from heavy falls) increases over most areas	Likely	More likely than not (d)	Very likely
Area affected by droughts increases	Likely in many regions since 1970s	More likely than not	Likely
Intense tropical cyclone activity increases	Likely in some regions since 1970s	More likely than not (d)	Likely
Increased incidence of extreme high sea level (excludes tsunamis) (e)	Likely	More likely than not (d, f)	Likely (g)

▲ Figure 4: The various phenomena of climate change and their trends, past and future.

Notes

'More likely than not' = more than 50% chance of occurring
'Likely' = more than 66% chance of occurring
'Very likely' = more than 90% chance of occurring
(a) Decreased frequency of cold days and nights (coldest 10%)
(b) Warming of the most extreme days and nights each year
(c) Increased frequency of hot days and nights (hottest 10%)
(d) Magnitude of anthropogenic contributions not assessed. Attribution for these phenomena based on expert judgement rather than formal attribution studies.
(e) Extreme high sea level depends on average sea level and on regional weather systems. It is defined here as the highest 1% of hourly values of observed sea level at a station for a given reference period.
(f) Changes in observed extreme high sea level closely follow the changes in average sea level. It is very likely that anthropogenic activity contributed to a rise in average sea level.
(g) In all scenarios, the projected global average sea level at 2100 is higher than in the reference period. The effect of changes in regional weather systems on sea level extremes has not been assessed.

Source: 'Climate Change 2007: The Physical Science Basis', contribution of Working Group I to the *Fourth Assessment Report* of the IPCC, p. 8. www.ipcc.ch

Summary

This chapter has demonstrated that climate change is not a new phenomenon. The earth's palaeoclimatic record reveals that the earth's climate has been warmer in the past than it is at present.

The changes that the earth is experiencing in the natural world demonstrate that the impact of climate change is already being felt. Although climate change itself is not unprecedented, it is the rate at which the climate is changing that is the real cause for concern.

The work of the Intergovernmental Panel on Climate Change has been fundamental to our understanding of the mechanism of global warming and the process of climate change. There is now much evidence to suggest that it is anthropogenic factors which are most responsible for the present phenomenon of climate change.

The burning of fossil fuels to power human industries releases damaging greenhouse gases into the atmosphere. The gases of most concern include carbon dioxide, methane and nitrous oxide. The world must act to reduce the emission of such gases immediately.

MCQ

Exam practice

Study the map below – Who's to blame?

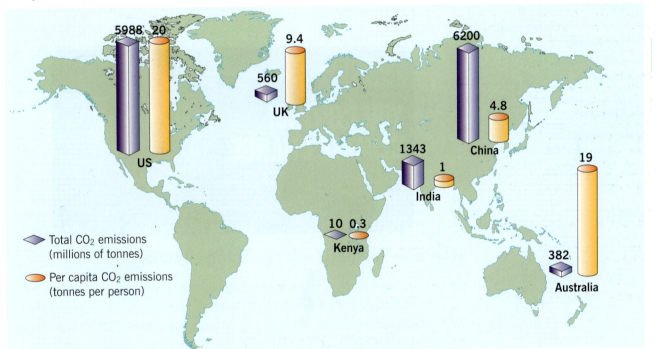

(a) Name the two countries with the highest overall emissions. For each, suggest a reason. [4]

(b) (i) Name the country which has the lowest emissions per capita. [1]

    (ii) Suggest reasons for this. [3]

(c) Suggest reasons for the differences shown between the overall emissions totals and the per capita emissions for the six countries shown. [4]

CHAPTER 5 What are the impacts of climate change and why should we be concerned?

Key terms

Adaptive capacity
Best case scenario
Coral bleaching
Dryland agriculture
Emissions
Eustatic
Feedback
Indigenous
Lag time
Marginal
Meltwaters
Multiple stresses
Permafrost
Sea ice
Scenario families
Special Report on Emissions
 Scenarios
Stern review
Storm Surge
Tipping point
Water stress
Worst case scenario

Learning objectives

After studying this chapter, you will be able to discuss these ideas and concepts and provide located examples of them:

- The direct impacts of projected climate changes.
- Environmental and ecological impacts of Arctic warming in the Arctic region.
- The complexities of environmental impacts across the African continent and how they could lead to disasters for those people living in poverty.
- The indirect impacts of projected climate changes, such as the eustatic rise in sea level (global inundation).
- Impacts of climate change are difficult to predict, and emissions scenarios (such as the IPCC model) may vary – from 'business as usual' to 'sustainable' – and could be affected by attempts to manage the impacts of climate change.
- Evidence that combined impacts could lead to catastrophic, irreversible changes and contribute to a more hazardous world.

► **Figure 1:** A European Commission advertisement. There is now a global consensus that climate change is real. We must recognise that through our actions we can at least mitigate some of its impacts.

Acknowledgement of a changing climate

Global warming has been better understood by the scientific community in recent years. At the same time, there has been a growing consensus about the nature of climate change and the way that its effects are already being felt on the planet. The international community at last acknowledges that climate change is the most pressing issue that confronts humankind. The consensus in the international community now acknowledges that climate change is the one of the most pressing issues confronting humankind.

Even so, climate scientists tend to release a range of change forecasts because of the natural variability in climate. These forecasts range from 'best case scenarios', in which the degree of change is the least, through to 'worst case scenarios', which, as the name suggests, are the least desirable options for humankind, and predict negative impacts on a massive scale.

At this stage, it is important to note that even the best case scenarios of climate change carry with them significant impacts, both for the human race and the general health of the planet. The minimum rise in average global temperature for the present century is expected to be more than double the increase that occurred throughout the twentieth century. This forecast, and other examples of climate change which will be explored in this chapter, are indicative of the fact that the rate at which the climate is changing is faster than had been previously imagined.

Research carried out by Working Group II for the Intergovernmental Panel on Climate Change (IPCC), who reported on 'Impacts, adaptation and vulnerability in relation to climate change' concluded that some regions will be more vulnerable to the effects of climate change than others. In the same sense, some regions will be better able to address and deal with the likely changes because they have a higher 'adaptive capacity' than other regions.

Key terms

Adaptive capacity: the ability of a nation to adapt to and overcome the obstacles that change presents.

Case study: The price of emissions

The present phenomenon of global warming is occurring at an unprecedented rate. Potentially more frightening is the fact that even if humankind could instantly cut its greenhouse gas emissions to the point where they had no net radiative forcing, the climate would continue to change for some time. An analysis of the earth's climatic record has shown that there is a 'lag time' between the emission of greenhouse gases and the warming effect that results from their entry into the atmospheric system. Therefore, the impacts of climate change that are being felt today are the 'price tag' for emissions that occurred decades ago. Moving forward in time, humankind can expect to pay a similar or even heavier price for the emissions that have occurred more recently, in addition to those of today and tomorrow.

Compulsory case study

Africa – the economic impact on the poor

There is little doubt that Africa is one of the planet's most vulnerable regions in terms of climate change. Much of the continent is characterised by large variations in climate, with tracts of land that are considered 'inhospitable' or of low development potential, and yet still have people living on them. At the same time, the adaptive capacity of most African nations is relatively low. This increases the potential for significant impacts to be felt by the African population.

Changing patterns of rainfall are expected to have an immediate impact on the existing forms of agriculture that occur in Africa. The worst affected agricultural regions are likely to be those that currently occupy the more marginal areas of the continent, in arid and semi-arid regions. As rainfall declines, growing seasons will shorten correspondingly. The net result of these changes is that the potential yield of many of Africa's farming areas will be significantly reduced. In areas of dryland agriculture, where the water needs of farmers are completely dependent on rainfall (Figure 2), potential yields may decrease by as much as 50% by 2020, exacerbating existing problems of malnutrition. Broadly, changing patterns of rainfall will effectively reduce the total amount of land in Africa that is considered to be 'arable'.

Taking it further

To learn more about the causes of famine in regions of Africa read 'Natural or human disaster?' on your Student CD-ROM.

▲ **Figure 2:** The impact of declining rainfall will hit hard in areas of dryland agriculture.

In these dryland areas of Africa, as rainfall declines, significant water stress is likely to occur in communities that are already under pressure from drought and famine. It is estimated that between 75 and 250 million Africans will face increased levels of water stress by 2020. This could be exacerbated if Africa experiences a growing demand for water over the course of the next decade. Such demand could emanate from increases in population or to meet the needs of developing agricultural and industrial activities.

The indirect impacts of climate change in Africa

Taking it further

What other indirect costs would be felt as a result of sea-level changes in Africa?

In addition to the direct climatic changes in temperature and rainfall patterns, there are other indirect impacts that are likely to be felt within Africa. As global temperatures continue to rise, there will be a corresponding rise in the water temperature of lakes, rivers and streams, making them less hospitable to many species of fish. Freshwater sources in coastal areas are also likely to be contaminated by the encroachment of salty seawater, which will negatively affect fish stocks. As a result, food supplies in communities that are dependent on locally caught fish are affected.

The adaptive capacity of many African nations will be severely challenged by the threat of sea level rise. For coastal or low-lying African communities, adaptive work will need to be undertaken in response to the rising level of the sea, but it will be costly. This will include direct costs, such as those incurred as land use activities are relocated to other areas. There is also a range of indirect costs inherent in adaptation. For example, some nations will bear the obvious cost of the loss of previously productive farmland to the rising sea.

Case study: The complications posed by multiple stresses

Recent estimates show that in those African nations likely to be affected by sea level rise, as much as 5 to 10% of GDP might need to be spent on adaptive work. For many nations on the African continent, spending such amounts of national wealth to adapt to climate change may just not be possible. Of course, African nations face a range of multiple stresses from a whole host of issues, not just those relating to climate. Those nations beset by poverty, disease or conflict (in addition to drought, famine and climate change) will struggle to adapt and, as such, are highly vulnerable to the impacts of a changing climate.

Compulsory case study

The Arctic – the environmental and ecological impact

Like Africa, the polar regions of the world are also severely challenged by climate change. The Arctic has in fact warmed more quickly than any other region on earth whilst the Antarctic Peninsula has also experienced significant warming. In recent years, the global community has been shocked by images from these isolated and remote parts of the planet. Large chunks of ice collapsing into the sea, rapidly melting glaciers and polar bears struggling to find enough ice to live on are images that have quickly brought home the realities of global warming, as they appear much starker in the bleak polar regions.

Put at its simplest, global warming will significantly reduce the area and thickness of ice and snow coverage in polar regions. In the unique Arctic environment, this problem will be compounded by the melting of sea ice and permafrost. Reductions in the area of ice will bring significant impacts to the wildlife found in the Arctic, especially the higher-order animals that operate at the top of food chains, such as polar bears, seals and whales (Figure 3).

People who live in the Arctic are also likely to experience some significant changes to their way of life as the environment around them changes. Some of the environmental changes will be direct, such as the loss or extinction of species that have been a traditional part of indigenous diets. Other changes will, at first, be subtle, such as variations in the migration patterns or breeding habits of polar wildlife. It is important to note the significance of these changes to indigenous communities, who have traditionally co-existed with their environment.

▲ **Figure 3:** Polar bears and other higher-order Arctic predators are expected to suffer as climate changes significantly reduce the area of sea ice and permafrost.

Much like people living in Africa, the human inhabitants of the Arctic will also face losing some of their land to the sea. However, the nature of this loss will be quite different. Quite literally, the melting of sea ice and permafrost will result in the direct loss of hunting grounds for them, as land slips into the sea. Infrastructure, although relatively limited over much of the Arctic, is also threatened.

The indigenous people of the Arctic have a relatively low adaptive capacity, much like the nations of the African continent. Their ability to relocate dwellings or associated infrastructure in the face of reductions in the area of sea ice and permafrost is limited by low levels of development and, in some case, their traditional ways of life. There are concerns that without substantial assistance from sources outside of the Arctic communities, whole cultures and ways of life could be at risk.

Taking it further

To learn more about the impact of Arctic warming read 'It's getting warmer — one cheer, two cheers?' on your Student CD-ROM.

Case study: Could the Arctic 'benefit' from climate change?

Interestingly, climate change brings a strange 'benefit' to the Arctic, but whether this is a 'positive' depends on your point of view. With global warming reducing the area of sea ice in the Arctic, the whole region in fact becomes more navigable by canoe, boat or ship. This is especially true with respect to the Arctic winter, when large areas of the polar region are usually inaccessible due to ice. Reductions in the area of sea ice could have the effect of improving transport and communication for the local communities. And in a bizarre twist, in a warmer world, heating costs are also expected to be lower in the Arctic.

The global impact of sea level rise

Here is one indirect impact of climate change which will register across the globe – in regions as diverse as Africa and the poles. This is the eustatic (global) rise in average sea level. Just as it is now accepted that the earth has warmed significantly since the Industrial Revolution, it is also generally accepted that significant changes in sea level have occurred. Today's average global sea level is 10 to 20 cm higher than compared to pre-industrial times.

Sea level rise is a serious threat to nations across the globe. Not only will the basic shape of nations and continents be affected, but also significant tracts of land, much of it highly productive, will be lost to the oceans. Compounding this is the threat to the populations and infrastructure of coastal and low-lying communities. The inestimable loss of biodiversity that would occur as habitats such as coral reefs, coastal mangroves and river deltas disappear is yet another problem, and one that is often overlooked.

Many nations will face some tough decisions in the face of rising sea levels. It will be the job of politicians and decision-makers to balance the potential losses of productive land to sea level rise with the costs of relocating the land uses affected. Current projections suggest that by 2080, millions of people have been flooded each year by the rising seas. There is no doubt that the relocation of people and land uses from affected regions would be extremely costly – as we have already seen it would be well beyond the adaptive capacity of many of the world's poorer nations. Deaths are expected to occur as a result of the inability of some nations to address the relocation needs of their populations.

The impact on small islands and deltas

Some of the areas likely to be worst affected by sea level rise are the small islands. Many of these are found within the tropical oceans, especially within the Indian and Pacific Oceans. Other small islands are located throughout the higher latitudes of the Atlantic Ocean. Regardless of their geographical location, small islands are particularly vulnerable to climate change, and especially to sea level rise. In the short term, sea level rise is expected to increase the exposure of small islands to storm surges, coral bleaching and erosion. These impacts will have a negative effect on the island community, threatening local industries such as fishing and tourism. In the longer term, the very existence of many small islands is threatened by potential inundation by the sea.

As we have seen in Chapter 2, rapid development and urbanisation has occurred within the megadeltas of the earth, including the Nile, the Mekong and the Ganges-Brahmaputra. Climate change brings disaster for these highly populated regions when sea levels rise. Of all the coastal areas within Asia, it is the megadeltas of South, East and South East Asia that are most at risk. These areas can expect to be among the first to be flooded by the sea. It is projected that in some instances megadeltas could also be flooded by the rivers which create them as their volue is swelled in areas that experience an increase in rainfall or snowmelt due to climate change.

Case study: The hidden impacts of sea level rise

Sea level rise has the added negative impact of contaminating supplies of freshwater. Above ground, salty seawater can pollute rivers, estuaries, lakes or any freshwater system, including irrigation systems vital to farming. Salt water can also contaminate groundwater. This has already occurred in Israel and Thailand, where underground supplies of freshwater have become salty. The deltas of the world are affected in a similar way. In addition, their highly fertile soils are becoming corrupted with salt and rendered useless for farming. This has already had significant impacts in China's Yangtze Delta.

Sea level rise set to continue

Due to climate processes and feedbacks, it is apparent that the sea level will continue to rise in coming decades, irrespective of future reductions in greenhouse gas emissions. In a warmer world, sea level rise occurs because of two reasons. The first reason is that the oceans will absorb some of this extra heat and that water molecules will expand because of this. This is referred to as thermal expansion. Secondly, because warmer temperatures will result in melting of snow and ice cover, meltwaters form which have the potential to raise sea levels significantly more than thermal expansion. For example, the melting of Greenland's ice and snow coverage is expected to make a contribution to the rising sea level long after 2100, whatever the level of emission reductions made between now and the end of this century. If, in the worst case scenario, the Greenland ice sheet was to melt completely, the corresponding rise in average global sea level would be an incredible 7 metres! It is estimated that the complete melting of the ice sheet that overlays West Antarctica would, by itself, contribute a further 5 metre rise in the average global sea level.

Taking it further

Only the melting of snow and ice on land surfaces will contribute to sea level rise – the melting of sea ice will not. Can you explain why? (Hint: consider what happens to the level of liquid in a glass as ice blocks melt in your drinks.)

Simulating the future

It is evident that across the globe, much more work needs to be done as various regions adapt to climate change. This adaptation needs to occur in relation to both observed changes in the climate (things that have already happened) and anticipated changes (things that are expected to happen in the future). For example, the Australian government is talking of a national plan to 'tackle' the water crisis, in recognition of the fact that Australia's climate is drying and that a joint approach of the various Australian states is required to successfully adapt to this change. Other adaptive projects have tackled the anticipated climate changes. In the Netherlands, recent work on the coastal defences have factored predictions of rising sea levels into calculations.

One of the factors that increases the difficulty of predicting the future climate is that the nature of how the climate will change in the future is dependent upon other factors. Principal among these is the consideration of the amount of greenhouse gases that will be emitted from anthropogenic sources in the decades to come. Above all else, our attempt to reduce the amount of greenhouse gases that we produce has the potential to at least slow down the pace of climate change.

Emissions scenarios

To assist with its predictions and projections of the planet's future climate, the IPCC has recently published a *Special Report on Emissions Scenarios*. In this report, various 'storyline' and 'scenario families' were used to illustrate the effects that varying degrees of greenhouse gas mitigation will have on the climate of the future world. By basing climate projections on the average family unit in various global scenarios, the IPCC has in effect shown that we all have a part to play in the reduction of emissions.

Within the *Special Report on Emissions Scenarios* each storyline and scenario family is indicated by a letter and a number. The six scenarios and the themes associated with their storylines are as follows:

A1FI – a fossil fuel intensive future
A1T – non-fossil fuel energy sources
A1B – not relying too heavily on any one energy source (note: all A1 scenarios are based on a converging world with large reductions in regional differences in per capita income)
A2 – self-reliance and preservations of local identities
B1 – global solutions and improved equity
B2 – local solutions toward environmental protection.

It is worth investigating the various storylines and scenario families that were developed in this report as they give us an insight into how the future may play out (Figure 4).

▶ **Figure 4:** The six storylines and family scenarios that were developed as part of the IPCC's *Special Report on Emissions Scenarios*.
Source: 'Climate Change 2007: Impacts, Adaptation and Vulnerability', contribution of Working Group II to the *Fourth Assessment Report* of the IPCC, p. 22.

A1. The A1 storyline and scenario family describes a future world of very rapid economic growth, global population that peaks in mid-century and declines thereafter, and the rapid introduction of more efficient technologies. Major underlying themes are convergence among regions, capacity building and increased cultural and social interactions, with a substantial reduction in regional differences in per capita income. The A1 scenario family develops into three groups that describe alternative directions of technological change in the energy system. The three A1 groups are distinguished by their technological emphasis: fossil intensive (A1FI), non fossil energy sources (A1T), or a balance across all sources (A1B) (where balanced is defined as not relying too heavily on one particular energy source, on the assumption that similar improvement rates apply to all energy supply and end use technologies).

A2. The A2 storyline and scenario family describes a very heterogeneous world. The underlying theme is self reliance and preservation of local identities. Fertility patterns across regions converge very slowly, which results in continuously increasing population. Economic development is primarily regionally oriented and per capita economic growth and technological change more fragmented and slower than other storylines.

B1. The B1 storyline and scenario family describes a convergent world with the same global population, that peaks in mid-century and declines thereafter, as in the A1 storyline, but with rapid change in economic structures toward a service and information economy, with reductions in material intensity and the introduction of clean and resource efficient technologies. The emphasis is on global solutions to economic, social and environmental sustainability, including improved equity, but without additional climate initiatives.

B2. The B2 storyline and scenario family describes a world in which the emphasis is on local solutions to economic, social and environmental sustainability. It is a world with continuously increasing global population, at a rate lower than A2, intermediate levels of economic development, and less rapid and more diverse technological change than in the B1 and A1 storylines. While the scenario is also oriented towards environmental protection and social equity, it focuses on local and regional levels.

An illustrative scenario was chosen for each of the six scenario groups A1B, A1FI, A1T, A2, B1 and B2. All should be considered equally sound.

The SRES scenarios do not include additional climate initiatives, which means that no scenarios are included that explicitly assume implementation of the United Nations Framework Convention on Climate Change or the emissions targets of the Kyoto Protocol.

Clear paths to follow

The IPCC used the storylines and scenario families in their projections of future climate change to produce models of how the future climate may look (Figure 5).

With reference to the multi-model diagram (Figure 5), it is apparent that the best result in terms of future climate would be achieved by maintaining the concentration of atmospheric greenhouse gases at their level in the year 2000. Whilst this is not likely to occur, it is clear that the next best scenario for the planet is B1 (see Figure 4). This scenario was characterised by its focus on 'global solutions to economic, social and environmental sustainability'.

Compare this to the result achieved under the conditions of scenario A2. This storyline featured a world where the preservation of local interests and regional development was paramount. Self-reliance was favoured in preference to working in partnership with other affected parties. The net result of a scenario which very closely matches the present global village situation is a much, much warmer world.

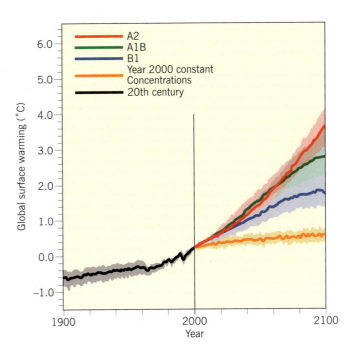

▲ **Figure 5:** Multi-model averages for surface warming, based on the scenarios used in the IPCC's *Special Report on Emissions Scenarios*.
Source: 'Climate Change 2007: Impacts, Adaptation and Vulnerability', contribution of Working Group II to the *Fourth Assessment Report* of the IPCC, p. 11.

The image of a catastrophic future

It is apparent that by warming the world we have created the potential for natural hazards to occur with greater magnitude. Storms have become noticeably more severe and their associated flood events more disastrous. Whilst there is some debate about how climate change will affect the frequency of tropical cyclones, it is agreed that the warmer oceans are helping to generate more intense hurricanes and typhoons. People living in coastal communities or on the flood plains of rivers are those most threatened by changes to the frequency or magnitude of extreme weather events. What worries some observers most is the notion of a 'tipping point'. Tipping points can occur during climate change when strong 'positive' feedbacks are set in motion by only moderate additional warming, rather like a snowball effect. Some studies find that global warming of 0.6 °C in the past 30 years has been driven mainly by increasing greenhouse gases, and only moderate additional climate change is likely to set in motion disintegration of the West Antarctic ice sheet and Arctic sea ice. Positive feedback that amplifies the change (makes the snowball bigger) includes increased absorption of sunlight as melting exposes darker surfaces and speedup of iceberg discharge as the warming ocean melts ice shelves that otherwise inhibit ice flow. Thus the trend accelerates beyond our control; hence the idea of a tipping point.

The latest predictions from the IPCC also point to significant changes in the general pattern of rainfall as it is experienced across the planet. For example, the 'Grain Belt' of North America, Australia's 'Wheatbelt', and much of southern Asia, are likely to experience a significant drying of the climate.

In Africa, the region that straddles the mid-latitudes south of the Sahara Desert, will experience declining rainfall. Reduced yields will impact on existing problems of malnutrition and disease in many parts of the African continent.

Taking it further

To read about the 2006 government review of global warming read 'The Stern Review' on your Student CD-ROM.

Key terms

The tipping point is when damage from climate change occurs irreversibly at an increasing rate.

Case study: Disaster for the natural world as well

Climate change does not affect humankind alone. The increasing warmth of the planet is also having a very real impact on the natural world. Latest estimates point to the possibility that up to 25% of the world's mammals and 12% of its bird species may be lost to extinction over the course of the next few decades. These high rates of extinction are in response to the effect that climate change is expected to have on the particular ecosystems that mammals and birds inhabit, with forests, rangelands and wetlands expected to be particularly badly affected. All of these areas will be more prone to damage from drought, fire and pests. This will also have an impact on how these natural resources can be utilised by humankind (see Figure 6).

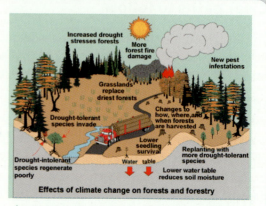

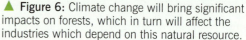

▲ **Figure 6:** Climate change will bring significant impacts on forests, which in turn will affect the industries which depend on this natural resource.

In the face of rapidly changing habitats, the opportunity for plants and animals to migrate to other, more hospitable areas is lessened by the continued degradation of the global environment by humans. This is thought to be in stark contrast to natural episodes of climate change that have occurred throughout the earth's long history. In prehistoric times, when the anthropogenic impact at a planetary scale was much lower, the natural world was better able to respond to a changing climate through the migration of species to more hospitable climes. Overall change occurred much more slowly than it is at present.

The same rings true for the human population. Within the course of human history, small groups and even larger populations of humans were able to respond to climate change by moving to new, uninhabited areas of the planet. In our currently overcrowded state, when there have never been more people on the earth, this option does not exist in the same way as it did in the past. There are fewer unoccupied places on the globe and ultimately, fewer ecological niches to be filled.

An inequitable future

The most striking aspect of everything we have considered so far about global warming is the inequity with which it will be experienced by the human population. The effects of climate change are not likely to be felt equally around the globe. There is no doubt that the people currently living in the more marginal areas of the planet will be the most affected by the changing climate. Most of these marginal areas exist in parts of the less developed world.

The paradox of global warming is that it is the developed world that is most responsible for the greenhouse gas emissions which have caused global warming, yet it is the people of these nations who can expect to be *least* affected by the changing climate. The relatively poor people of the less developed world are not only more vulnerable to climate change, but they also have less capacity to adapt to and cope with the onset of more frequent and intense natural hazards, a rising sea level, changing rainfall patterns and shortages of both food and water.

The challenge now is for our politicians and decision-makers to build on the hard work of the climate scientists. Global solutions are needed to these global problems, and the time to act is now.

Summary

The direct impacts of climate change are being felt in ecosystems across the planet. Average global temperatures have risen since the Industrial Revolution. Some regions of the earth are more vulnerable to change than others, and this chapter has looked at case studies of the impacts of the warming trend in Africa and the Arctic.

There are also a number of indirect impacts of climate change. The most significant of these is the eustatic rise in sea level. This will affect the millions of people who live in low-lying coastal regions, on the so-called megadeltas or on small islands.

Climate change will continue to occur in decades to come, as a result of greenhouse gas emissions that have been made in the past. Whilst it is difficult to predict the future, the projected impacts of climate change are also very serious. The IPCC has produced a range of future 'emissions scenarios' intended to help us predict the likely impacts of climate change in years to come. It is clear that work must be done now to reduce the emissions of the future.

MCQ

Exam practice

1. (a) (i) What is the tipping point?   [1]
        (ii) Suggest why there is such great concern that it could be reached.   [2]
    (b) Explain why the melting of glaciers and ice sheets can be concerns.
         (A) in the local area   (B) globally.   [4]
    (c) (i) Choose one area which is experiencing changing precipitation patterns.
        (ii) Suggest reasons why this is a problem.   [3]
    (d) Explain, with examples, how climate change could lead to growing numbers of
         environmental refugees.   [3]

2.

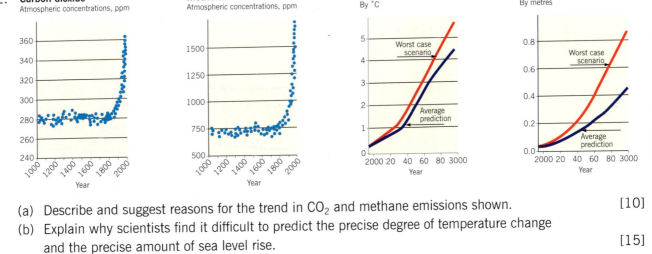

    (a) Describe and suggest reasons for the trend in CO$_2$ and methane emissions shown.   [10]
    (b) Explain why scientists find it difficult to predict the precise degree of temperature change
         and the precise amount of sea level rise.   [15]

CHAPTER 6 What are the strategies for managing climate change?

Key Terms

Annex 1 countries

Carbon sink

Clean development mechanism

Commitment period

Development pathway

Economies in transition

Emissions targets

Joint implementation

Marrakesh Accords

Non-climatic stresses

Offsetting

Organisation for Economic Co-operation and Development (OECD)

Peak emissions

Learning objectives

After studying this chapter, you will be able to discuss these ideas and concepts and provide located examples of them:

- Strategies attempt to limit the impacts of climate change at various scales.
- A number of strategies involve adapting to climate change.
- There are conflicting views on how to manage climate change.
- The key players involved in managing climate change include governments, businesses, non-governmental organisations (NGOs), individuals and groups.
- Global agreements are complex and affect specific countries.
- Global strategies for managing climate change are needed at all scales, and progress is likely to be incremental.

▶ **Figure 1:** One popular way to deal with gas emissions is to wear a face mask. But is this a strategy to address climate change or a short-term adaptation?

Climate change is now widely considered to be a reality. In the face of unprecedented social and environmental changes, the nations of the world are now looking for strategies to help them deal with it.

It is also acknowledged that the impacts of climate change will continue to be felt for many decades into the future. The climate will continue to change as a result of the greenhouse gas emissions that were made long in the past. Present emissions, and those that will occur in the near future, will also contribute to climate change.

Adapting to the changing climate and mitigating its impacts

It is clear that action is required to help the communities of the world to adapt to the climatic conditions that will prevail in the future. Adaptation suggests that nations will need to make changes in order to protect their populations, infrastructure, and ultimately, their standard of living. Adaptive practices are already starting to occur at the local, national and international levels.

It must be stressed that adaptive practices do not help to solve the problem of climate change. They are not focused on reducing harmful greenhouse gas emissions, and as such, do nothing to prevent global warming. The sole purpose of adaptive practices is to manage the impacts of climate change – to protect populations and infrastructures. Adaptation refers to the idea that, even if we can't control or limit climate change, there are things we can do to lessen its impacts.

Case study: Encouraging adaptation

The European Union (EU) is dedicated to helping the nations of Europe work together to achieve 'peace and prosperity'. Currently, the EU has 27 member nations. The EU has been heavily involved in helping its member nations to prepare for and adapt to climate change. In the face of changing rainfall patterns across the European continent, the EU has encouraged farmers to take a flexible approach to managing their farms. A key feature of this flexibility has been the diversification of crops. Diversification insulates the food security of Europe against the (as yet unseen) impact that climate change might have on the traditional crops grown in Europe. The EU has also advised national governments to modify their agricultural subsidy and incentive programmes to encourage farmers to continue with flexible farm management practices. This is considered the best way of ensuring that the agricultural sector can cope with and adapt to the changes that lie ahead.

Variations in adaptive capacity

The ability of a nation to make the changes that are necessary to adapt to climate change is referred to as its adaptive capacity. Sadly, the world's adaptive capacity is not equal amongst nations, nor within communities. This is because the ability of any given community to successfully adapt to climate change is affected by a range of other factors, or 'non-climatic stresses'. These include:

- Conflict
- Disease
- Food shortages
- Poverty
- Unequal access to resources
- Water stress.

Those nations that are affected by significant non-climatic stresses at the local or national level tend to give these issues urgent and immediate attention. Because of this, and also because of their limited financial resources in the first instance, the less developed nations of the world are likely to have a lower adaptive capacity in terms of addressing the impacts of climate change.

Developing sustainability

One of the keys to improving development pathways is ensuring that development exists in harmony with the systems and processes that occur in the natural environment. Effectively, sustainable development reduces the vulnerability of a community to climate change by strengthening its adaptive capacity.

Taking it further

To learn more about sustainability read 'Sustainability and climate change' on your Student CD-ROM.

Mitigating climate change

There would be less need for adaptive changes, of course, if the process of climate change itself could be limited or stopped. Whilst the climate system would still continue to change for a number of decades into the future (as a legacy of past emissions), the risk of compounding these changes would be significantly reduced. However, a complete cut in emissions is probably unlikely to happen. There may be other forms of limiting climate change that are more easily achieved.

Case study: The importance of limiting climate change

To the vast majority of people limiting climate change is absolutely essential. In fact, without this limitation the idea that global communities can 'adapt' to the changes in the climate becomes redundant. Unless we do something to limit our production of greenhouse gases, there is no point in trying to adapt to climate change. And although they go hand in hand, it is clear that most effort should be given to limitation in preference to adaptation.

Some attempts have already been made to limit climate change by reducing the global emissions of greenhouse gases. The gases that have been the main focus of these efforts include:

- Carbon dioxide (CO_2)
- Methane (CH_4)
- Nitrous oxide (N_2O)
- Hydrofluorocarbons
- Perfluorocarbons
- Sulphur hexafluoride (SF_6)

The nations of the EU are working hard to reach agreement on how to reduce the emissions of CO_2 that emanate from vehicles. According to the EU, for every kilogram of petrol or diesel burnt in cars, lorries or aircraft, approximately 3.5 kg of CO_2 are released into the atmosphere. The EU is planning to reduce the emissions of CO_2 from all new cars to just 140 g/km. This target represents a 25% reduction in CO_2 emissions based on 1995 levels, although there is some debate in relation to the date by which this target should be achieved.

In spite of attempts at limiting the emission of these gases, the trends remain a cause for concern. Between 1970 and 2004, the emission of the greenhouse gases listed above increased by 70%. Most of this increase occurred in the early part of this period, with the increase since 1990 being just 24%. At the current rate, it is estimated that by 2030 the increase in the emission of greenhouse gases (relative to emission levels in 2000) will lie somewhere between 25% and 90%.

The carbon dioxide story

In terms of the greenhouse gases, the CO_2 situation is by far the worst. Since 1970, emissions of CO_2 have grown by 80%. There have been some recent reductions in the energy intensity of production, which has helped to slow emissions (since 1990, the increase in CO_2 emissions has grown by just 28%). However, corresponding increases in global population and average income has driven the need to burn more fossil fuels, releasing ever-greater quantities of CO_2 into the atmosphere. The total amount of CO_2 emanating from an activity, industry or even a nation is referred to as its 'carbon footprint' – its mark left behind on the atmosphere of the planet.

With the continued dependence of the world's industries on fossil fuels, prospects for the future do not seem much brighter. Between now and 2030, it is estimated that emissions of CO_2 will grow by somewhere between 40% and 110% (relative to emissions in 2000). In the future, and on a per capita basis, the emission of CO_2 will be lower in the developed countries than in the developing world. However, statistics can be misleading, and must be interpreted carefully. Most tellingly, although they will produce less emissions on a per capita basis, the people of the developed world will still contribute two-thirds to three-quarters of the total future increase in CO_2 emissions.

Limitation scenarios for carbon dioxide

It would be wonderful to think that a reduction could occur in the total global emissions of CO_2. For this to occur, emissions of CO_2 must first reach their maximum concentration (or 'peak') within the atmosphere, and thereafter enter a decline. As shown in Figure 2, the projected rise in global average temperature is directly linked to the eventual 'peak' atmospheric concentration of CO_2. How quickly the peak of emissions is reached will determine the global mean temperature increase that can be expected.

CO_2 concentration (ppm)	Global mean temperature increase (°C above pre-industrial temperatures)	Peaking year of CO_2 emissions
350–399	2.0–2.4	2000–2015
400–439	2.4–2.8	2000–2020
440–484	2.8–3.2	2010–2030
485–569	3.2–4.0	2020–2060
570–660	4.0–4.9	2050–2080

◀ Figure 2: The projected rise in global temperatures is directly linked to the peak concentration of CO_2 in the atmosphere, as well as the year in which this peak occurs.
Source: United Nations Framework Convention on Climate Change

Clearly, it is in the interest of the global population to work towards achieving the peak concentration of atmospheric CO_2 as soon in the future as possible. This will be one of the most effective ways to limit climate change.

Case study: Denmark

Denmark has worked hard to reduce its emissions of greenhouse gases and, in so doing, play its part in helping to limit climate change. Between 1990 and 2000, industries across Denmark were encouraged to make the switch from coal-based energy production to cleaner forms of energy, such as natural gas. Many industries also took the opportunity to switch to renewable forms of energy such as solar power and wind power. The benefits of this change have been twofold. Not only did the nation reduce its emissions of greenhouse gases, but it also enjoyed a 27% increase in Gross Domestic Product over the course of the decade.

Forging an international agreement on climate change

One of the best attempts so far to manage climate change has been the aforementioned 'United Nations Framework Convention on Climate Change' (UNFCCC). The UNFCCC was created in 1994 and was an important first step in recognising that global warming was a significant problem for the international community. The stated aim of the UNFCCC is to stabilise the emission of greenhouse gases at a level that would 'prevent dangerous anthropogenic [human-induced] interference with the climate system'.

Developed nations	Economies in transition
Australia	Bulgaria
Austria	Croatia
Belarus	Czech Republic
Belgium	Estonia
Canada	Hungary
Denmark	Latvia
Finland	Lithuania
France	Poland
Germany	Romania
Greece	Russian Federation
Iceland	
Ireland	Slovakia
Italy	Slovenia
Japan	Ukraine
Liechtenstein	
Luxembourg	
Monaco	
Netherlands	
New Zealand	
Norway	
Portugal	
Spain	
Sweden	
Switzerland	
Turkey	
United Kingdom	
United States of America	

▲ **Figure 3:** The Annex 1 nations as referred to in the Kyoto Protocol.
Source: United Nations Framework Convention on Climate Change

This aim must be placed in the context of the time in which it was formulated. Back in 1994 there was less scientific evidence to support the notion of climate change and much debate about whether global warming was related to the activities of humans. The establishment of the UNFCCC with the then rather lofty aim of preventing dangerous human interference with the climate system was visionary, showing remarkable prescience of the impacts that would come to light over the course of the next decade.

The importance of reducing the projected impacts of climate change is clearly acknowledged in the UNFCCC. In relation to the stabilisation of greenhouse gases at an acceptable level, the UNFCCC indicates that:

> 'such a level should be achieved within a time-frame sufficient to allow ecosystems to adapt naturally to climate change, to ensure that food production is not threatened, and to enable economic development to proceed in a sustainable manner.'

Source: United Nations Framework Convention on Climate Change

The UNFCCC required a 'benchmark' upon which to base all future reductions of greenhouse gases. This would allow nations to standardise and monitor their emissions as they worked towards reducing them. The base year chosen by the UNFCCC to be the benchmark was 1990. Hence, when the UNFCCC refers to 'reductions in emissions', it is important to remember that this is with respect to the level of emissions that existed in the year 1990.

Some nations are more responsible than others

The UNFCCC also identified that some nations carried a greater responsibility for the phenomenon of global warming than others. As more research on global warming was undertaken, it became clear that the developed nations of the world were primarily responsible for the emission of the greenhouse gases that had led to the rise in average global temperatures. As a consequence, the UNFCCC subsequently charged these nations with doing the most to address the needs of the planet in relation to climate change.

The countries most responsible for climate change were already recognised as the richest nations of the world, and mostly, they already belonged to a group known as the Organisation for Economic Cooperation and Development (OECD). These nations were listed in the first annex to the UNFCCC agreement and have since been referred to as the 'Annex 1' countries (Figure 3).

Whilst the Annex 1 countries mostly belonged to the developed world, there were also some nations who were classified as 'economies in transition'. Most of these were located in Central and Eastern Europe, with many being former states of the Soviet Union. The economies of these newly independent nations were identified as transitioning from being centrally planned to being market-based, following the collapse of the Soviet Union.

The UNFCCC required the Annex 1 nations to begin to cut their emissions of greenhouse gases immediately. By the year 2000, these countries were expected to have reduced emissions back to 1990 levels. As a group, they were able to achieve this goal. However, not every nation managed this task, and the good work of some was needed to make up for the inability of others to meet the target. Only in this way was the group, as a whole, able to meet the target.

The development pathway

Recent findings by Working Group II, as reported in the *Fourth Assessment Report* of the Intergovernmental Panel on Climate Change (IPCC), confirmed the importance of considering 'development pathways' in projections of climate change. A development pathway refers to the course of economic and social development that is assumed will occur in a given nation in future years. The lower development pathway of the less developed nations effectively reduces their ability to adapt to climate change.

The UNFCCC recognised that many nations of the developing world were already on the pathway to development that had been blazed by the richer nations. This pathway was characterised by rapid industrialisation and high levels of greenhouse gas emissions. The richer nations accepted that whilst they were cutting their emissions, the developing nations of the world would continue to increase their emissions, as they developed. Extra cuts in emissions would eventually be required in the developed world in order to compensate for the emissions that would continue to occur in the developing and less developed worlds.

As well as cuts in their emissions, the Annex 1 nations were called upon to make financial contributions to help support the rest of the world with its efforts to fight climate change. In effect, this meant that over and above the aid activities that they were already engaged in, the Annex 1 nations were also expected to contribute financially to climate change projects in the less developed and developing worlds. Through the UNFCCC's 'Global Environment Facility', less developed nations can access grants and loans that are funded by the Annex 1 countries. Agreement was also reached for the richer nations to freely share their technological advances in the fight against climate change with other nations.

The Kyoto Protocol

The UNFCCC was designed as a 'framework' rather than a fixed set of rules and regulations. As scientific research continued, it was intended that the UNFCCC could be adapted to incorporate the new understandings about climate change that this would inevitably bring. An important first addition to the UNFCCC was the Kyoto Protocol. Work on this addition to the UNFCCC began in 1995, only one year after the UNFCCC had been signed, reflecting the growing commitment of the global community to working towards the management of climate change.

Taking it further

Complete an analysis of the *Fourth Assessment Report of the Intergovernmental Panel on Climate Change*. Study the findings of the three Working Groups that compiled this report and briefly summarise the conclusions of each.

Case study: Making the Kyoto Protocol work

The Kyoto Protocol was officially added to the UNFCCC in 1997, being adopted unanimously by those countries that had been signatories to the original framework. However, it took a number of years for these nations to work out how it would take effect and be monitored. Many groups and committees were set up, and at one of the most important meetings, held at Marrakesh in 2001, a set of 'rules' was developed to help the nations operate the Kyoto Protocol. These rules are now known as the 'Marrakesh Accords'. Following continued negotiations over many years, the Kyoto Protocol finally came into effect on 16 February 2005. The Kyoto Protocol's so-called first 'commitment period' began in 2008 and runs through to 2012. The lagtime between signing and implementation again highlights the amount of dialogue and negotiation that is required in order for nations to cooperate in this fashion. A similar amount of work will need to be done between now and 2012 to make sure that the groundwork is laid for future commitment periods (after 2012).

Case study: The nature of an international agreement

The targets set by the Kyoto Protocol, whilst binding, have been designed with a degree of flexibility. It is useful to read the actual text of international agreements such as the Protocol to gain an understanding of the careful and deliberate way in which the nations of the world have chosen to express their commitment to the management of climate change.

Nations	Australia	European Union	Canada	Central and Eastern Europe (most states)	Hungary	Iceland	Japan	New Zealand	Norway	Poland	Russia	Switzerland	Ukraine	United States of America
Emissions target (relative to 1990)	Increase by 8%	Decrease by 8%	Decrease by 6%	Decrease by 8%	Decrease by 6%	Increase by 10%	Decrease by 6%	Stabilise	Increase by 1%	Decrease by 6%	Stabilise	Decrease by 8%	Stabilise	Decrease by 7%

▲ Figure 4: The emissions targets of the nations covered by the Kyoto Protocol.
Source: United Nations Framework Convention on Climate Change

'Article 3

The Parties included in Annex 1 shall, individually or jointly, ensure that their aggregate anthropogenic carbon dioxide equivalent emissions of the greenhouse gases . . . do not exceed their assigned amounts, calculated pursuant to the quantified emission limitation and reduction commitments . . . with a view to reducing their overall emissions of such gases by at least 5 per cent below 1990 levels in the commitment period 2008 to 2012.'

Source: United Nations Framework Convention on Climate Change

Subsequently, the emissions targets that are set for the first commitment period differ greatly between nations. Some nations are even allowed to increase their emissions (relative to 1990) in recognition of their particular development pathway. The emission targets for the signatories to the Kyoto Protocol are shown in Figure 4.

Binding targets, but individualised

The Kyoto Protocol adds power to the UNFCCC because it is legally binding on those nations who have ratified it. The Protocol sets future targets that the signatory nations are to achieve in relation to their emissions of greenhouse gases. It recognises the need for global action, whilst acknowledging that there are circumstances and factors within nations that necessitate some flexibility in terms of the reduction targets that are set. As such, the Protocol serves as an excellent model of the type of compromise agreements that are needed in the fight against climate change.

During the first commitment period from 2008 to 2012, nations that have ratified the Kyoto Protocol are expected, as a group, to reduce their emissions to 5% below the level of their emissions in 1990. Therefore, in meeting the goals of the group, there is also the capacity to produce individualised targets for different nations.

Withdrawal of support of some nations

Following the setting of these targets, some of the signatories to the Kyoto Protocol subsequently withdrew their support for the agreement.

Unhappy with their emissions targets, Australia and the USA simply refused to ratify the agreement. Australia remained opposed to the ratification of the Kyoto Protocol until 2007, when a change of government brought about the political will to agree to the terms of the treaty. The USA still refuses to ratify the Kyoto Protocol. This does the agreement great damage, not only because of the political and economic clout of the United States, but also because it is one of the world's highest emitters of greenhouse gases.

The refusal of the USA to ratify the Kyoto Protocol demonstrates the conundrum of international agreements and treaties. Over time, it has been found that those treaties with real power (of which the Kyoto Protocol is a good example) often have difficulty garnering widespread support. This is because, inevitably, there will be some nations who consider that they will be adversely affected by its terms. The reverse is also true – those treaties that are universally accepted often lack the binding clauses and 'targets' that are necessary to make them truly effective.

This is the exact reason that the UNFCCC was designed as a flexible framework that could grow and develop within the international community. It is also the reason that an amendment such as the Kyoto Protocol has been added, in an effort to strengthen the effectiveness of this international agreement.

Case study: Other agreements to have come out of the Kyoto Protocol

The setting of emission targets in the Kyoto Protocol has also led to the formation of other international agreements. The nations of the EU met separately to the other signatories to the Protocol, to discuss how, as a group, they would meet their target of an 8% reduction in greenhouse gas emissions by 2012. The EU decided to share the responsibility of reducing emissions. This meant that some nations significantly decreased their emissions by a large amount so that others could increase their emissions and continue on the development pathway. For example, Luxembourg agreed to take a 28% reduction, and Germany and Denmark 21%, so that Greece and Portugal could increase their emissions by 25% and 27%, respectively.

Lateral thinking encouraged

The Kyoto Protocol has encouraged the nations of the developed world to think laterally about how to meet their emission targets. For example, for those nations who consider themselves unable to meet their designated cuts in greenhouse gas emissions, there is the option of offsetting some of their carbon emissions through the creation of 'carbon sinks'. Natural carbon sinks can be found in oceans and forests, and help to remove CO_2 from the atmosphere. By planting more trees, countries can, in effect, compensate for or 'cancel out' any part of their greenhouse gas emissions that are above target. Under the rules of the Kyoto Protocol, it is even possible for nations to fund the planting of trees beyond their own borders.

There are also other ways that nations can cancel out their excess emissions. Nations who have exceeded their target can fund projects that lead to greenhouse gas reductions in other countries. In this way, the reduction of emissions in one country can compensate for the excess of emissions in another. This sophisticated form of emissions trading is referred to as 'joint implementation'.

Key terms

Offsetting – the ability to cover increases in CO_2 emissions by sponsoring programmes that reduce emissions in other communities or nations.

Taking it further

To learn more about carbon offsetting read 'Offset – and fly to the Maldives with a clear conscience' on your Student CD-ROM.

Case study: The 'clean development mechanism'

Not all nations who have ratified the Kyoto Protocol will be able to meet their reduction targets. Another way for these nations to compensate for their excess emissions of greenhouse gases is through the 'clean development mechanism'. This process recognises that greenhouse gas emissions are equally damaging, irrespective of where they originate. Using the clean development mechanism, Annex 1 nations can fund projects that reduce emissions in nations that are not covered by the Protocol. In this way, they compensate for their own emissions whilst encouraging reductions in greenhouse gas emissions in parts of the world that are not yet subject to international agreements such as the Kyoto Protocol.

Apparent achievements so far – much work to be done

For many years the popular slogan in relation to the management of climate change was 'think global, act local'. We all have a part to play and every contribution is important. However, it remains apparent that the efforts of the large, industrialised nations to reduce their greenhouse gas emissions will be most effective in the fight against climate change.

There appear to have been some good achievements so far in relation to the targets that were set for the developed nations by the UNFCCC. Between 1990 and 2000, the greenhouse gas emissions of these countries were found to have decreased by 5.6%. However, when explored further, it is apparent that this time period coincided with the break up of the Soviet Union. As the former Soviet states gained their independence, they faced significant economic hardship as their economies adjusted from being centrally planned to being market-based. These nations experienced a 37% decrease in greenhouse gas emissions between 1990 and 2002 as their economies dealt with these changes.

These are the economies that the UNFCCC referred to in Annex 1 as 'economies in transition'. In effect, their emission reductions masked an 8.2% increase in greenhouse gas emissions that occurred in the other Annex 1 nations during the same period. Now that many of the 'economies in transition' have established themselves, there will be increases in emissions from these nations as well, meaning that there is much work to be done by all Annex 1 countries to meet the targets set by the Kyoto Protocol in the first commitment period.

Case study: Greenhouse gas reductions in the United Kingdom

Heading into the first commitment period of the Kyoto Protocol, the UK was 'doing its bit' to reduce greenhouse gas emissions. The UK's total emission of greenhouse gases has now steadily fallen below the level of emissions in the base year of 1990.

When these reductions are considered in relation to various sectors of the economy (see Figure 5), it is clear that it is the joint effort of government, businesses and individuals that is helping to reduce the 'carbon footprint' of the nation.

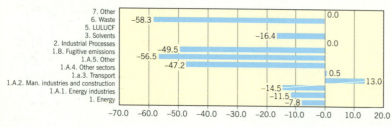

◀ **Figure 5:** Sector-by-sector reduction in greenhouse gas emissions, 1990–2005. Large reductions have been made in the sectors of waste and industrial processes. The emissions emanating from transport is an area of concern for the future.

Source: United Nations Framework Convention on Climate Change

Summary

One of the priorities for the nations of the world is to reduce the effects of climate change upon their people and their infrastructure. Through adaptation, nations are hoping to lessen the impact of the projected future impacts of climate change.

Efforts must also be made to limit and manage climate change itself. Global emissions of greenhouse gases must 'peak' early in this century and enter decline thereafter in order to reduce the amount by which the planet is expected to warm.

The United Nations Framework Convention on Climate Change is an international agreement that will help to facilitate this goal. Importantly, the UNFCCC recognises that some nations are more responsible for the present phenomenon of climate change than others.

The complexities of an international agreement designed to address climate change are significant. Progress at reducing greenhouse gas emissions has been made, but it is slow, and is characterised by the need for much preliminary discussion, debate, negotiation and, above all, compromise.

MCQ

Exam practice

Study the diagram which compares the carbon footprints of the USA and the UK.

(a) (i)   Define the term 'carbon footprint'.   [1]
    (ii) State two ways in which the carbon footprint of the USA and the UK are different and give a reason why.   [4]

(b) (i)   Choose **two** of the strategies shown for home energy use and lifestyle and suggest how they would cut the carbon footprint.   [2]
    (ii) What **further** two suggestions would you offer to cut down on the transport footprint?   [2]

(c) Explain how the Kyoto Protocol has developed a range of strategies aimed towards managing climate change.   [4]

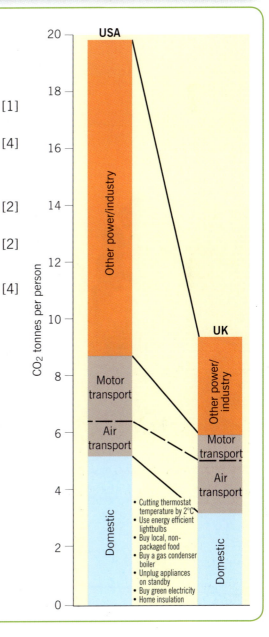

Chapter 7 How should we tackle the global challenges of increasing risk and vulnerability in a more hazardous world?

Key terms

Biomass fuels
Carbon capture
Carbon market
Climate-friendly technology
Combined cycle turbine
Expert Group on Technology Transfer
Fluorescent bulb
Incandescent bulb
Low-carbon energy
Technology transfer

Learning objectives

After studying this chapter, you will be able to discuss these ideas and concepts and provide examples of them:

- Increasing risk and uncertainty threatens major disruption to people and the environment at a global scale.
- Such disruption brings water shortages and food insecurity.
- Global warming will result in a more hazardous world; it is one of the biggest challenges humankind has faced. Its people should make innovative choices, adopt sustainable strategies and understand the costs and benefits involved.
- Solutions to a hazardous world, at all scales, need to focus on the underlying issues of risk and vulnerability.

The future of the planet is clouded by risk and uncertainty in relation to the health and well-being of the global environment. Whilst massive efforts have been made to better understand the mechanism of global warming, efforts to tackle climate change are still in their infancy.

It is now clear that the present rate of climate change is faster than at any stage in the recent history of the earth. Climate change is a problem that will be felt globally, though its effects are likely to be felt differently in various regions.

Food and water supplies under threat

Climate change will threaten world food supplies. Already we have seen how rainfall in the sub-tropics and mid-latitude areas is expected to decline. This will have the corresponding effect of lowering

▲ **Figure 1:** Queuing for water, like this, is an everyday occurrence in some parts of the world.

potential crop yields. For those parts of the world that already experience famine this is a great concern. By 2020, an extra 50 million people could be at risk of hunger. Working Group II of the Intergovernmental Panel on Climate Change (IPCC) estimates that this number could rise by an additional 266 million people by 2080. It is predicted that crop yields in Asia will be dramatically affected by the rising temperature. For example, a 2 °C rise in average global temperature could result in a 5 to 12% reduction in China's rain-fed rice production, which will have a significant impact on its 1 billion plus population.

Rainfall decline will also place increased pressure on water supplies. This, coupled with ever-increasing populations, will lead to higher levels of water stress in many regions of the world. It is estimated that by 2020, as many as 250 million Africans could live in areas that are affected by water stress. By the middle of the century, the availability of water in the drier regions of the mid-latitudes is expected to have declined by as much as 30%. Increases in the frequency and intensity of both floods and droughts are also expected as the planet continues to warm. Already there are many millions of people worldwide who cannot access freshwater on a regular basis – and climate change only threatens to make their situation worse, whilst plunging many millions more into water stress.

Sea level rise brings further risks and uncertainties. Freshwater supplies in coastal or low-lying areas, and especially on small islands, are threatened by intrusion from salty sea waters, further exacerbating the water supply problem. A range of coastal hazards will increase with the rising sea level, including storm surges, inundation and erosion. For those living on the world's megadeltas, particularly those in Asia, there is the added concern of flooding, as meltwaters from mountainous regions swell the level of the rivers that formed them.

▲ **Figure 2:** Droughts are expected to occur more frequently and become more intense in the future.

The vulnerable state of the planet

In the face of the present phenomenon of climate change, it is accurate to say that the planet has never been more vulnerable than it is now. Our exploitation of the earth's physical environment has destroyed many of the natural buffers that would have served to mitigate some of the effects of climate change. Mining and agricultural practices have cleared the earth of vegetation and stripped it of resources. These practices have exposed topsoils to erosion by wind and water, whilst also increasing the likelihood of landslides and avalanches on hillsides. Forestry and the development of land for housing have severely reduced the area of the earth covered by trees. This has reduced the capacity of the earth's forests to act as carbon sinks and to remove at least some of the greenhouse gas emissions that emanate from anthropogenic activities.

There is the added complication of the increasing human population. Rapid population growth, particularly within the less developed world, has resulted in many more people living in marginal areas of the planet. These are the areas that are most exposed to the impact of climate change. With a heavily populated planet, people living in these marginal areas have neither the option nor the means to move to uninhabited areas that would be less exposed to the perils of a changing climate. The same is true for the organisms with which we share the planet. Hunting, exploitation and habitat destruction have already led to the extinction of thousands of species of plants and animals. By destroying so much of their natural environment, humans have also reduced the opportunities for these organisms to migrate or adapt in the face of unprecedented climate change.

The present rate of climate change, coupled with the loss of the earth's protective buffers and the rapid increase in the human population, results in humankind facing its greatest ever challenge. And of course, there remains the great paradox of climate change. The rich nations of the world, those most directly responsible for global warming, are the best equipped and best resourced to deal with and adapt to the changing climate. Yet it is the people of the less developed world – those least responsible for the changing climate – who face the greatest risk and uncertainty in the future.

Strategies to manage global warming

Plant a tree

One of the best ways to fight emissions of greenhouse gases is to plant more trees. As previously discussed in Chapter 6, trees serve as excellent carbon sinks by removing CO_2 from the atmosphere. Unfortunately, anthropogenic activities have removed many of the world's forests. Technological change has meant that forests are cut down faster than ever before. Deforestation not only diminishes the capabilities of this global carbon sink, but the destruction of each individual tree also releases the CO_2 that it stores back into the atmosphere.

The rapid deforestation that is occurring across the globe is a matter of short-term gain versus long-term sustainability. The simple act of planting more trees is an excellent example of the costs and benefits associated with trying to reduce the impact of global warming. In order to plant more trees, other land uses must make way for the return of the forested areas which once covered a much greater proportion of the earth than at present. The cost of this will be felt in terms of losses in production, jobs, and ultimately, national incomes. There are few politicians or governments around the world who could advocate such change and expect to be re-elected, such is the degree of investment in the status quo of industrialists, workers and their families.

The great contradiction of forests is that they tend to be controlled by the local population, yet they have an importance for the global community. In the longer term, the role that forests play as carbon sinks will be to the benefit of all of humankind. There is room within the Kyoto Protocol for countries that have an economic or developmental need to utilise particular forestry resources to 'pay' for forests to be planted elsewhere in their country or within another. However, the global community is a long way from reaching a consensus on how to deal with this issue.

A time for innovation

In order to tackle the increased risk and vulnerability that accompany living in a more hazardous world, the global community must start to employ some innovative strategies against climate change. One of the best ways to combat climate change is for us to end our dependence on fossil fuels. Whilst the search for suitable alternatives continues, the planet would benefit from some innovative approaches to how fossil fuels are used. In the short term, our aim should be to use fossil fuels more efficiently – so that the energy derived from their use is increased.

Some fossil fuels are less harmful ('cleaner') than others and, wherever possible, these should be used in preference to the 'dirty' options.

Taking it further

To learn more about the role of forests in controlling climate change read 'Plant a tree to save the world' on your Student CD-ROM.

Taking it further

Research the latest developments in terms of automobiles that use alternative fuels. Consider the specifications of these vehicles and compare their price and performance to those that operate on fossil fuels.

Recent work in the automobile industry has seen many vehicles, from standard family cars right through to buses, converted to operate on natural gas. Vehicles that are powered by natural gas, in preference to petrol or diesel, are much better for the environment. This is because natural gas, even though it is a fossil fuel, releases less CO_2 per unit of energy than petrol, coal or oil.

Case study: The combined cycle turbine

Already there are machines and technology that can utilise fossil fuels in a more efficient way. One such example is the 'combined cycle turbine'. Like most turbines, this one operates by burning fossil fuels to generate heat, which in turn drives steam turbines. The innovative part of this particular turbine is that extra energy is generated from the use of its exhaust gases. The thermal expansion of the exhaust gases is harnessed in order to drive additional gas turbines. As a result, the combined cycle turbine is 70% more efficient that traditional steam turbines, culminating in the more efficient use of fossil fuels.

Alternatives to coal and oil

There are a range of other, innovative alternatives to oil and coal – the most widely used fossil fuels. A number of 'biomass fuels', which originate from biological sources, are now available. Like fossil fuels, the biomass fuels must be burnt in order for them to provide energy for use by humans (Figure 3), but their big advantage is that they are a much cleaner source of energy, resulting in less greenhouse gas emissions per unit of energy produced.

Examples of biomass fuels include:

- Fuel wood
- Ethanol and biodiesel
- Alcohol fermented from sugar
- Oils extracted from soybeans
- Methane gas which emanates from rubbish dumps.

Since plants are a major carbon sink, helping to remove CO_2 from the air, it is vital that any use of plants as biomass fuels is accompanied by large scale re-planting. This is a very important measure to help offset the loss of these plants from the global carbon sink.

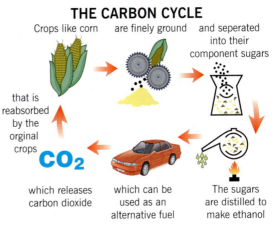

THE CARBON CYCLE

Crops like corn are finely ground and seperated into their component sugars

that is reabsorbed by the orginal crops

CO_2 which releases carbon dioxide

which can be used as an alternative fuel

The sugars are distilled to make ethanol

▲ Figure 3: The process of using biomass fuels as an alternative to fossil fuels.

Case study: Capturing carbon?

Carbon capture is a radical concept in the fight against climate change. Although this is not a technique that could be described as a 'renewable' or 'sustainable' solution to climate change, it is currently being trialled in some parts of the world in the hope that it will help to reduce the effects of climate change.

Carbon capture works on the principle that greenhouse gases can be 'caught' before they are released into the atmosphere. The captured carbon is then stored safely in a designated carbon sink, where it is 'sealed off' and unable to enter the atmosphere. Typically, this storage may occur under the ground. It is thought that geological formations or even depleted oil and gas reservoirs may make ideal storage points. In effect, this would return the carbon that has emanated from the burning of fossil fuels to its original location below the surface of the earth. The deeper parts of the ocean are also being considered as storage points.

There is much work to be done on the environmental implications of carbon capture, yet it is an example of the type of innovative thinking that is occurring in relation to reducing the impact of climate change.

Reducing our carbon footprint

Innovative thinking should not be thought of as the preserve of the big industrialists or the automotive industry alone. It is important that we all make a contribution to reducing our greenhouse gas emissions. In homes, there is much that can be done to reduce the 'carbon footprint' of individuals or families. Many governments have developed rating systems to help householders choose energy-efficient appliances. This is especially important for white goods such as fridges, air conditioners and washing machines, which traditionally consume large amounts of energy. In addition to these technological improvements, simple behavioural changes such as switching off electrical items after use, instead of leaving them on 'standby', have also been shown to bring about significant energy savings. Whilst these practices might seem small or insignificant in isolation, when taken on by local communities or entire nations, they can result in a significant reduction in greenhouse gas emissions.

Case study: The end of the line for the incandescent light bulb?

One piece of innovative thinking that has really been popular is the replacement of incandescent light bulbs within the homes and workplaces of the world. The incandescent bulb was a 100-year-old piece of technology which was very inefficient in its use of energy, producing vast amounts of heat as well as light. An alternative, the energy-saving fluorescent bulb, had been available in the marketplace for many years, but its higher cost was thought to be a deterrent to its widespread use. However, in 2007 a number of governments moved to gradually phase out the use of the incandescent bulb. Although more expensive, the energy-saving bulb has the dual advantage of lasting longer and being much better for the environment than the incandescent bulb. The higher costs in the short term will benefit all of humankind in the longer term.

Alternatives to fossil fuels – nuclear power

One of the most controversial alternatives to the use of fossil fuels for energy generation is the use of nuclear power. Currently, nuclear power accounts for approximately 7% of the world's energy supplies. Whilst it is not a renewable form of energy production, nuclear power has the advantage that it produces virtually no emissions of greenhouse gas. However, there is a serious issue of safety in relation to the generation of power in this fashion. Nuclear power plants deal with highly radioactive materials in the course of energy production, and a by-product of the process is a large amount of radioactive nuclear waste. There are many issues connected with the use, transport and storage of this waste, in addition to the ever-present threat of nuclear accidents.

The fact that nuclear materials intended for nuclear power plants could be used in the construction of weapons of mass destruction is also a concern. Such fears have been heightened in this millennium by the advent of global terrorism, revolving around the idea that terrorists or rogue states will obtain nuclear material intended for energy production and put it to use in the construction of nuclear weapons. There is even a school of thought that suggests that nuclear power plants serve as targets for terrorist activities. It is thought that these reasons, coupled with concerns about the safety of nuclear power and its by-products, will prevent nuclear power from coming to replace fossil fuels as the primary form of energy production, in spite of nuclear power's clean bill of health in relation to greenhouse gas emissions.

Sustainable forms of energy production

There is a growing push for the development of sustainable technologies that will replace fossil fuels. Without some fundamental and at times radical changes to our practices and processes, more and more of the earth's population becomes vulnerable to the impacts of food and water shortages, sea level rise and spiralling global temperatures.

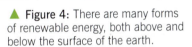

Taking it further

To learn more about wind and solar power read 'It's blowing in the wind' on your Student CD-ROM.

Solar-, water- and wind-power generation techniques have long been known to be entirely sustainable and are therefore referred to as 'climate-friendly technologies'. These, and a range of other renewable energy options, have the capacity to generate millions of joules of energy each year (see Figure 4). The sustainability of these forms of energy production arises from the fact that they are renewable – unlike fossil fuels, the energy that is obtainable from the sun, wind and water will never run out or be depleted. Yet together, solar and wind power account for only 2% of the world's electricity production.

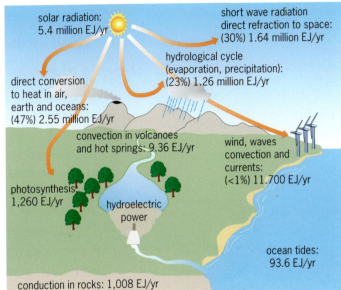

▲ Figure 4: There are many forms of renewable energy, both above and below the surface of the earth.

Criticisms of climate-friendly technologies

It has long been claimed that some of the climate-friendly technologies have serious flaws that would prevent them becoming the primary source of energy production across the globe. Solar power has long been thought to be difficult to generate in areas that lack sunshine hours or which experience long, dark winters. The generation of wind power has been thought to be dependent upon prevailing conditions within the environment, whilst the generation of hydroelectric power is often criticised because of the environmental impacts that are associated with the damming of river catchments.

Taking it further

To learn more about alternatives to oil read 'We'll always find a way, perhaps?' on your Student CD-ROM.

These criticisms tend to be based on the idea that one climate-friendly technology will be the answer to the world's energy production needs. It is gradually becoming clearer that only by diversifying the way in which we produce energy for our homes and workplaces, and doing so in a sustainable way, will we be able to meet our energy needs and protect the environment.

The cost of climate-friendly technologies

The cost of switching existing systems of electricity generation over to these sustainable forms is a major factor preventing their widespread use. For the uptake of such technologies to occur, a win–win situation must develop that sees benefits for the environment as well as for national economies. Governments are not inclined to move towards technologies that reduce national income. This is particularly true for the less developed nations, who have an equal right to development as the rest of the world, and much less flexibility in how this is possible to achieve. In the words of the UNFCCC, climate-friendly technologies will need to 'enable a transition to a carbon-constrained economy and de-couple economic growth from emissions growth'.

Innovative ideas, especially when they are in their infancy, tend to be accompanied by a higher cost with respect to existing technologies. The same can be said of climate-friendly technologies. One of the biggest barriers to the introduction of such technologies is their high cost compared to existing fossil-fuel-based practices. However, it has always been clear that high start-up costs would be covered by savings in the longer term. It must be noted that comparisons of costs often fail to incorporate the environmental costs of our continued dependence on fossil fuels, usually because these are largely hidden, occur in the longer term and are very hard to estimate accurately. However, this 'true cost' of technologies based on fossil fuels should be recognised by governments and policy-makers.

The role of market forces

According to market principles, the price of climate-friendly technologies will fall once demand for them increases. However, for this to occur, the marketplace will need some assistance from governments and regulatory bodies. Innovative thinking by these groups and the use of rebate schemes and assistance packages can encourage the uptake of climate-friendly solutions by industry and householders alike. This has the added advantage of stimulating change within established patterns of human behaviour, and can be the impetus for encouraging a more efficient use of energy.

In the same way that market forces will contribute to the uptake of clean technologies within a nation, it is important to remember that a 'carbon market' exists within the international community as well. The carbon market refers to the idea that emissions of CO_2 can be regulated globally, and that 'emissions trading' can take place between nations. Many rapidly developing nations are currently establishing fossil-fuel-based energy-production facilities which are intended to drive their development over the next thirty to forty years. Whilst recognising the development pathways of these nations, it makes sense for the developed nations of the world, who are better placed to afford to move towards the more expensive climate-friendly technologies, to be able to 'trade off' some of their carbon emissions to these developing nations. There is already provision within the Kyoto Protocol for this emissions trading to occur (see Chapter 6).

The transition to clean forms of power generation would also be the impetus for the creation of a range of jobs in a diverse array of new industries. It is estimated that by the year 2050, products that relate to the low-carbon energy market are expected to have a global value of $500 bn. This represents many new opportunities, and the role that business and government will play in helping this market to grow and develop in coming decades is crucial.

Case study: Technology transfer

It is important to remember that under the terms of the UNFCCC, Annex 1 nations are expected to share climate-friendly technologies with the nations of the less developed world. To assist them in this task, the 'Expert Group on Technology Transfer' has been established, with the goal of promoting ways to share technology between nations. At the same time, the UNFCCC's 'Global Environment Facility' is responsible for distributing grants that will help to strengthen the global market for low-carbon technologies. These grants, worth an estimated $259 m annually, help to transfer technology from the developed to the less developed world. This in turn helps to increase energy efficiency by establishing sustainable practices and encouraging the use of renewable energies.

Summary

Global warming and climate change are now recognised as the biggest challenges facing humanity. Whilst many non-climatic stresses also exist at the local and national levels, climate change is a truly global problem which will be felt in every region of the world.

In the future, access to food and water is likely to become more difficult for many millions of the world's inhabitants. Large-scale environmental degradation by humankind has left the planet in a vulnerable state, with many of the natural buffers that would help to protect us against climate change having been removed.

There is much that can be done to fight climate change and return the planet to a healthier state. The simple act of tree-planting is a good example. However, more work needs to be done to find alternatives to fossil fuels. Our industries and our homes must be powered in a more sustainable way.

Whilst some progress has been made in this area, the world must move past the short-term costs of changing our methods of power generation and focus on the long-term benefits to the climate system and the health of the planet. Mechanisms have already been established to encourage cooperation between nations. Governments have a key role to play in this process, but first the political will for such change needs to exist.

MCQ

Exam practice

1. Study the diagram which shows the factors that are likely to influence a country's or a community's vulnerability to global hazards in the future.
   (a) (i) Define the term 'adaptive capacity'. [1]
   (ii) Choose two of the factors shown and state how each is likely to influence adaptive capacity. [2]
   (b) (i) Name two hydro-meteorological hazards. [2]
   (ii) Suggest reasons why exposure to your two chosen hazards is likely to increase in the future. [3]
   (c) Choose one environment and explain how in the **future** it will become more **vulnerable** to a range of climate change impacts. [4]

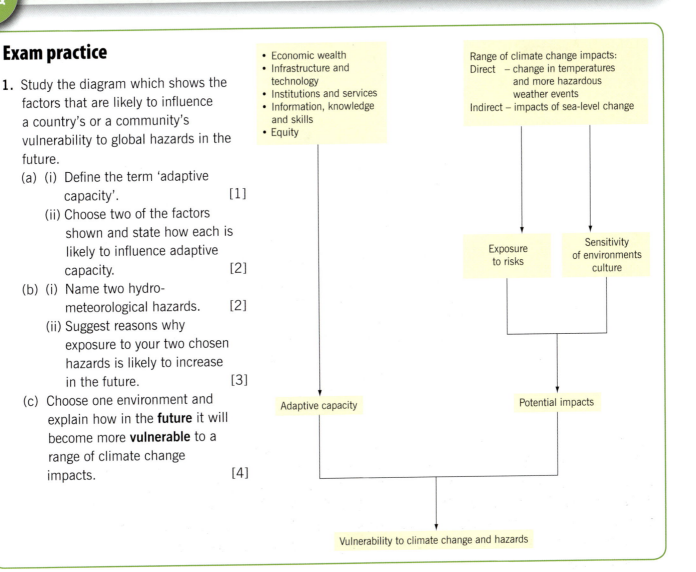

- Economic wealth
- Infrastructure and technology
- Institutions and services
- Information, knowledge and skills
- Equity

Range of climate change impacts:
Direct – change in temperatures and more hazardous weather events
Indirect – impacts of sea-level change

Exposure to risks

Sensitivity of environments culture

Adaptive capacity

Potential impacts

Vulnerability to climate change and hazards

CHAPTER 8 What is globalisation and how is it changing people's lives?

Key Terms

Climate change
Democracy
Demography
Demographic Transition
 Model
Destination
Free trade
Globalisation
Infant mortality
Push and pull factors
Source
Transnational/multinational
 companies

Key terms

The IMF defines globalisation as 'the growing economic interdependence of countries worldwide through increasing volume and variety of cross-border transactions in goods and services, freer international capital flows, and more rapid and widespread diffusion of technology'.

Learning objectives

After studying this chapter, you will be able to discuss these ideas and concepts and provide examples of them:
• The development of globalisation.
• The link between globalisation and population change.
• The components of population change.
• The factors which have accelerated globalisation.
• The effects of globalisation on population movements, through a number of topical examples.

Globalisation has a number of different aspects. It refers, first, to a process in which national economies are becoming more integrated into a single global economy. This means that the actions and decisions in one part of the world have knock-on effects in other parts, because all parts of the world are becoming linked economically.

Many argue that the main aspect of globalisation is this economic interdependency that occurs between countries on a global scale. The spread and development of technology – which has fuelled this interdependency – is another aspect of globalisation.

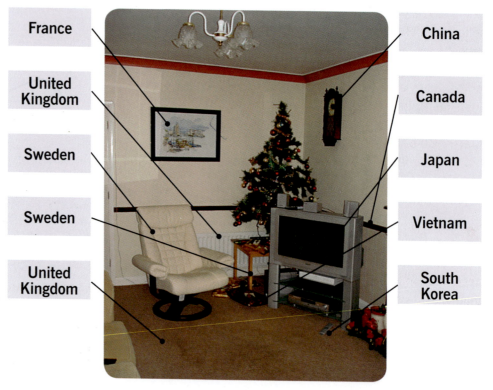

France
United Kingdom
Sweden
Sweden
United Kingdom
China
Canada
Japan
Vietnam
South Korea

▶ Figure 1: The global sitting room. Consider your own home. Where do the goods come from? Where would they have come from 50 years ago?

Some people believe that the world is also becoming very similar politically, with many countries developing the ideas of democracy, freedom and free trade. A 'cultural globalisation', which refers to the tendency for western cultural norms to spread to other parts of the world, is also developing. 'Demographic globalisation' reflects the increasing numbers of migrants in the world and the mixing of ethnicity. Some environmental problems have also gone global. The 2007 Bali Conference, for example, was an example of global concern for an environmental problem – climate change.

Population distribution

The population of the world has experienced radical changes over the final 50 years of the last century and is predicted to change even more in the next 50 years. Figure 2 shows the vast growth in population in that time, from 2.5 billion to nearly 10 billion. It also displays the shift in population between the continents. All continents are experiencing growth but the growth is more marked in some continents than others, which affects the global distribution of population. Asia and Africa, for example, are rapidly increasing their share of the world's growing population, while North America and Europe are growing relatively slowly. Increased population puts pressure on resources in the areas of growth. The world is already experiencing the effect of rapid population growth – the industrialisation of China, for example, one of the main contributors to world climate change due to its dependence on fossil fuels. There has also been a recent trend for China to look to African countries to fulfil its demand for resources.

Population change

Population change is the outcome of two processes: natural change and migrational change. The natural change in a population is the difference between the crude birth rate and the crude death rate. If births exceed deaths there is a natural increase in population and if deaths exceed births, there is a natural decrease in population. Many demographers believe that the fertility rate is a more accurate measure of population change than crude birth rate. The fertility rate is the number of births in a year per 1,000 women who are in the normal reproductive age group (15 to 44 years).

Migrational change can lead to either a fall or rise in population. A net migration gain occurs when more people immigrate than emigrate; a net migration loss is when more people emigrate than immigrate. Therefore there are many different factors that contribute to population change.

Taking it further

To learn more about global integration read 'One world? Take a further look at integration' on your Student CD-ROM.

Taking it further

To learn more about fertility rates around the world read 'Global fertility rates' on your Student CD-ROM.

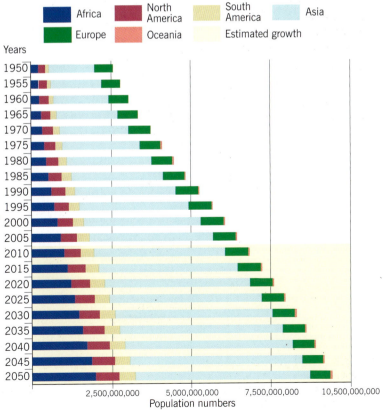

▶ **Figure 2:** World population distribution 1950–2050.
Source: www.timeforchange.org

The Demographic Transition Model

The Demographic Transition Model (DMT) can be used to portray population change on a global scale (see Figure 3). The DTM portrays:

- Change over space – a number of countries at the same time can show the population characteristics of one stage.
- Change over time – a country should theoretically progress through each of the stages.

Stage 1
Birth and death rates are both high. There may be fluctuations in the birth and death rates between years. There are no countries in the world that are still in this stage, although parts of countries may be. The reasons for the high birth rates are little access to birth control and high levels of infant mortality. Reasons for the high death rate are poor diet and hygiene and little medical science.

Stage 3 (e.g. Bangladesh)
Birth rates now fall rapidly due to improved knowledge of family planning, different aspirations and different role of women in society. Death rates continue to fall.

Stage 5 (e.g. Russian Federation)
Some countries are now moving towards what is called a fifth stage, where death rate is higher than the birth rate. In these countries there is a natural decrease in population.

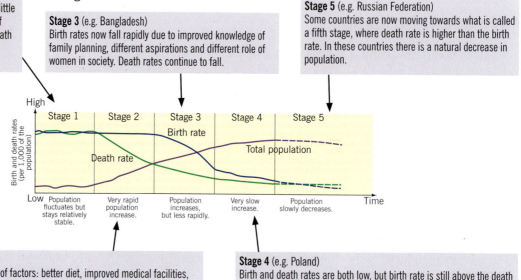

Stage 2 (e.g. Ethiopia)
Death rates are falling due to a number of factors: better diet, improved medical facilities, and better sanitation and water supply. Birth rates remain high and this leads to high population growth. A number of the least economically developed countries of the world are in this stage of the model.

Stage 4 (e.g. Poland)
Birth and death rates are both low, but birth rate is still above the death rate. This stage is characteristic of many of the more economically developed countries in the world.

▲ **Figure 3:** The Demographic Transition Model.

Taking it further

Find out three more countries for each stage of the Demographic Transition Model. Justify your choice of countries.

Factors affecting migration

The effect of migration on societies has increased dramatically since the early 1900s. We only have to look at British society to see the mix of races that now inhabit the islands of Great Britain. This globalisation of population has many causes. In some ways, international migration of people is the most important of globalisation changes because it takes with it beliefs and cultures, and mixes societies. There are many factors that cause migration, which can be divided into push and pull factors.

Other models of migration, for example Lee's model of migrations, do not refer to push and pull factors. Instead it sees places as possessing a number of attributes which individuals perceive in different ways, depending on their personal characteristics. His model also introduces the idea of intervening obstacles which need to be overcome for migration to take place. These intervening obstacles include:

- Social obstacles, such as family ties, illiteracy or lack of education.
- Economic obstacles, such as the cost of setting up a new home, the cost of moving or the need to help run a family business.
- Lack of information about the destination – where to stay when they arrive, for example.
- Intervening opportunities and places. Migrants may move to intervening places rather than their original destination, due to obstacles such as costs, family pressure or other opportunities that present themselves during the migration.

▶ Figure 4: Push and pull factors for migration.

Push factors include:		Pull factors include:	
Natural disasters (such as volcanic eruptions or floods), harsh climates		Hazard-free areas of the world	
War and political conflicts		Political asylum, freedom of speech	
Unemployment, poverty, growing inequality between the rich and poor nations of the world		Employment opportunities, high living standards	
Declining neighbourhoods, shortage of housing		Good welfare services, plenty of available housing	

Factors that accelerate globalisation

The factors that help to speed up globalisation are many and varied. We will examine four of them in this chapter and show how they are interrelated.

Since the 1970s the development of new technologies have played a part in the 'shrinking world'. Transport technology has seen the development of bigger jet aircraft, more high-speed trains and better road systems in many countries. There has also been the development of electronic technology (e-technology), using the internet to link parts of the globe. In 1998 it was estimated that 2.3 million UK households (9%) had access to the internet, but this had risen to 14.3 million (58%) by 2006.

One of the most influential factors in the rapid acceleration in globalisation is the development of multinational or transnational companies (TNCs). These companies have their headquarters in their country of origin but have branch plants throughout the world. The ability to locate anywhere in the world has been enhanced by the other globalisation factors, such as the development of technology. As an indication of the early origins of TNCs it is worth recalling that the first cars made in the United Kingdom were produced by the German company Daimler. Although many modern TNCs bear the name of a country on their logos – British Petroleum (BP), for example – and they frequently have their HQ in their country of 'origin', they owe no real loyalty to those countries. The people who manage the corporations do not own them. The corporations are legally obligated to maximise profit on behalf of their owners – the shareholders – and must therefore continually look for ways to increase profitability. Companies frequently become 'transnational' in order to reduce costs or improve sales. Hence Honda produce cars in the UK at Swindon to improve sales in Europe, whereas Levi-Strauss produce their clothes in Central America and China to reduce costs. Needless to say the senior personnel working within TNCs are very keen on globalisation.

▲ Figure 5: Factors that accelerate globalisation.

Transnational companies
Index of transnationality*, 2005

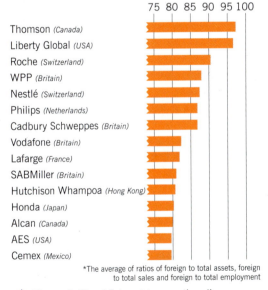

*The average of ratios of foreign to total assets, foreign to total sales and foreign to total employment

▲ Figure 6: The 15 'most transnational' companies in the world.

Source: UNCTAD

Taking it further

To learn more about the impact of a more integrated world read 'A world turned upside down. Who owns what today?' on your Student CD-ROM.

There are many ways to assess the world's most transnational firms. The United Nations Conference on Trade and Development assessed how 'transnational' a company was by calculating the proportions of its assets, sales and employment located abroad. According to this calculation, Thomson, a Canadian media company, is the world's most transnational firm. Thomson has 97.8% of its assets, 96.6% of its sales and 97.3% of its jobs outside its Canadian homeland. Figure 6 shows that, although some of these top TNCs are familiar, many of the world's best known brands – McDonald's, Nike, Coca-Cola, Toyota, etc. – are not included.

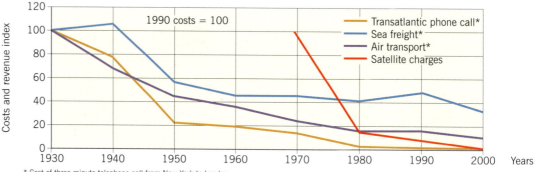

▶ Figure 7: The falling costs of transport and communication.

* Cost of three minute telephone call from New York to London
* Average ocean freight and port charges per short ton of import and export cargo
* Average air transport revenue per passenger mile

Taking it further

To learn more about the role of TNCs in the global economy read 'Who benefits exactly? Are TNCs the good guys or the bad guys?' on your Student CD-ROM.

The decreasing cost of transport and communication, especially since 1950 (see Figure 7), has affected many TNCs. They now have easier access to their headquarters via satellite, or can travel to them much more quickly and cheaply. The availability of improved transport and communications has also encouraged people to migrate for employment. Internet search engines have given people access to companies worldwide and home shopping is becoming increasingly important. Transnational companies now control 70% of the world's trade.

The opening up of new markets would not be possible without the new technologies. Customers are now more aware of the possibilities and the goods they order can be transported more cost effectively. Countries such as China and India, with their increasing wealth and their greater availability of employment, have helped to fuel this growth and are now home to many global manufacturing plants.

Many of the international organisations established since the Second World War (see table) have also increased globalisation.

▼ Figure 8: Some organisations that have influenced globalisation since 1945.

Organisation	Full name	Date founded	Task
GATT	General Agreement on Tariffs and Trade	1948	To promote free trade and reduce barriers to trade
IMF	International Monetary Fund	1945	To promote international monetary co-operation, currency stability and international trade
UN	United Nations	1945	To increase international co-operation and reduce conflicts
World Bank (IBRD)	International Bank for Reconstruction and Development	1946	To provide funds and expertise to promote economic development
WTO	World Trade Organization	1995	The WTO promotes 'free trade' or 'trade liberalisation' – the economic exchange of goods and services between countries, without government intervention and regulation

Effects of globalisation on population movements

Globalisation has led to a greater ease of movement for money, food and goods, as technology and global awareness has increased. However, the effect of globalisation on population movements is more complex. The ability of people to migrate has indeed increased, but many countries have begun to protect their boundaries as an increasing number of people want to move from poor to rich areas. The best way to explain the effects of globalisation on population movements is through a range of examples.

The UK, the EU and migration

There is supposed to be a greater freedom of movement between the countries of the European Union (EU), but this is not always the case. The populations of the first 15 member countries of the EU are allowed free movement between all their countries. Since the inclusion of ten more countries in 2004, however, the original member states have been tightening their borders. And when two further countries – Romania and Bulgaria – joined the EU in January 2007, they were not allowed the free movement of labour that other countries were allowed. Only Sweden and Finland allowed Romanians and Bulgarians to enter freely.

The UK is tightening its immigration laws to all economic migrants. Unskilled migrants will not be allowed into the country at all (except those from the first 25 EU countries). Skilled migrants will have to fulfil a points quota (see table). As is the case in most countries of the world, highly skilled migrants are still welcome in the UK – as long as they attain 75 points. The quota systems for skilled workers, students and temporary workers have yet to be announced.

Qualifications	Points	Previous earnings (£000)	Points	Age	Points	Other	Points
Bachelor's degree	30	16–18	5	Under 28	20	If earnings/ qualifications were gained in the UK	5
Master's degree	35	18–20	10	28–29	10		
Ph.D.	50	20–23	15	30–31	5		
		23–26	20				
		26–29	25				
		29–32	30				
		32–35	35				
		35–40	40				
		40+	45				

▲ Figure 9: UK entry points system for highly skilled migrants.

Case study: Talented migrants – footballers

Other migrants, who have exceptional talents, such as footballers, are also welcomed to the UK. Work permits are usually granted to players who have played in a number of matches for their national sides. The countries have to be ranked in the top 70 by football's governing body, FIFA. There has been a tremendous increase in the number of foreign players in the Premier League since 1992 (see Figure 10). Take, for example, the Manchester United player, Ji-Sung Park, from South Korea. As well as being a brilliant footballer, Ji-Sung attracts the South Korean audience to Manchester United matches, thereby increasing the Manchester United fan base and the club's profits through merchandising. Games are now transmitted using the global communications network through satellite TV and the internet, and this will help to increase the revenue for the club.

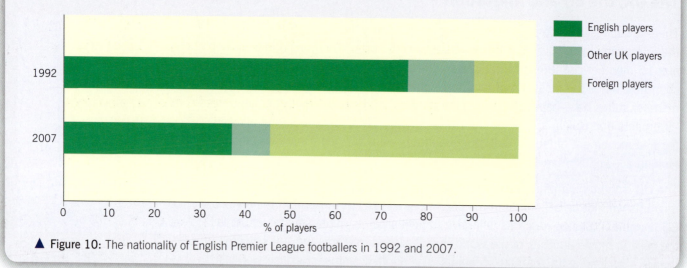

▲ **Figure 10:** The nationality of English Premier League footballers in 1992 and 2007.

Crossing the border

Globalisation is fuelling many attempts to move from poor countries to rich countries, especially if those countries are visible just across the border. This is the case, for example, with Mexicans trying to cross the border into the USA, and they will often risk their lives in attempts to join their more affluent neighbours. The border into the USA, which is nearly 2,000 miles long, used to be relatively open, and the many Mexicans who crossed over provided much-needed cheap labour as agricultural workers and as domestic helps in American homes.

▲ **Figure 11:** The barrier erected to stop Mexicans crossing illegally into the USA.

Since the 1980s, however, the border has been more tightly patrolled, mainly to stop drug trafficking. Of the 11,000 Border Patrol agents in the USA, 89% work on the USA–Mexican border. The agents are helped by long sections of barriers in the urban areas along the border, security cameras, electronic sensors, night-vision scopes, ground vehicles, aircraft and unmanned aerial vehicles. In 2004 they apprehended nearly 1.25 million immigrants trying to cross the border illegally. All of these security measures have not made the crossing impossible, only more expensive and dangerous. Mexicans who are desperate for a better life will simply try other ways of getting into the USA, such as crossing the Arizona desert. Since 2000, for example, more than 750 would-be migrants have been found dead in the Arizona desert. These are only the documented deaths; no one knows how many more lie out there unknown, unrecovered and unrecoverable (after skeletons are bleached by the sun for long enough, animals eat them for the calcium).

By closing the border, the USA has made the crossing more of a challenge. There has even been a theme park set up in Mexico, part funded by the government, which simulates the border crossing. Eco Alberto Park in Ixmiquilpan – about 700 miles south of the border – represents crossing the border as a form of 'extreme sport'. Taking part involves enduring a 5-hour trek (that usually finishes about 2 a.m.) in freezing cold temperatures. Customers pay to walk in mud, balance on ledges in the pitch black, tackle rickety bridges, sprint across cornfields and wade through fast-flowing rivers, as they are chased by pretend US border patrol guards, who fire blanks at them. The customers pay £10 for the privilege. Some say the Park is a way for Mexicans to practise the crossing, others say it is an effective deterrent. Either way, it is definitely a tourist attraction which is becoming ever more popular.

The real border guards are unimpressed and have condemned the Park, pointing out that if it is used for training, the event should last for days rather than hours! They have also criticised the government for funding an illegal and dangerous activity.

Summary

Having studied this chapter, you should be able to discuss these ideas and concepts and provide located examples of them:

- What globalisation is and why it has developed.
- The link between globalisation and population change.
- The components of population change.
- The factors which have accelerated globalisation.
    - The effects of globalisation on population movements, such as footballers to the UK and Mexicans to the USA.

MCQ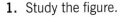

Exam practice

1. Study the figure.

    (a) Which region has the highest weekly passenger kilometres in:

    2006.................

    2026 .... (2)

    (b) Which regions appear to be 'left behind' by the growth in air travel?
    Explain your answer. (3)

    (c) Briefly explain the link between the process of globalisation and the growth in international air travel. (4)

    (d) The projected growth in air travel can be said to have costs as well as benefits. Outline some of the costs. (3)

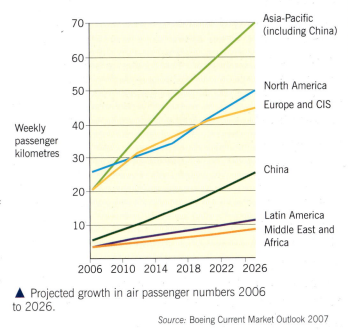

▲ Projected growth in air passenger numbers 2006 to 2026.

Source: Boeing Current Market Outlook 2007

CHAPTER 9 What are the main groupings of nations and what differences in levels of power and wealth exist?

Key terms

Economic groupings
GNP
International trade
Multiplier effect
Political groupings
Supply chain

Learning objectives

After studying this chapter, you will be able to discuss these ideas and concepts and provide examples of them:

- Disparities in global wealth.
- There are economic and political groupings of countries.
- These groupings change over time.
- The role that TNCs play in the development of global business.
- Specific information about one particular TNC.

▲ Figure 1: A McDonald's restaurant. But which country is it in? What does your answer tell you about McDonald's?

Introduction

Since the beginning of trade, countries have grouped together to form alliances that gave them mutual benefits. The first trading patterns were developed during colonial times between the 'mother country' and its colonies. Britain, for example, traded goods with all the countries of its empire, and many products were shipped from them back to Britain. In time, this developed into special agreements, which survived after the empire had been dismantled. New Zealand, for example, had special agreements for many years about exporting meat and dairy products to the UK (though the UK's involvement in the EU has since weakened those agreements).

There are many different groupings of countries in the world. Some, like the EU or OPEC, are deliberately organised groups – generally for economic or political reasons – that are recognised throughout the world. A country can belong to more than one of these groups – and would probably benefit from doing so.

There are other types of groups that have been chosen and named by geographers, economists and politicians to help them in their work. Countries are classified according to their level of development, their wealth or some other measure, and then referred to as a group – less economically developed countries (LEDCs), for example, or more economically developed countries (MEDCs). Countries have no say about what group they are put in and there is no formal connection between the countries in a group. It's just a convenient way for everyone to view the countries of the world.

Global disparities

There are very great differences in wealth in the world. These can be measured both between countries and within them. Many researchers recognise that these differences have increased in recent years. In broad terms there is no doubt that globalisation has made the rich richer, but it is much more arguable whether it has benefited the poor.

The usual measurement of wealth variation *between* countries is Gross Domestic Product (GDP) per head. But measurement of variations *within* a country is often done by using a combination of GDP per head – an average figure – and the 'Gini coefficient' (sometimes known as Lorenz curves). The Gini coefficient measures how the total income is distributed within a society. Nations with a relatively even spread of wealth – with few mega-rich individuals and few living in poverty – have Gini coefficients of 0.25–0.30; examples would be Scandinavian countries, such as Sweden. Countries where a very large proportion of the total income is earned by a small percentage of the population – resulting in many disadvantaged and poor people – have coefficients of between 0.50 and 0.60. A number of South American countries, such as Brazil and Bolivia, figure amongst this group.

If we look at the world as a whole, then the coefficient is about 0.65. This reflects a world in which the richest 20% of the population consume well over 80% of its resources. A study by the World Institute for Development Economics Research at United Nations University reports that the richest 1% of adults alone owned 40% of global assets in the year 2000, and that the richest 10% of adults accounted for 85% of the world total. The poorest half of the world adult population owned barely 1% of global wealth. It is important to note that most commentators agree that these disparities are increasing – that, in other words, both within countries and globally the gap between the rich and poor is widening. In rich MEDCs, although outward signs of absolute poverty are unusual, relative poverty is increasing and societies are becoming more divided.

Global groupings – levels of development

LDCs – Less developed countries
The poorest countries in the world are known as the LDCs. The GNP in these countries is very low and their economy has hardly started to develop. These include countries such as the Maldives, where the only development that has taken place is tourism, or countries like Ethiopia, which is continually struggling with the effects of drought and war.

LEDCs – Less economically developed countries
The term LEDCs can be used loosely for the next grouping of countries economically. These countries have started to develop their economies and this can be seen in their increasing GDP, their calorie intake per day and their birth and death rates.

MEDCs – More economically developed countries
The term MEDC refers to countries that have highly developed economies. They have high levels of calorie intake and GDP. Their birth and death rates are low, and in some cases their death rate is higher than their birth rate.

NICs – Newly industrialised countries
NICs have improved their economy – relatively recently – through the development of a strong manufacturing base. These countries have been recognised by geographers and economists as a distinct group since the late 1960s.

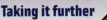

Taking it further

To learn more about measuring inequality read 'The gap between the rich and the poor' on your Student CD-ROM.

Taking it further

To learn more about colonialism read 'A look at colonialism' on your Student CD-ROM.

Key term

GNP – Gross National Product: the total value of goods and services produced by a country in a given period (GDP), plus the money earned by its investments abroad. GNP does not include the money earned by foreigners who live in that country.

Global groupings – political-economic alliances

G8 – the Group of Eight
The eight most powerful countries in the world are known as the G8 – Canada, France, Germany, Italy, Japan, Russia, the UK and the USA. Their leaders meet annually to discuss global issues.

The Commonwealth
The Commonwealth is an association of 53 countries, all of which are former British colonies, except the UK itself and Mozambique. Although the member countries are very diverse, they all try to uphold the same values.

OECD – the Organisation for Economic Co-operation and Development
The OECD consists of the richest and most powerful countries, and is therefore one of the world's most powerful economic organisations. Its members (currently 30 countries) share the principles of market economy, democracy and respect for human rights.

EU – the European Union
The EU is an economic and political grouping of European countries. It now has 27 members who contribute to a central European Parliament, Commission, Court of Justice, etc. Members can trade freely within the union and are protected to some degree from external trade by trade barriers. The EU is becoming an increasingly influential group in global economics and politics.

Global groupings – trade blocs

APEC – the Asia Pacific Economic Co-operation
APEC is a group of 21 Pacific rim countries that meet annually to discuss the regional economy, co-operation, trade and investment. APEC members (who include Australia, China, Japan, Russia and the USA) account for approximately 41% of the world's population, 56% of world GDP and 49% of world trade.

OPEC – the Organization of the Petroleum Exporting Countries
Most of the members of OPEC are Middle East countries, but the organisation also includes countries such as Venezuela and Nigeria. When these countries act collectively they are extremely powerful because they control most of the world's oil.

NAFTA – the North American Free Trade Agreement
NAFTA, which came into being in 1994, is a free trade agreement between the three North American countries – Canada, USA and Mexico. It remains the largest trade bloc in the world in terms of the combined GDP of its members.

Taking it further
Name five countries that belong to each of the following 'groups': LDCs, LEDCs, MEDCs, NICs.

The role of transnational companies (TNCs)

Transnational companies operate globally for a number of reasons, all of which are about growing (or at least safeguarding) their profits.

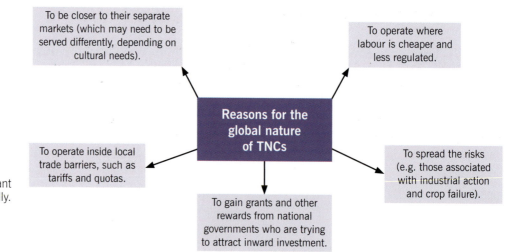

To be closer to their separate markets (which may need to be served differently, depending on cultural needs).

To operate where labour is cheaper and less regulated.

Reasons for the global nature of TNCs

To operate inside local trade barriers, such as tariffs and quotas.

To spread the risks (e.g. those associated with industrial action and crop failure).

To gain grants and other rewards from national governments who are trying to attract inward investment.

▶ Figure 2: Why companies want to operate globally.

TNCs have a major role in the global economy and, as such, they are themselves agents of global change. They link groups of countries together as they produce goods for a global market. The economist, Adam Smith, argued that an invisible hand was required to ensure that the demand of customers was met by the creation of goods and services by suppliers. In a global economic system a mechanism is required to ensure that these goods and services are provided to the global consuming community. TNCs provide this role. Therefore globalisation is an economic solution to the movement of goods and services from the producers to the consumers.

In one production line the goods may be sourced from many different countries. TNCs can also influence culture as they shape global patterns of consumption. For example, McDonald's burgers are eaten in over 100 countries around the world.

TNCs are also of economic importance to a country as they bring direct foreign investment. TNCs invest money in each of the countries they operate in, setting off a multiplier effect. They do not always produce all of their goods or components themselves – they often subcontract the work to other companies who then produce the goods under the name of the TNC. (It is very difficult to know who actually owns companies nowadays because of the many acquisitions and mergers that take place. Brands that have always been in the market place could actually be owned by other companies.)

TNCs have to deal with the various trade blocs and protectionist policies, such as tariffs and quotas. Honda, for example, was restricted to importing a limited number of cars into the UK every year, but it decided to locate its next factory in Swindon, so now it can sell as many cars in the UK as it likes, because they are being manufactured within the country.

Although there are many restrictions on the movement of people, many countries have free trade agreements. This applies between the EU countries, and between the USA, Canada and Mexico.

The presence of the free market in Europe can be witnessed every day on a drive along the motorway where many foreign lorries can be seen transporting goods all over the country (Figure 3). Many of these lorries are transporting goods produced by TNCs.

▲ **Figure 3:** Foreign lorries transporting goods all over the country.

Taking it further

To learn more about the theory behind trade rules read 'How the classical economists got it wrong' on your Student CD-ROM.

McDonald's: a service sector TNC

McDonald's is one of the world's best known TNCs. Its growth into a global brand is one of the success stories of the last 50 years. The first restaurant opened in the US in 1955 and there are now 30,000 restaurants in 120 countries. It is the largest fast food service company in the world, with 50 million people a day using its restaurants. The first restaurant in the UK opened in 1974 and now there are over 1,200 restaurants that serve 2 million customers a day.

▲ **Figure 4:** McDonald's on Galle Road, Colombo, Sri Lanka.

▲ **Figure 5:** Exterior of McDonald's, High Street, Windsor.

Taking it further

To learn more about how TNCs operate read 'Research your own TNC' on your Student CD-ROM.

McDonald's have had some negative publicity in the past, due primarily to the public's misunderstanding with regards to their practices concerning pay and food production.

The company realised that, if they were to continue to succeed and expand as a TNC, they must regain the public's goodwill. For a TNC, they are quite radical. Their preference has always been to source locally, therefore fulfilling the ideals of sustainability. This fact, along with their policy to be totally open, has impressed the British public and ensured the continuing success of McDonald's in the UK. Figures 6 and 7 portray the supply chain for a number of McDonald's products in the UK.

In most other ways, McDonald's is a typical TNC. Its profits, for example, go to the USA where the company is based. Remember that in many countries McDonald's is organised as a franchise. In the UK, for example, 50% of McDonald's branches are franchises, in which individuals (many of them previous McDonald's employees) have made a financial commitment – often more than £250,000 – to run a restaurant for at least 20 years. The profits from these enterprises do circulate 'locally', with the subsequent multiplier effect.

Figure 1 shows a McDonald's restaurant in Colombo in Sri Lanka. The people in the photograph could be eating anywhere in the world. The products and the packaging on the tables are very similar to those used in the UK – because the McDonald's customer culture shares commonalities throughout the world. Many people prefer this, as they know what to expect and it makes them feel secure, no matter which country they are in – the brand and experience is the same. Figure 4 shows the outside of the same restaurant with the usual McDonald's sign, also instantly recognisable. One of the few restaurants that does not have the usual McDonald's frontage is opposite Windsor castle on High Street Windsor, as shown in Figure 5, as it did not get planning permission from the local authority.

By retaining product commonalities across different countries, although with some local variances, McDonald's is spreading a part of western culture throughout the world. This widespread shaping of common patterns of consumption is one of the characteristics of all TNCs.

Although the products are very similar, their prices vary throughout the world. In the UK, the average McDonald's meal costs approximately £4, whereas in Sri Lanka it costs £1 and in the USA it costs £3. This is because of the varying wages and costs of supplies in the different countries. Although the products are similar, the local price reflects the country's stage of development, because the McDonald's is aware of the cost of living in the area but wants to maintain its profit margins. If a McDonald's in Sri Lanka charged £4 then only the tourists would eat there but, as you can see from Figure 1, it is very popular with the locals. In 2007, McDonald's spent over £460 m through its UK supply chain. This involved over 17,000 farmers working with 6,000 food supply companies. Figure 6 shows the location of many of the suppliers and what they supply. The majority of the produce for the company's UK outlets comes from the UK, just as, for example, produce for the Brazil outlets comes from Brazil. In some instances, for example in an emerging market where a country does not have the infrastructure in place to support local sourcing, then McDonald's do have to source from further afield. However, they continue to support a local sourcing policy.

The company is trying to be more sustainable and to 'think local' in all of its outlets. However, although the UK is fairly self-sufficient, other countries are not. The UK companies that supply McDonald's in the UK also export products and packaging to other countries.

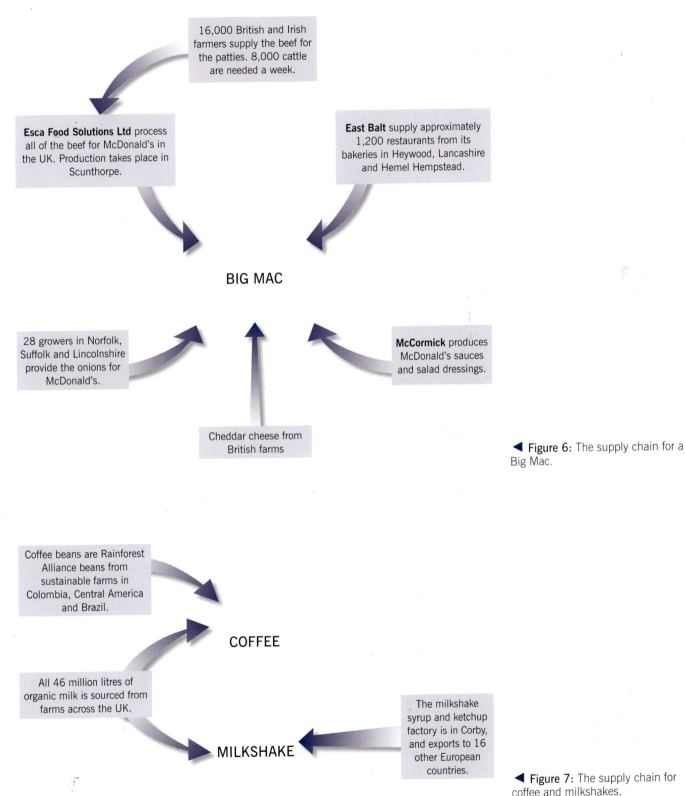

16,000 British and Irish farmers supply the beef for the patties. 8,000 cattle are needed a week.

Esca Food Solutions Ltd process all of the beef for McDonald's in the UK. Production takes place in Scunthorpe.

East Balt supply approximately 1,200 restaurants from its bakeries in Heywood, Lancashire and Hemel Hempstead.

28 growers in Norfolk, Suffolk and Lincolnshire provide the onions for McDonald's.

McCormick produces McDonald's sauces and salad dressings.

Cheddar cheese from British farms

BIG MAC

◀ **Figure 6:** The supply chain for a Big Mac.

Coffee beans are Rainforest Alliance beans from sustainable farms in Colombia, Central America and Brazil.

COFFEE

All 46 million litres of organic milk is sourced from farms across the UK.

The milkshake syrup and ketchup factory is in Corby, and exports to 16 other European countries.

MILKSHAKE

◀ **Figure 7:** The supply chain for coffee and milkshakes.

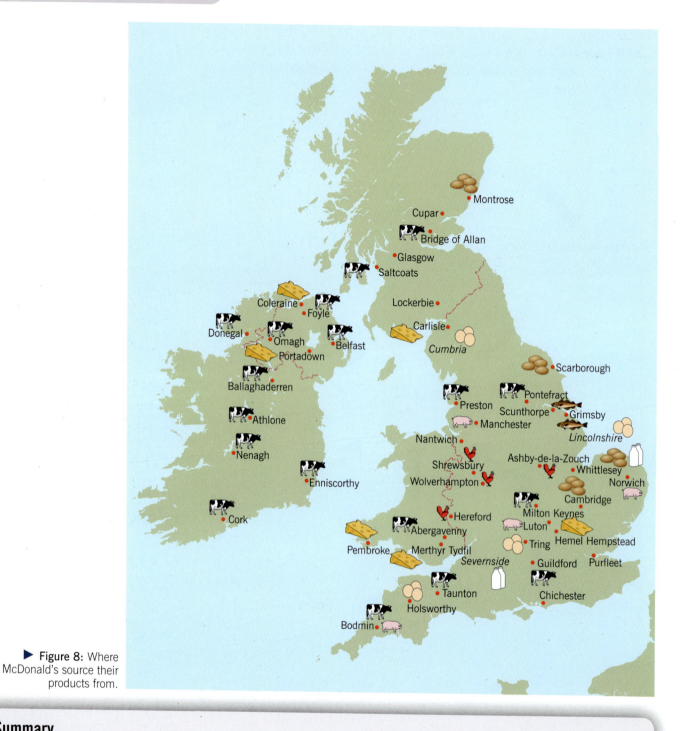

► **Figure 8:** Where McDonald's source their products from.

Summary

Having studied this chapter, you should be able to discuss these ideas and concepts and provide located examples of them:

• Wealth is not spread evenly across the world.

• The main economic and political groupings of countries in the world.

• These groupings change over time.

• The role that TNCs play in the development of global business .

  • Information about McDonald's, a service sector TNC.

MCQ

Exam practice

1. Study the figure.

World's top 20 TNCs	Economic sector	Home country	Revenue (sales) in 2007 ($US bn)	Total GDP of selected countries, 2006 ($US bn)
1. Wal-Mart	Retail	🇺🇸	351	Saudi Arabia, 349
2. Exxon Mobil	Oil & Gas	🇺🇸	347	
3. Shell	Oil & Gas	🇳🇱	318	Denmark 276
4. BP	Oil & Gas	🇬🇧	274	
5. General Motors	Vehicles	🇺🇸	207	
6. Toyota	Vehicles	🇯🇵	204	Portugal 194
7. Chevron	Oil & Gas	🇺🇸	200	
8. DaimlerChrysler	Vehicles	🇩🇪	190	
9. ConocoPhillips	Oil & Gas	🇺🇸	172	
10. Total	Oil & Gas	🇫🇷	168	United Arab Emirates 168
11. General Electric	Industrial	🇺🇸	168	
12. Ford Motor	Vehicles	🇺🇸	160	
13. ING Group	Banking & Finance	🇺🇸	158	
14. Citigroup	Banking & Finance	🇺🇸	146	Malaysia 148
15. AXA	Banking & Finance	🇫🇷	139	
16. Volkswagen	Vehicles	🇩🇪	132	Singapore 132
17. Sinopec	Oil & Gas	🇨🇳	131	
18. Crédit Agricole	Banking & Finance	🇫🇷	128	
19. Allianz	Banking & Finance	🇩🇪	125	Pakistan 127
20. Fortis	Banking & Finance	🇳🇱	121	

◀ The World's top 10 TNCs in 2007 by revenue.

(a) Which economic sector dominates the global TNC top 20? (1)

(b) Briefly state the key characteristics of a TNC. (3)

(c) What benefits do TNCs bring to their home country? (3)

(d) Referring to the figure, comment on the significance of TNCs when compared to the total GDP of some countries. (4)

2. (a) Describe how and explain why production of the Honda Civic has 'globalised' since the 1970s. (10)

(b) With reference to named TNCs, explain its role in development and globalisation. (15)

1 1975 Production begins in Indonesia
2 1977 Production begins in Mexico
3 1984 Production begins in Thailand
4 1986 Production begins in the U.S.
5 1988 Production begins in Canada
6 1992 Production begins in the Philippines
7 1994 Production begins in the UK and Pakistan
8 1997 Production begins in Brazil and Turkey
9 2006 Production begins in China

NB: Honda is a Japanese TNC. The first Honda Civic was produced in Japan in 1972. Honda Civic's are small family cars.

◀ Globalisation of Honda Civic car production

Chapter 10 Why, as places and societies become more interconnected, do some places show extreme wealth and poverty?

Key Terms

Global hub
Global network
'Switched-on' countries
'Switched-off' countries

Learning objectives

After studying this chapter, you will be able to discuss these ideas and concepts and provide examples of them:

• Global networks, such as air travel and tourism, create flows of money, trade and information.
• Some places are more involved in these flows than others, and this connectivity can be assessed through energy usage and ecological footprints.
• The places that are more 'switched on' (connected) are wealthier and more powerful.
• The places that are 'switched off' (not connected) remain poor.
• The role of technology in our shrinking world.
• Who the winners are and who the losers are, and their reasons.

The term 'global network' refers to the links between different countries in the world. These links include the flows of capital, traded goods and services, information and – to a lesser extent – people. Some areas are well connected, and these are usually high income areas. Other areas are poorly connected and are generally low income areas.

Taking it further

To learn more about interconnectivity read 'The connected world – taking a look at the network' on your Student CD-ROM.

◀ **Figure 1:** Great Britain's motorway network. Which areas would you say are the winners and which areas are the losers? Which areas will be switched on and which switched off by this network?

The 14 countries that have the most trading partners are shown in Figure 2. Trading with several other countries implies a great connectivity. If this map is compared with the flows of air travel shown in Figure 3, it can be seen that there is a direct correlation between the number of passengers travelling by air and the countries with the most trading partners. These countries would appear to be the most connected and 'switched on' countries of the world.

Rank	Area	% of world's trade in 2006
1	European Union	17.0
2	USA	15.6
3	China	8.9
4	Japan	6.3
5	Canada	4.2
6	South Korea	3.4
7	Hong Kong	3.4
8	Singapore	2.6
9	Mexico	2.6
10	Russia	2.3
11	Switzerland	1.7
12	India	1.7
13	Malaysia	1.5
14	Australia	1.4

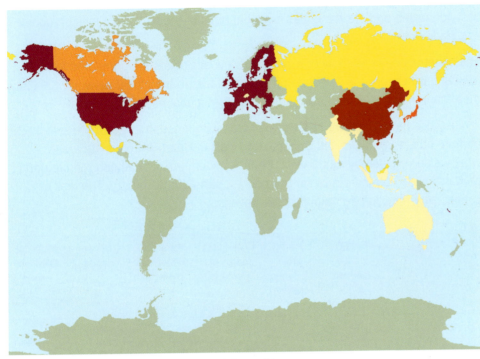

▲ Figure 2: The top 14 trading countries in the world.

	Europe	Northern America	Latin America	Pacific Asia	South Asia	Middle East and North Africa	Sub-Saharan Africa	Oceania	Former Soviet Union / Central Asia
Europe	79.8								
Northern America	25.8	78.2							
Latin America	6.0	15.8	12.8						
Pacific Asia	8.4	12.3	0.3	20.7					
South Asia	2.5	2.0	0.02	2.5	3.1				
Middle East and North Africa	8.2	2.5	0.1	1.6	4.4	6.5			
Sub-Saharan Africa	4.1	0.9	0.09	0.3	0.3	0.7	4.1		
Oceania	1.6	1.2	0.09	3.8	0.1	0.2	0.2	7.0	
Former Soviet Union / Central Asia	2.2	0.5	0.04	0.2	0.06	0.1	0.02	0.009	0.3

▲ Figure 3: Number of air passengers (millions) between and within areas of the world, per year.

Another way to assess the connectivity of a country – or indeed a city – is to look at its energy use. The countries which appear as having the most trading partners also appear as having the highest usage of energy (Figure 4). This is due to the amount of energy that is being used both personally and by business to sustain the economy. There also appears to be a direct correlation between energy usage and ecological footprints of a country. The countries that have the most trading partners, the highest ecological footprints, energy usage and GNP appear to be the best connected and are the nodes or global hubs of the world for flows of money and trade but not workers.

The countries that have low energy usage, low ecological footprints and few trading partners are the switched off poorer places in the global network. Spatially, these countries are located away from the main global networks links.

It must also be remembered that some areas within countries are more switched on than others. In Figure 1 the prosperous part of Great Britain is the area which is served well by motorways. Counties such as Cornwall and remote parts of Wales and Scotland are by far the poorest parts of the country. The lack of connectivity may, in part, explain their poverty.

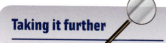

Taking it further

To learn more about patterns of deprivation read 'Pockets of poverty and wealthy elites' on your Student CD-ROM.

Country	Energy usage (tonnes of oil equivalent)	Rank for energy usage	Ecological footprint (hectares per person)	Rank for ecological footprint	GNP per capita	Rank for GNP per capita
United States	8.35	1	12.22	2	44,000	6
Canada	8.16	2	7.66	9	32,000	19
Finland	6.4	3	8.45	8	37,500	13
Belgium	5.78	4	5.88	21	36,000	17
Australia	5.71	5	8.49	7	32,000	20
Norway	5.7	6	6.13	18	40,000	2
Sweden	5.7	7	7.53	10	41,000	8
New Zealand	4.86	8	9.54	5	26,000	25
Netherlands	4.76	9	5.75	22	36,500	15
France	4.25	10	7.27	11	36,000	16
Japan	4.13	11	5.94	20	39,000	11
Germany	4.13	12	6.31	14	35,000	18
United Kingdom	3.89	13	6.29	16	37,500	12
Ireland	3.86	14	9.43	6	40,000	9
Switzerland	3.7	15	6.63	13	55,000	3

▲ Figure 4: Energy usage, ecological footprint and GNP for the top energy using countries in the world in 2006.

Achieving connectivity

The ways in which these countries – and indeed cities – have achieved this connectivity now needs to be looked at in more detail. Is the world really shrinking? Technology is perhaps the main influence on globalisation. 'Technology' includes communication technology, such as telephones and the internet, but also refers to the developments in transport technology.

Telegraph communication

The development of the telegraph was a major breakthrough in communication technology. In its time, the telegraph was as important as the internet is now in shrinking the world. Before the telegraph, news took at least 10 days to be shipped across the Atlantic. Therefore news from Europe – where most of the Americans had come from – was always at least 10 days old. This is very difficult for us to comprehend in our world of 'breaking news'. The newspapers in New York demanded that the service be improved, and from 1857 onwards ships started laying cables across the Atlantic, with little practical success at first. In 1858, for example, when Queen Victoria sent a message to the American President, it took more than 16 hours to transmit, despite having fewer than 100 words. The technology improved, however, and the first commercial telegraph was in operation by 1868. In the twentieth century, telephone cables became more important, and now satellites are used instead of cables to convey a whole range of electronic messages. Figure 5 shows the Satellite Earth Station at Goonhilly in Cornwall, the largest in the world. There are 60 dishes on the site which are continually busy sending and receiving TV pictures all over the world, while simultaneously handling thousands of international phone, fax, data and video calls. The large dish on the right of the picture (called 'Merlin') carried the 1985 Live Aid concert to 2 billion people around the globe. It is this sort of technology that is making the world appear to shrink.

Internet communication

The internet is the major breakthrough in communication technology of the late twentieth century. Figure 6 shows the phenomenal growth of the internet since 1977. But why has it grown so much, and what does this mean for our shrinking world? By 2010 much of the planet will be using the internet. The internet is a way of communicating with other people simply and in many cases, securely. This means that transnational companies can keep in touch with their branch plants easily. It has also enabled many people to work from home, if only for part of the week, using their computers as a way of communicating with their company. By making information about places and people far more readily available, the internet is also a way of learning about the world.

Perhaps one of the most amazing facts about the internet's growth, compared with earlier technologies, is that, to get a market of 50 million people, it took radio 38 years and TV 13 years but, once it was open to the public, it took the internet only 4 years.

▲ **Figure 5:** Goonhilly Satellite Earth Station in Cornwall.

Year	Number of hosts (servers)
1977	111
1981	213
1983	562
1984	1,000
1986	5,000
1987	10,000
1989	100,000
1992	1,000,000
2001	175,000,000
2002	200,000,000

▲ **Figure 6:** The growth in internet usage.

"I always fly from Luton to Edinburgh. The total travel time including check in is only about 7 hours and cost me just £65."

Air travel

The technology revolution has hit the travel industry with both barrels. The internet has totally changed peoples perception of the world, and now people want to travel further than they ever did before. And using the internet shows them what is there and allows them to book online. For example, if a family wanted to travel to Sri Lanka, even 10 years ago, it would have been a very expensive place to go to and a complicated process to organise. Now, with online holiday booking and the airline technology to take them there directly, it has become relatively easy and inexpensive. More holidays are now booked online than at high street travel agents. As a result, many high street and local travel agents have closed down, and tour operators have had to adapt to the evolving market.

The revolution in air travel began in the 1950s, when airlines started to use jet aircraft, such as the Comet and Boeing 707 for both charter and scheduled trips. The introduction of wide-bodied jets in the 1970s meant that more people could be transported more cheaply than ever before, and now 300 to 400 people can be transported on one jet airplane. The more recent rise of low-cost budget airlines then further revolutionised the marketplace.

For some journeys, low-cost budget airlines are often a cheaper and faster way of travelling than the train (see Figure 7). As well as revolutionising the business world, they are also opening up many cities and countries to tourists. The numbers of people who now have two or three foreign holidays a year by taking cheap weekend breaks has increased significantly. With the development of the tourist industry comes the multiplier effect, creating more wealth and opportunity for the destination. One place that has benefited greatly from this trend is Prague.

"Perhaps I should try it. I always take the train from Luton to Edinburgh. The total travel time is over 12 hours for the return journey and I have to change trains 5 times. It can be very tedious and it costs me just over £100."

These examples illustrate that the world is indeed shrinking for some but, as technology continues to bring some places closer by increasing their connectivity, other places now suffer. The islanders of the Pitcairn Islands in the Pacific Ocean, for example, have become more isolated as now fewer ships pass their shores because of the switch to air travel.

Connectivity and natural resources

The connectivity of places is a function of their economic success and potential. In turn, once places are well connected this feeds further growth, producing a virtuous circle that often extends the wealth gap between rich global regions and poor global regions.

▲ Figure 7: A discussion between two businessmen on the comparative costs of train and air travel.

Case study: Prague

Prague opened up to tourists during the 1990s, but it wasn't until the low-cost airlines started to fly there in 2003 that tourist numbers increased. Many British people fly to Prague using easyJet or Ryanair and stay for 3 or 4 nights. There has also been a development in the number of people who celebrate their stag and hen nights there. In 2004, 3.5 million tourists visited Prague, with the British being the second-largest group, at 650,000. Germany provided the largest number of tourists, many using its budget airline Germanwings. The figures continued to rise, and in 2006 stood at 6.6 million. This example shows how the development of budget airlines has increased one city's connectivity and made it more of a global hub.

In the pre-modern world the great fertile plains of South and East Asia were the hub of civilisations that were interconnected through trade and political alliances, long before European development. Pre-modern wealth was quite closely related to physical factors, such as soil fertility, climate and accessibility. The picture has been much less clear since the dawn of the colonial age. The search for raw materials and their exploitation led to the development of the slave trade and the impoverishment of many global regions for the benefit of the 'mother' countries. Modern countries that are richly endowed with raw materials such as the Democratic Republic of the Congo (once Zaire) or Bolivia are not wealthy (although they have a number of very wealthy individuals) whereas other countries without enormous reserves of natural wealth have achieved dramatic economic success through the development of their human resources. An obvious example is South Korea, which became a separate nation after the Korean War. This divided it from communist-led North Korea, which had a virtual monopoly of the natural resources. South Korea's progress and emergence as one of the first NICs – through foreign investment and enormous emphasis on education – is in marked contrast to the disappointing economic performance of North Korea, which, despite its natural resources, remains one of the poorest nations on earth.

Taking it further

To learn more about the relationship between natural resources and economic development read 'We've got the gold so why aren't we rich?' on your Student CD-ROM.

▲ **Figure 8:** Shanghai, China

Case study: China

The economic development of China is a relatively recent phenomenon. In 1995, China's GNP per capita was $620, but by 2005 it had risen to $1,700 – nearly a threefold increase. China's development is aided by both natural and human resources. It has a great wealth of natural resources, having vast reserves of coal, oil and natural gas. These are used to fuel the industrial development of the country. Since the 1990s China has also been developing its energy base, with new hydroelectric and nuclear power stations. China's geographical position in the world is also beneficial for its development as all around it are the developing markets of South Korea, Taiwan and India, and it is on the major trade routes.

China has a great human resource in its vast population, who are willing to work hard – in education and in employment. China trains 600,000 new engineers every year. However, the millions of rural labourers who are fuelling China's economic growth are not treated well by their employers. Despite recent reforms, they are shut out of the health care system and state education, live in appalling, overcrowded conditions and are routinely exposed to some of the most exploitative working conditions. They are forced to work long stretches of time under hazardous conditions for very low wages. Many managers withhold pay for 2 to 3 months to ensure that they hold on to their workers, who are in short supply in this rapidly industrialising country.

So China has become a divided society. Not only is it divided within the cities, it is also developing a regional split between the developed urban eastern regions, where most production is concentrated – Shanghai, Tianjin and Guangdong, and the underdeveloped western regions of Shaanxi, Guangxi, Sichuan and Gansu, where the majority of poor Chinese live. So although China, as a country, appears to be developing fast, there is a social cost to this rapid development.

The two photographs (Figures 8 and 9) illustrate the results of the rapid industrialisation of China. Figure 8, of Beijing, shows the new industry with the blue roofs in the foreground. The skyscrapers in the background show the phenomenal growth of the city. The second photograph, Figure 9, shows the living conditions of the poor migrants. Notice the roofs that open to allow light and air into the very confined spaces.

▲ **Figure 9:** Housing in Shanghai, China.

The physical and human resources of a country can also play an important role in determining its role in the world. Some countries appear to have all the opportunities, while others are lacking in the physical and human resources that will help them to succeed in a competitive world. Yet other places have become global hubs despite lacking the valuable physical and human resources, and vice versa.

Case study: The Gambia

The Gambia is one of the 'loser' countries which remains poorly connected. It is not developing at the same rate as China because it lacks physical and human resources. Between 1995 and 2005, the Gambia's GNP per capita dropped from $320 to $290. The Gambia has no confirmed mineral or natural resource deposits and has a limited agricultural base. About 75% of the people depend on crops and livestock for their livelihood. Small-scale manufacturing activity includes the processing of groundnuts, fish and hides, which are then exported. The country is dependent upon aid for any development that it may achieve. The government is trying to aid development with spending in the social sector. For example, a girls' scholarship programme was started in 2001, and met with great success, enrolling girls from poor households in school. However, without natural and human resources, the Gambia will find it hard to become a global hub of activity in the way that China is now.

◀ **Figure 10:** A shanty town in Banjul, the Gambia.

▶ **Figure 11:** Traditional groundnut farming in the Gambia.

Summary

Having studied this chapter, you should be able to discuss these ideas and concepts and provide located examples of them:

- Global networks create flows of money, trade and information.
- Some places are more involved in these flows than others.
- Some places are more switched on (connected) and as a result are gaining wealth and power – China, for example.
- Some places are switched off (not connected) and as a result are remaining poor – the Gambia, for example.
- The reasons why some places are switched on and others are switched off.
  - The role of technology in our shrinking world.

MCQ

Exam practice

1.

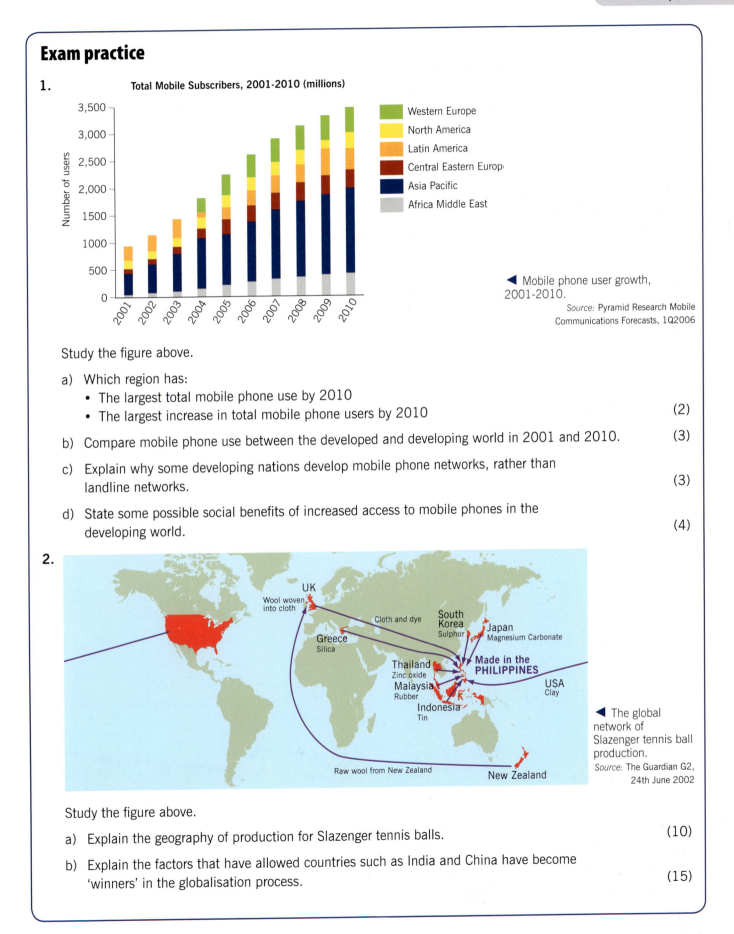

Total Mobile Subscribers, 2001-2010 (millions)

◀ Mobile phone user growth, 2001-2010.

Source: Pyramid Research Mobile Communications Forecasts, 1Q2006

Study the figure above.

a) Which region has:
   • The largest total mobile phone use by 2010
   • The largest increase in total mobile phone users by 2010 (2)

b) Compare mobile phone use between the developed and developing world in 2001 and 2010. (3)

c) Explain why some developing nations develop mobile phone networks, rather than landline networks. (3)

d) State some possible social benefits of increased access to mobile phones in the developing world. (4)

2.

◀ The global network of Slazenger tennis ball production.
Source: The Guardian G2, 24th June 2002

Study the figure above.

a) Explain the geography of production for Slazenger tennis balls. (10)

b) Explain the factors that have allowed countries such as India and China have become 'winners' in the globalisation process. (15)

CHAPTER 11 How does evidence from personal, local and national sources help us understand the pattern of population change in the UK?

Key terms

Ageing population
Dependency ratio
Education Maintenance
   Allowance (EMA)
Global depression
Pathfinder project
Population structure
Post-war baby boom
Replacement rates

Learning objectives

After studying this chapter, you will be able to discuss these ideas and concepts and provide examples of them:

• The changes in the structure of the population of the UK.
• Migration has had an impact on some families but not others.
• The changing employment patterns during the twentieth century.
• The social and economic factors that have had an impact on UK population.
• The challenges that are presented by a greying population.

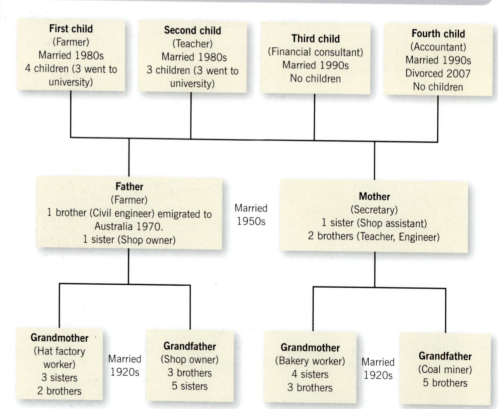

▶ Figure 1: A typical British family tree. How does this family tree reflect the changes in the UK population structure during the twentieth century?

Taking it further

Research your own family tree.

The structure of the population of the UK changed greatly during the twentieth century. A number of trends can be identified, such as a change in the size of families, people living longer, family members emigrating, new immigrants arriving, and a change to the employment base of the country. These changes have been brought about by a number of economic and social factors which will be examined in this chapter.

The social and economic factors that have had an impact on UK population

The birth rate of the UK declined for much of the twentieth century. There were occasions when there was an increase in birth rate, such as the years immediately after the Second World War when men were reunited with their families (known as the 'baby boom' period); however the overall trend was one of decline. In 1940, 11% of women in the UK had no children. By 2000 this figure had more than doubled. According to the latest reports, two out of three women born in the 1970s are yet to have children. In comparison, half of the women born in the early 1960s had had children by the time they were 25. Figure 2 further exemplifies this trend in various European countries. A rate of 2.1 children is considered to be the population replacement level, so these countries are not replacing their populations, whereas in the early 1960s they all were.

Ireland	1.99
France	1.90
Norway	1.81
Sweden	1.75
UK	1.74
Netherlands	1.73
Germany	1.37
Italy	1.33
Spain	1.32
Greece	1.29

▲ Figure 2: Replacement rates in selected European countries.
Source: Eurostat 2004 figures

So what are the reasons for this dramatic decrease in birth rate in European countries? One of the reasons for the decline is the changing status of women within society. As more women receive the same education as men, and laws change to give them equal rights in the workplace, more women want to have a career rather than staying at home to raise a family. It is not only women who do not want to have children. Many are fully supported by their partners because of the freedom, lifestyle and income that they as a couple can enjoy if they don't have children. And once women have a career, they may not want to give it up to have children, for several reasons (see Figure 3).

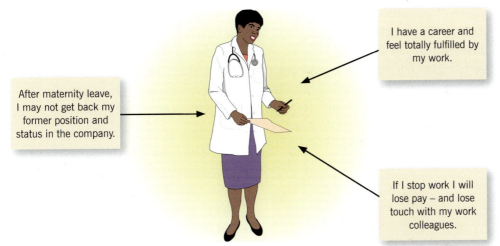

I have a career and feel totally fulfilled by my work.

After maternity leave, I may not get back my former position and status in the company.

If I stop work I will lose pay – and lose touch with my work colleagues.

◄ Figure 3: Reasons for not having a family.

In addition, many women who have put off having children until they have established their careers and then find that their fertility levels are low and they cannot actually conceive. The average age for mothers having their first child was 26 in 1971, this figure had risen to 29 in 2002, but could be broken down into two: 26 outside of marriage and 31 inside marriage. Thus, in addition to the many women taking a decision not to have children, women generally are having children later in life. Many women have children but continue to work full time. This option – which was not available to their mothers' generation – has been brought about partly by the development of labour-saving devices (such as automatic washing machines and dishwashers) and partly by developments in childcare facilities.

Taking it further

To learn more about falling fertility in Europe read 'Falling fertility in the developed world' on your Student CD-ROM.

Academic year	Numbers enrolled
1988	365,000
1989	369,000
1990	389,000
1992	455,000
1994	517,000
1996	538,000
1998	576,000
2000	618,000
2002	628,000
2004	647,000
2006	679,000

▲ **Figure 4:** Numbers of students (under 21) enrolled on full-time higher education courses.

Taking it further

To learn more about employment structure read 'Are part-time, temporary female workers the future?' on your Student CD-ROM.

Changes in government policies have also had an effect on lowering the birth rate. The availability of contraception and legal abortion, together with the provision of family planning clinics, make it easier for couples to limit the size of their family. The awareness of contraception has also been heightened by government advertising campaigns and by sex education being part of the school curriculum. The establishment of the National Health Service in 1948 means that there is free health care for all British citizens, which has led to an increase in life expectancy. Life expectancy has also increased because of better nutrition, helped by increased affluence and the greater variety of foods available (because of globalisation), allowing for a more balanced diet.

Changing work patterns are one of the significant economic factors affecting the population. There has been a steady decline in primary and secondary industry and a rise in the numbers employed in tertiary industry. In the primary sectors, this change has been driven by the mechanisation of agriculture and the closures of mines – due to exhaustion of raw materials and cheap imports. In the secondary sectors, there has also been a global shift in manufacturing to south-east Asia, where labour is cheaper and items can be produced at a lower cost. The growth of wealth and the consumer society has led to greater demand for services and a rise in the tertiary sector.

The UK has also seen a rise in the school leaving age during the twentieth century – to 14 in 1918, to 15 in 1947 and to 16 in 1972. A larger number of students are now staying on beyond 16, in colleges and sixth forms. This has been fuelled by the introduction of Education Maintenance Allowance (EMA) which pays students of lower-income families while they study. There has been a lot of investment in universities and there is now a much greater selection of courses available for study. As a result, many more young people are deciding to go to higher education than ever before. Figure 4 shows the rise in the numbers of young people (the figures are for under 21s) who enrolled on full-time courses between the years 1988 and 2006. This has led to an educated population who demand highly paid jobs in the tertiary sector.

There has also been a distinct movement of the population from the north of England to the South East. In many cases, this has been economic migrants looking for better jobs, and in some cases it has been people looking for a better lifestyle. Between 1991 and 2001 all regions of the country saw a growth in population, except the North East which saw a 0.2% decline and the North West which remained constant. Figure 5 shows the actual and the expected population changes between 2001 and 2011.

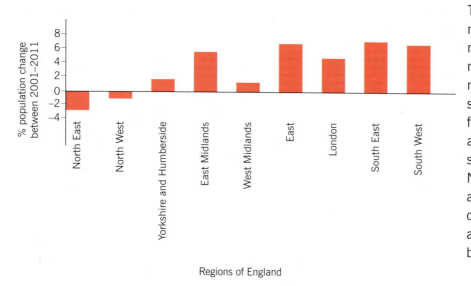

▶ **Figure 5:** Projected change in populations of the English regions between 2001 and 2011.

Again, all the growth regions are in the south of the country and the regions of decline are in the north. The government has tried to overcome this with 'Pathfinder projects' to try to regenerate failing communities. In 2005, £24 m went to the Yorkshire and Humberside region, £18 m to the North West, and £2 m to the North East.

The challenges presented by an ageing – 'greying' – population

By an 'ageing population' geographers mean that more of the population are either at or approaching retirement age. The population of the UK in 2000 is shown in Figure 6, and it is clear by looking at the columns that the population is ageing. By 2003 there were 20 million people aged 50 and over in the UK. This was a 45% increase over 50 years, from 13.8 million in 1951. The number is projected to increase by a further 36% by 2031, when there will be 27.2 million people aged 50 and over. This is a large burden for the economically active members of the population to carry, and will mean that the dependency ratio will continue to rise. The challenges that an ageing population presents are the pension burden and an increase in demand for specialist nurses and equipment, care homes and housing.

Taking it further

Find out more about Pathfinder projects in the north of England.

Taking it further

To explore this topic further you should look closely at the material covered in Chapters 26 and 30. These will give you plenty of ideas about how the population shift in the UK has been a function of industrial decline and employment shift, and how efforts to regenerate urban places in the north of the country have been met with variable success.

◀ **Figure 6:** Population pyramid for the United Kingdom in 2000.
Source: US Census Bureau, International Data Base

Taking it further

Research the 1970s oil crisis.

The Depression in the 1930s saw a decline in the birth rate as many people did not have the money to start a family. This effect has largely disappeared from the 2000 pyramid.

This is the 'baby boom' caused by an increase in the birth rate as soldiers returned from the war and were reunited with their families.

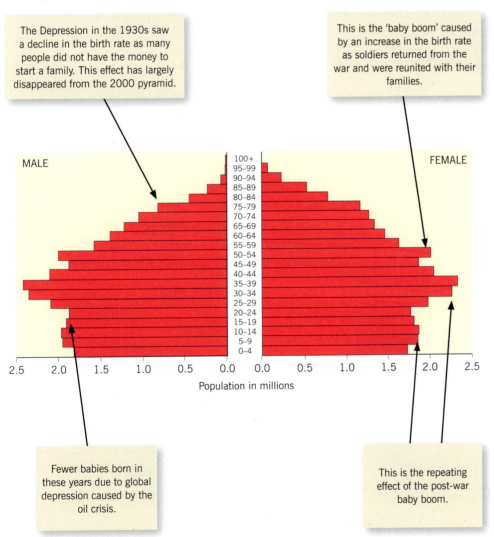

Fewer babies born in these years due to global depression caused by the oil crisis.

This is the repeating effect of the post-war baby boom.

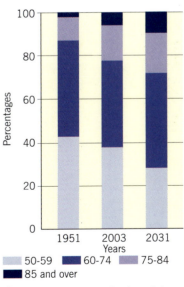

▲ **Figure 7:** Age distribution of the UK population over 50.

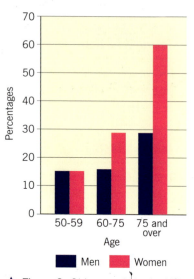

▲ Figure 8: Older people in the UK in 2002 who live alone, in selected age groups.

Taking it further 🔍

To learn more about the impact of an ageing population read 'Old, I'm not old. A further look at ageing in Europe' on your Student CD-ROM.

▶ Figure 9: Population pyramids for Reading and Christchurch (Dorset).

Pensions: There will be an increase in the number of people receiving state pension as the number of older people continues to increase. In 1950 there was only one pensioner for every five economically active people, but now there are three. The government has already taken action by raising the age that people will receive a state pension. It will go up from 65 to 66 in 2026, up again to 67 in 2036, and 68 in 2046.

Hospitals and care homes: Elderly patients require different health care to younger patients. As the population becomes older there will be a greater demand on specialist nursing staff, for example, in cardiac units. There will also be a greater demand for hospital beds, as elderly patients cannot be discharged if they live alone and have no one to care for them. The number of care homes will have to grow, because fewer elderly people will be able to go and live with their families when both the partners have full-time jobs. This is another aspect of the change in women's position in society.

Housing: As people live to an older age there will be an increase in demand for housing. Many elderly people live alone especially elderly women, see Figure 8. It is also the case that women live longer than men and therefore there will be a need for more housing stock as the population continues to age. This will also cause an increase in house prices as demand exceeds supply. It may also be a different kind of housing stock which is required as more people live alone or in warden assisted flats.

Distribution of the ageing population

The effects of an ageing population will not be felt equally across the country. Some local authorities that have large numbers of older people will have more challenges than local authorities who have large numbers of economically active people. Figure 9 shows two contrasting population pyramids. The one for Reading shows many people in the economically active age group, which means that there will be a large number of people to contribute to local taxes, and the local council will be able to provide services for this population structure. The contrasting pyramid for Christchurch, however, shows a much older population. Here the local council will have to provide extra facilities such as specialist hospital units and care homes to deal with the challenges this population structure presents.

Reading

Christchurch

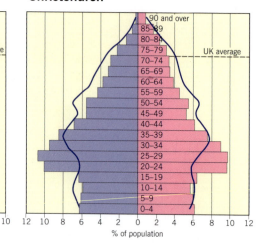

Summary

After studying this chapter you will have learnt:

• That there have been changes to the structure of the population of the UK which have been brought about by social and economic factors.

• That family trees of some British citizens reflect these changes.

• That migration has impacted on some families, but not on others.

• About the changing employment patterns during the twentieth century, from a country based on primary and secondary employment to a country with the majority of its population working in the tertiary sector.

• The fact that the UK has an ageing population and about the challenges that presents.

MCQ

Exam practice

1.

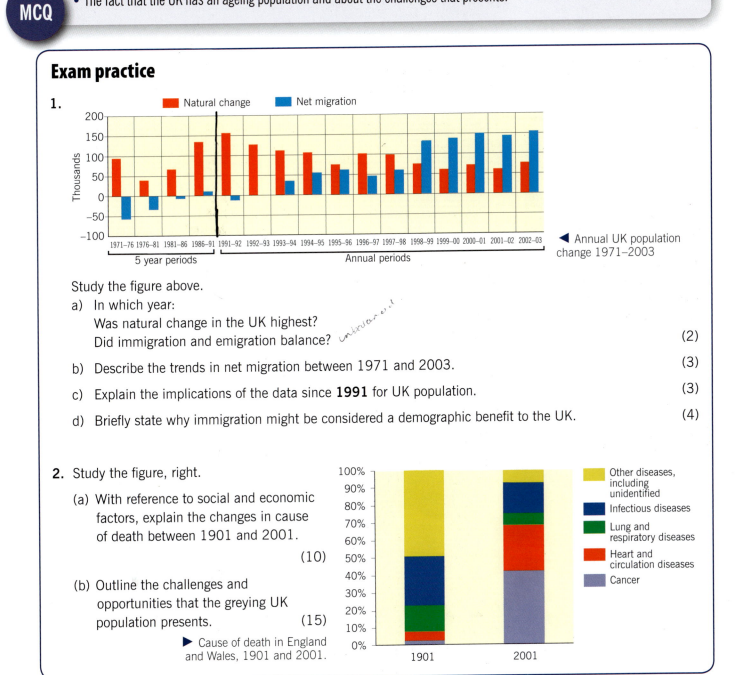

◀ Annual UK population change 1971–2003

Study the figure above.

a) In which year:
   Was natural change in the UK highest?
   Did immigration and emigration balance? *continuous* (2)

b) Describe the trends in net migration between 1971 and 2003. (3)

c) Explain the implications of the data since **1991** for UK population. (3)

d) Briefly state why immigration might be considered a demographic benefit to the UK. (4)

2. Study the figure, right.

(a) With reference to social and economic factors, explain the changes in cause of death between 1901 and 2001. (10)

(b) Outline the challenges and opportunities that the greying UK population presents. (15)

▶ Cause of death in England and Wales, 1901 and 2001.

Other diseases, including unidentified
Infectious diseases
Lung and respiratory diseases
Heart and circulation diseases
Cancer

CHAPTER 12 How is migration changing the face of the EU?

Key terms

Demography
Economic migration
European Union
Migrant
Military juntas
Net migration
Political migration
Post-colonial

Learning objectives

After studying this chapter, you will be able to discuss these ideas and concepts and provide examples of them:
- The most important migration patterns into Europe in the late twentieth and early twenty-first centuries.
- The importance of cultural and economic links between European countries and the wider world.
- The pattern of labour migration from eastern Europe to the UK after countries became members of the European Union.
- The flow of retired Britons to Mediterranean locations, such as France.
- The economic, social, environmental and political consequences of these movements.

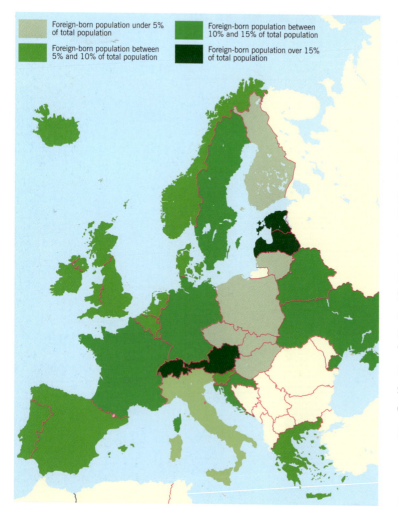

Foreign-born population under 5% of total population

Foreign-born population between 5% and 10% of total population

Foreign-born population between 10% and 15% of total population

Foreign-born population over 15% of total population

Before 1960, Europe was a continent of zero net migration. During the 1960s emigration was greater than immigration, and it took until the mid-1970s for this trend to be reversed.

The European Union (EU) was formed by a group of countries in Europe who share an economic and political vision. Net immigration into the EU is estimated to have been 1.7 million in 2005, which was slightly lower than in the previous four years. About 70% of these migrants moved into Spain, Italy, Germany and the UK.

The population of many European countries has been levelling off, with decline a real possibilty in a number of them. Migration will change this, both because of the arrivals adding to the numbers and also because migrants' fertility rates are often higher than the 'native' population's. The total number of foreign-born residents makes up about 5.5% of the EU population. Figure 1 shows the percentage of foreign-born residents, by country, in 2005.

But where did these migrants come from?

◀ **Figure 1:** The percentage of foreign-born populations in Europe in 2005. What does this pattern show?

In this chapter the term 'migration' refers to permanent migration. The United Nations defines a 'migrant' as a person living outside his or her country of birth. People migrate to get away from something they do not like (a push factor), or may be attracted to another area that is of greater benefit to them (a pull factor). People may migrate to find work (economic migration), or they may migrate to get away from oppression (political migration).

The migration flow patterns into Europe are many and varied. They also relate to the history of the individual countries being discussed. During the sixteenth and seventeenth centuries, many European countries occupied territories in other continents and developed colonies. When these colonies were given their independence, their residents were able to apply for passports to the mother country and they were given work permits. This greatly influenced the flow of migrants and now, in these 'post-colonial' times, the largest groups of international migrants to all European countries are from their original colonies.

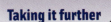

Taking it further

To learn more about ethnic diversity read 'Foreign-born' on your Student CD-ROM.

Key term

Migration is the movement of people from one place to another. Migration may be permanent or temporary.

Case study: African migrants to the Canary Islands

During 2006, about 6,000 African economic migrants lost their lives or went missing on the sea journey to the Canary Islands in their desperate bid to get into 'Fortress Europe'. Some 31,000 illegal migrants reached the islands, which is six times as many as in 2005. Many were subsequently returned to Africa. Spain (which controls the Canary Islands) asked the European Union for help to control the flow, and two boats and two aircraft from the EU border control agency were sent to patrol the shores of Senegal and Mauritania, but this measure only lasted for a few weeks.

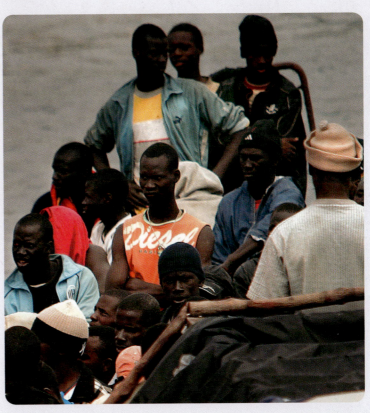

▲ Figure 2: African migrants risk their lives sailing to the Canary Islands.

Taking it further

To learn more about Europe's ethnic variation read 'Investigating migration' on your Student CD-ROM.

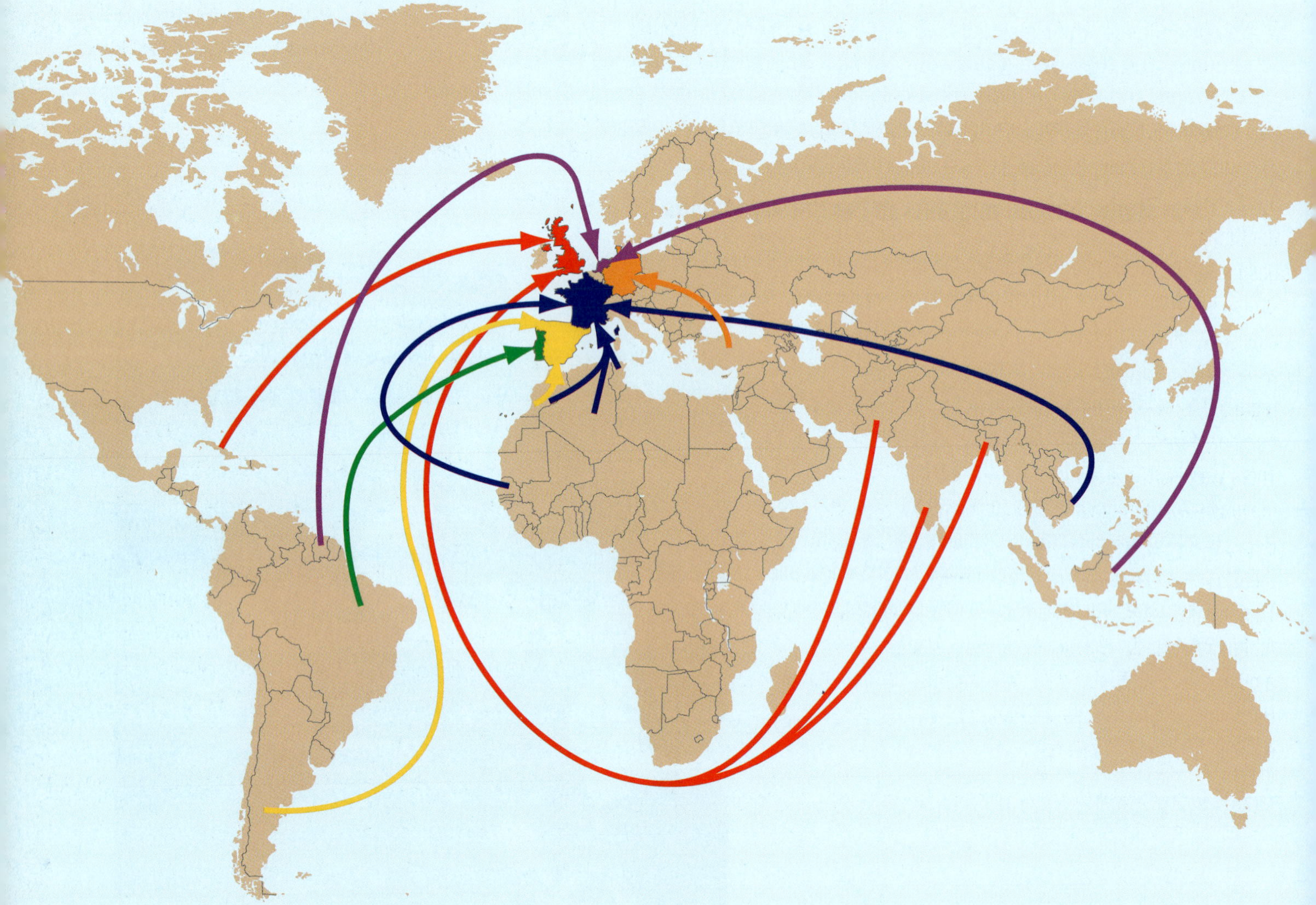

▲ **Figure 3:** Migration flows into Europe

Netherlands

The Netherlands, like all other European countries, was short of unskilled labour after the Second World War. It actively recruited migrants from its colonies, especially from Indonesia after its decolonisation in 1949. In the 1960s the Netherlands changed from a country of net emigration to a country of net immigration because of the influx of economic migrants from Suriname after it gained independence.

United Kingdom

When the British Empire was at its most powerful, over a third of the world's population lived under British rule. The vast majority of immigrants to the UK are from former colonies, most notably from the Caribbean and the Indian subcontinent, although there have also been substantial flows from Kenya and South Africa. In the1950s the British government actively recruited Bangladeshis to work in London, especially on public transport. West Indians worked in the health service as nurses and ancillary employees. Many Pakistani citizens were recruited to work in the textile mills in northern England, and a large number of Indian doctors were recruited to work in the health service. There were no language problems due to the fact that English was the language of government and business within the British Indian colony. Between 1965 and 1972 the flow of Indians peaked, with the arrival of the Gujarati Indians who had been expelled by Idi Amin from Uganda. They were granted asylum because of their unusual circumstances. All this immigration has produced a diverse culture in the UK, with a number of events that celebrate the diversity. The annual Notting Hill Carnival, for example, a Caribbean celebration, is one of the UK's established cultural events.

Germany

After the Second World War, Germany had a chronic shortage of workers to rebuild its cities. It attracted migrants from many countries by instigating liberal asylum laws. Most of the migrants were from Turkey, although there were also considerable flows of people from Africa and Asia. These migrants were expected to return to their countries of origin once Germany was rebuilt. But many wished to stay, and have gained citizenship. By 2005 there were 2.6 million Turks living in Germany – 3% of the population. They have brought with them their culture, which has greatly enhanced life in Germany. They have also established economic links, as many of them send money back to their families in Turkey.

France

France has always been a country of net immigration, with more people moving into France than moving out. The inflow was generally from other European countries and, after the Second World War, France tried to recruit workers from its bordering countries, such as Italy, to help to rebuild the country. However, as the whole of Europe became wealthier, France failed to attract enough migrants to fill the jobs. It turned to its former colonies for workers, notably the 'Maghreb' countries in North-West Africa – Algeria, Morocco and Tunisia, and to Senegal. It also attracted migrants from South-East Asian countries, such as Vietnam. Between 1946 and 1990, 6.95 million people migrated from the Maghreb to France to fill vacancies in low-paid, low-esteem jobs.

Spain and Portugal

Between the 1960s and 1980s many European countries received political migrants who sought safety from political unrest and military juntas in Latin American countries, such as Argentina, Uruguay, Chile and Brazil. Many of these migrants were highly educated and easily found jobs in their new countries. For example, during the 1980s Spain benefited from the arrival of dentists from Argentina and Uruguay. Many educated Brazilians also migrated to Portugal to look for jobs in marketing and health care. Since the main language of Brazil is Portuguese, these migrants found it relatively easy to find jobs. The immigrants saw that a move to countries with flexible policies would enable them to move again to the more affluent western European countries after Spain and Portugal joined the EU in 1986. The past colonial links meant that there was already a shared culture and language, which helped the migrants integrate into their new countries. Spain has also received large numbers of economic migrants from Morocco, who risk their lives crossing the Mediterranean for the possibility of a life in the EU.

The post-accession labour flow from eastern Europe

Since May 2004, when eight new eastern European states joined the EU, there has been a large influx of migrants from these eight states into the existing EU countries. According to official figures, between May 2004 and June 2006, for example, 427,000 workers from these eight 'accession' states successfully applied for work in the UK, 62% of whom were Polish. By 2008, around 700,000 Poles were working in the UK. The highly respected Polish publication *Polityka,* however, estimates that 1 million people have moved to the UK from Poland alone, and there is a popular belief that between a half and two thirds of the Eastern-Bloc immigrants are from Poland. Perhaps the only truth that can be deduced from all of these figures is that the true number will probably never be known because of the official organisations' inability to obtain reliable data. The 'official' Polish workers brought with them 36,000 dependents – spouses and children. Most of the workers (82%) are aged 18 to 34, and 56% work in factories. Other migrants on the worker registration scheme are from the Czech Republic, Estonia, Hungary, Latvia, Lithuania, Slovakia and Slovenia.

The difference with this type of labour flow is that the migrants have moved into all areas of the UK and have not concentrated in the major cities. As is shown in the table, the most popular destination is East Anglia where the migrants work on farms and in food-processing factories. But what has brought so many young Eastern Europeans – and particularly Poles – to the UK?

Taking it further

To learn more about international migrants read 'Categories of international migrants' on your Student CD-ROM.

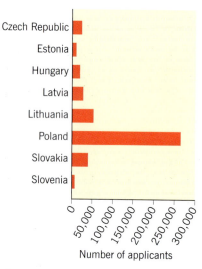

▲ Figure 4: Where the post-accession migrants came from.

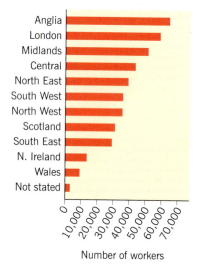

▲ Figure 5: Where the post-accession migrants settled in the UK.

Reasons for the migration

There are many push factors and pull factors that influenced the migrants' decisions, but the main motivation is economic – the eastern Europeans can earn much more if they work in western European countries. As only Sweden, Ireland and the UK would allow the migrants to work freely in their countries for many, the UK was their first choice. This labour flow was also influenced by recruiting agencies setting up in Poland to entice workers to the UK – to fill the demand for workers in jobs that British people did not want to do.

PUSH AND PULL FACTORS FOR MIGRANTS FROM EASTERN EUROPE

Employment and salaries

- Low salaries: many Polish workers earn about £200 a month. In the UK they can earn in a week what they earn in a month in Poland.
- Unemployment in Poland is between 20% and 25%, depending on where you live.
- In a recent internet survey, 40% of young medics in Poland declared that they would move abroad, the main reason being economic. Polish medical graduates, who will have spent 6 years at university, will earn only £220 a month – well below their counterparts in the UK.
- A 26-year-old teacher from Warsaw was earning £200 a month. Now he hands out leaflets in London and earns £600 a month.
- A primary teacher from Dzierzoniow earned £180 a month. Now he earns £1,200–£1,300 a month as a supervisor in a recycling plant.
- A maths graduate who was out of work in Poland is now earning six times the Polish average salary on a pizza-making production line.

Welfare state

- Once EU nationals have been working and paying tax in Britain for 12 months, they are entitled to the same level of state support as any British citizen, including child benefit for their children living in another EU country. Child benefit payments in the UK (£941 per year) are much higher than in Poland (£160 per year).
- They are also allowed access to the National Health Service and unemployment benefit.

Society and government

- Many young migrants come to experience a better standard of living and also a new lifestyle. There are many more opportunities for an excellent social life in the UK.
- Many migrants also feel that Britain is a more tolerant society than Poland and it is easier to get promoted on the basis of ability. It is also the case that the higher you rise in your profession, the more advantages there are in the life of an advanced democracy.
- The Polish government is still not truly democratic, and many people feel that EU money is not getting to the people who need it most.
- Many young people are moving out because they feel that the older generation hold all of the power and will not change their ways. Communism may be dead but the 'old school' is still very much alive, and many feel that it is holding the country back.
- Recruiting agencies – and indeed the Scottish Council – have set up in Poland to try to entice people to come to the UK to fill the job vacancies in the labour market.

Experts predict that this wave of immigration will be temporary, and that Poland is at the stage where Ireland was in the 1980s. It is exporting its unemployment abroad, because the economy is not able to generate enough jobs for everyone. When the economy finally takes off, these people will return home to Poland as this is where they want to be.

▶ Figure 6: A shop selling Polish food in the UK.

Impacts of migration on the host country

Many Poles prefer to shop in small local shops run by the Polish community, rather than integrating more with British society by shopping in Asda or Tesco. Many high streets now have a Polish shop, selling Polish produce, and there are Polish bars, newspapers and internet radio stations.

The migrants have fuelled economic growth, rather than undercut British workers in the labour market, as had been feared by some. The non-migrant unemployment rate has remained steady – the large increase in migrant workers did not take jobs away from the non-migrant population (although there may have been less availability of work for part-time and student workers).

The Polish and other eastern European migrants are making the UK workforce younger, which has eased the pension burden and helped to keep interest rates down – and low interest rates have helped all UK residents with mortgages.
The influx of young migrants needing accommodation has led to an upsurge in the buy-to-let market. There has also been an environmental impact, as many inner city areas are being regenerated to provide housing for the growing population. There has been a major shift in land use from secondary industry to housing. Although the new migrants cannot afford this new housing themselves, they occupy the houses and flats that have been vacated by those who can.

The Centre for Economics and Business Research has calculated that the average Polish migrant worker earns £20,000 per year, of which £6,000 to £7,000 is disposable income. As the exact number of migrants is unknown, the CEBR estimates spending power for this immigrant group to be somewhere between £3.5 and £4 bn. This is the equivalent of adding in to the economy the consumer demand of Liverpool in just 2 years, a major boost. However, if the migrants intend to stay and eventually retire here they must earn £27,000 a year to pay enough in taxes to support them in old age and only 20% of migrants currently earn this amount.

There has been an impact on the welfare state. Although 27,000 child benefit applications have been approved, some of these children still live in Poland and migrant workers are allowed to claim benefit for them.

On the whole, the young Polish workers have been well received and there has been little tension. Their hard-working, positive attitude has been praised by large organisations, such as Sainsbury's and the National Farmer's Union.

In Greater London, Polish immigrants now comprise one of the largest ethnic groups. Acton, Balham, Brixton, Ealing, Earls Court and Hammersmith have become known as 'Polish towns'.
There are now so many Polish children in British schools, especially Catholic schools, that Polish history and culture may be taught to all students, to help British children better understand their new classmates.

There are over 50 Polish 'Saturday Schools' around the UK, organised and financed by the Polish Educational Society, with very little local or central government funding. Their purpose is to ensure that the children of immigrants maintain their Polish language and cultural fluency in case they later return to Poland and re-enter the education system.

Research has shown that migrant workers are playing an increasingly pivotal role in some sectors where employers say they struggle to recruit. This is due to their willingness to accept forms of work that their British counterparts will not – 'working for 10 hours in a chiller', for example. The food industry is one of these sectors, with major farming-related employers in Cambridgeshire and neighbouring counties actively seeking eastern European workers to cope with their labour shortages.

When Polish migrants first arrived they worked in food processing and on farms, but now they are in all forms of industry. Recruitment fairs encourage this diversity, The last fair run by the Polish Express Newspaper, for example, was attended by 5,000 people. Recruitment agencies from all over the UK were represented, offering work in everything from catering and hospitality to care services, and in clerical, technical and engineering jobs.

Polish migrants are having an amazing impact on Catholic churches. In some neighbourhood parishes, masses in Polish are held, sometimes with standing room only. Indeed, this influx of Catholicism has meant that there are more practising Catholics in the UK than Anglicans.

Police in some areas of the country are complaining about being understaffed due to the extra demands put on the service by the migrants. In Cambridgeshire there has been a 17% increase in drink-driving offences amongst the migrant community. The police force there has to deal with 100 different languages, a situation which had landed the force with a translation bill of at least £800,000. They now employ community support officers to translate for the police.

▲ **Figure 7:** Impacts of Polish migration on the UK.

Impacts of migration on the source country

In Poland legislation is being drafted to try to encourage Poles to return home by offering them more lucrative salaries.

The fourth largest city in Poland, Wroclaw, is developing quickly. Over 100,000 jobs will be created over the next few years as companies such as LG, Phillips, Siemens, Volvo and Hewlett-Packard invest hundreds of millions of pounds. The problem is that there is a shortage of skilled construction workers and IT specialists — because they can earn seven times as much in the UK.

Many Polish government officials were against joining the EU because they realised what would happen to their services. In some areas of Wroclaw, for example, a quarter of all anaesthetists have emigrated. The ones who remain are having to deal with more than one operation at the same time, putting patients' lives at risk.

In 2005, 10% of jobs in the Polish construction industry could not be filled. But by early 2007 this figure had risen to 35% due to a shortage of workers caused by migration.

POLAND

The main Polish current affairs magazine, *Polityka*, has launched an incentive scheme called 'Stay With Us', sponsored by some of Poland's biggest companies, to persuade the country's leading young academics to resist the pull to emigrate. About a hundred scientists and researchers have each received a one-off payment of £5,000, equal to about 10 months' pay, to stay put.

Taking it further

To learn more about attitudes to migrants read 'Eastern European migrants' on your Student CD-ROM.

▲ **Figure 8:** Impacts of migration on Poland.

A retirement flow to a Mediterranean location – Spain

Every year, large numbers of British people decide to retire abroad. The country with the largest number of retired Brits is Canada, then the USA, Ireland and Spain. There are nearly a million British people who live either full or part time in Spain, with 80,000 of them being retired. A number of studies have been carried out to ascertain why so many Brits choose Spain as their retirement destination. The results of two of these studies are shown in Figures 9 and 10. In the first, respondents gave the 'most important' reason for moving to the Costa Del Sol. In the second, the respondents listed all the reasons for their choice of destination (without prioritising them) – hence the numbers add up to more than 100%. The same study also asked about the respondents' prior knowledge of Spain before they decided to retire there. The results are shown in Figure 11.

Most important reason for moving	Percentage of respondents
Lower cost of living (including tax reasons)	6.2
Climate (including other environmental factors)	48.1
Health, slower pace of life	18.4
Antipathy to the UK	6.8
Admiration of destination	5.0
Work or business connections	2.7
Family connections	8.9
Other	3.9

▲ **Figure 9:** Reasons why people leave the UK.

Factor of attraction	Percentage of respondents
Mediterranean climate	90.4
Lifestyle of the Spanish people	52.7
Spain's lower cost of living	28.7
Better health conditions	17.0
Accessibility to home country	14.4
Interest in Latin and Mediterranean cultures	9.0
Community of expatriate residents	11.2
Availability of leisure and recreational facilities	8.5
Spanish landscape	1.1

▲ **Figure 10:** What attracts migrants to Spain?

Prior knowledge of Spain	Percentage of respondents
Had enjoyed holidays	29.8
Already owned a house	19.1
Had received information	8.5
Had relatives living in Spain	1.6
Had worked in Spain	1.6
Other	3.7

▲ **Figure 11:** How UK residents find out about the Spanish lifestyle.

▲ **Figure 12:** Expats enjoying a round of golf in Spain.

Push and Pull Factors for UK Migrants to Spain

Mediterranean climate: The temperature in Spain is usually about 10 °C warmer than in the UK. There is also more sunshine and less rainfall. All of these factors are very important for retired people who are living on a fixed income and have to continually be aware of the cost of heating their homes. The climate in Spain is also seen as healthier, in that it enables a healthier lifestyle than in the UK.

Communication networks: Spain is about 2,000 km from the UK, but this distance has 'shrunk' because of the advent of 'no frills' airlines and the revolution in ICT. The cost of travelling to Spain by air is now cheaper than many train journeys in the UK and is in fact no more expensive than a UK internal flight. Therefore it is easy for retired people to come back to the UK to visit their families. They are also able to keep in touch easily with cheap telephone calls and the internet.

Lifestyle of Spanish people: Many people who retire to Spain are attracted by the slower pace of life that they have witnessed, for example, when they have been there on holiday. They are used to the frantic pace of life in the UK (especially in the South East) and now want a much quieter and slower pace of life. They are also attracted by the lower crime rates and an absence of 'youth culture' in the Spanish areas to which they have chosen to migrate.

Cost of living: People who retire to Spain receive their pension just as if they were in the UK. They are taxed by the Spanish authorities, but the tax rates in Spain are lower than in the UK. The cost of living in Spain is also lower than in the UK (but the difference is not as noticeable as it was the 1980s and 1990s). All these factors are very important for pensioners who are on a fixed income as they can buy food and drink more cheaply in Spain, leaving them more disposable income.

Property market: There has been a boom in house prices in the UK. This has meant that many people now have the capital to buy a property in Spain because their house in the UK is worth so much more than in the past. By selling up and buying a retirement home in Spain, where property is less expensive, pensioners are releasing equity and gain a lump sum of money to support them in their retirement.

	Jan	Feb	Mar	Apr	May	Jun	Jul	Aug	Sep	Oct	Nov	Dec
Max temp	16°C	16°C	18°C	21°C	23°C	28°C	31°C	31°C	28°C	24°C	20°C	18°C
Min temp	9°C	9°C	11°C	13°C	15°C	19°C	21°C	22°C	20°C	16°C	12°C	9°C
Hrs sun	6	7	7	8	10	11	11	11	9	7	6	5
Ave rainfall	15mm	14mm	15mm	16mm	17mm	21mm	21mm	23mm	21mm	18mm	17mm	14mm
Sea temp	14°C	13°C	14°C	15°C	17°C	21°C	21°C	25°C	24°C	21°C	18°C	15°C

▲ Figure 13: Climate figures for Spain.

Awareness of destination: The desire to migrate in retirement has also been fuelled by the development of tourism. People who have retired in the last 10 years were part of the boom in the tourism industry. These people have experienced foreign countries through their holidays and believe that 'the grass is greener ' there. This greater awareness of what is available in other countries has also been enhanced by the communications revolution and television programmes such as *A Place in the Sun*.

Expatriate community: The network of British people already living in the area who can be of support is also important. In fact, in one of the surveys discussed earlier, over 10% cited this as an important reason for choice of retirement migration. This is probably more important in choosing where in a country to live, rather than which country to choose in the first place. If there are existing residents who speak the same language as you do and can help solving problems (which they probably experienced when they arrived), then this is a strong pull factor for migrants.

Leisure facilities: These are another set of factors that are important, not as much for choice of country, but for choice of location within a country. For some it may be the availability of sporting activities such as golf courses or bowling greens; for others, it may be tea dances, coffee mornings and organised excursions. All these sorts of activity are important for retired people because they are a way of further developing social networks.

Living longer: In the 2001 Census of Population there were more people over 60 (21% of the population) than under 16 (20%) for the first time in England. People are living longer and will therefore need to plan for their retirement because they will be alive for a longer period of time. People are also healthier, due to better diets and knowledge about health and fitness. The generation now retiring to Spain are fit and healthy – and they expect to be for a good number of years.

Health care: In the past, people did not migrate when they retired because of the lack of free state health care in other European countries. This is no longer the case, because of the free movement of European people brought about by the EU. Now, if you receive a state pension in the UK you will be eligible for free state health care in Spain. There are also many private hospitals in Spain which did not exist 30 years ago. Therefore people today feel confident that if they are ill there will be plenty of health care experts available to treat them.

In the words of one expat:

'The United Kingdom is one of the most expensive countries in Europe. Taxes are high, the crime rate is rising, the weather is terrible, and a lot of British feel the Government stopped listening to them years ago. In a nutshell, the British, overall, are an incredibly unhappy people.'

'Then look at Spain. The weather is beautiful all year round and the Spanish beach resorts are some of the prettiest in the world. The way of life in Spain is more relaxed than in the UK. Taxes are lower, health care is excellent, the crime rate is lower than in the UK, and the Spanish still have family values. The UK now has the highest teenage pregnancy rate in Europe, the highest alcoholism rates, and parents spend less time with their children in the UK than anywhere else in Europe.'

Summary

Having studied this chapter, you should be able to discuss these ideas and concepts and provide located examples of them:

- The most important migration patterns into Europe in the late twentieth century and early twenty-first century.
- The cultural and economic links between European countries and the wider world.
- The reasons for and the economic, social, environmental and political consequences of the migration of eastern European (notably Polish) people into the UK since 2004.
- The reasons for movement of retired Britons to Mediterranean locations, notably Spain.

MCQ

Exam practice

1.

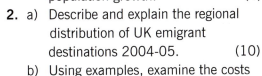

▲ Age distribution by ethnic group in the UK, 2001/02

a) Which ethnic group has:
   the lowest percentage of over 65 year olds
   the highest percentage under 16 years old? (2)

b) Referring to the figure above, explain the meaning of the term 'post-colonial' migrant flows. (2)

c) Explain why migrants are often younger than the host population. (3)

d) Using the figure, explain how immigration contributes to population growth. (4)

2. a) Describe and explain the regional distribution of UK emigrant destinations 2004-05. (10)

   b) Using examples, examine the costs and benefits to host countries of emigration from the UK to Mediterranean locations. (15)

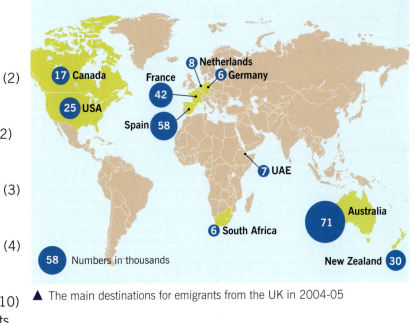

▲ The main destinations for emigrants from the UK in 2004-05

CHAPTER 13 What is driving the new urbanisation taking place and what are its consequences?

Key terms

Brownfield sites
Corporate sponsorship
European Union
Greenfield sites
Informal sector
Megacity
Out-source work
Shanty town
Squatter settlement
Urbanisation

Learning objectives

After studying this chapter, you will be able to discuss these ideas and concepts and provide examples of them:
- The growth of cities globally.
- The causes and processes of rural to urban migration.
- A megacity in an Asian country and the destination of its newcomers in shanty towns.
- A megacity in Europe and the destination of its movers in the suburbs.
- The consequences of the growth in these cities and whether the growth can be sustained.

▲ Figure 1: What is the message of this cartoon?

Taking it further

To learn more about successful cities read 'Why are some cities successful?' on your Student CD-ROM.

The world is becoming an increasingly urban place. By 2007, more than 50% of the world's population lived in cities, and the changing distribution of the predicted future growth is shown in Figure 2. A number of cities have grown into 'megacities'. These are commonly defined as urban regions with a population of more than 10 million, but the concept also encompasses the idea of global significance. Thus London, which sits in an urban region of more than 17 million (although its administrative area has a population of less than 8 million) is a megacity, in terms of both its size and its global significance – being one of the three most 'connected' cities on the planet (along with New York and Tokyo).

Whereas Europe had over half of the world's largest cities in 1900, Figure 3 shows how that pattern has changed in the last century, reducing Europe's share to 10%, whilst large cities have developed rapidly in Latin America, Asia and Africa. Although these huge cities are powerful and tend to dominate their countries in terms of manufacturing and investment they suffer a range of problems, from lack of housing, water, health and education, to the fact that they are continually encroaching upon their surrounding countryside.

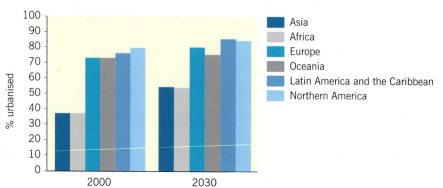

▶ Figure 2: Global urbanisation percentages.

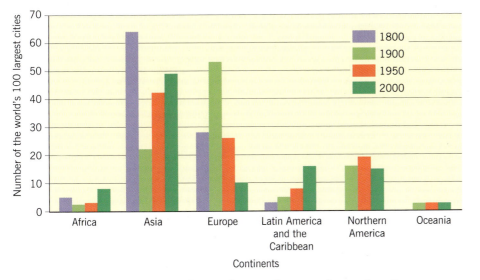

◀ **Figure 3:** The changing distribution, between 1800 and 2000, of the world's 100 largest cities.

Taking it further

To learn more about how we define megacities read 'Megacities – what they are and how they have grown' on your Student CD-ROM.

What are the causes of rural to urban migration?

The causes of rural to urban migration tend to differ between high-income and low-income countries but they all have one thing in common – migrants move from areas which lack opportunities to areas that they perceive as having opportunities. In LEDCs, rapid rates of rural to urban migration are often a result of profound changes in the countryside. Cities may be seen positively, but the primary reason for their growth is the transformation of the countryside. Of the thousand or so migrants who arrive each day in Mexico City the majority have no specific fixed employment to go to. In Bangladesh rural–urban migration contributes nearly 60% of the urban growth. Rural–urban migration is fastest when rapid commerce-centred growth takes place around major cities. Evidence suggests that the development of road infrastructure and transportation and the rapid expansion of manufacturing, trade, hotels, restaurants, housing and construction generate demand for unskilled and semi-skilled labour in LEDC cities. This has dramatically increased migration for job-related reasons. In addition, a major push factor in many regions has been the unequal land relations and the gradual commercialisation of agriculture, which has forced subsistence farmers off the land. Natural disasters, such as cyclones, can push large numbers into critical situations giving them no choice but to migrate. For example, in Bangladesh the top 10% of rural households controlled 51% of land and had 32% of the total income. Meanwhile, the bottom 40% of the households had only 2% of the land and 16% of the income. It is this marginal group who are most likely to migrate, providing three-quarters of rural out-migration. There had also been many cases of migration from the landowning households, but these were often for the purpose of maximising income from diversified sources, and they were usually only temporary, with household members returning to their villages after a few months. (see Figure 4).

▼ **Figure 4:** The causes of rural to urban migration.

Push factors	Pull factors
Drought and flooding	Global investment goes to cities not the countryside
Rural poverty	Cities becoming global hubs
Lack of services	Communications increases access to perceived urban opportunities
Lack of investment	Radios and in some cases televisions allows knowledge
Over population high birth rates	Services are perceived as better – health, education, entertainment, housing, jobs,

▲ **Figure 5:** Housing in Dharavi. The land that these shanty houses are built on is worth $10 bn.

▲ **Figure 6:** Squatter settlement housing and a water pipe in Dharavi.

▲ **Figure 7:** The rush hour in Mumbai. There are 15 people for every square metre of space on the train and 10 people a day die on the rail network.

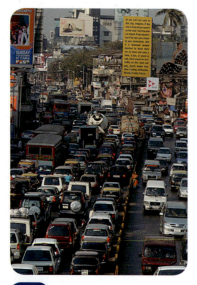

Mumbai, a megacity in Asia

Mumbai, the largest city in India, is situated on a long, thin island in a natural harbour on the west coast, in the opening of Thane Creek. There are 650 km² of island, of which more than 484 km² is densely urbanised, at an average population density of 30,000 people per square kilometre. The city is growing phenomenally – from approximately 3 million in 1951, to 14 million in 2007, to a projected 26 million by 2020. It generates 33% of India's entire tax revenue, and 40% of all international flights to India land in Mumbai.

There are a number of reasons why Mumbai has grown so rapidly. Its central position in Asia, with easy access to China and the West, has meant that it has become a global hub for the world's transnational companies. Mumbai is also the base for new Indian transnational companies, like Tata Steel and Godrej Retail – businesses that are fast equalling if not taking over from their European and American rivals. Its success is largely based on out-source work, but the city is also the home of 'Bollywood', the centre of India's film industry – now the world's biggest, with more films being made in Bollywood than in Hollywood. The phenomenal growth of Mumbai has had many consequences (see below), ranging from lack of space to overcrowded transport systems, to an acute shortage of water, much of which is transported to Mumbai from the mainland in enormous pipes.

Dharavi

Mumbai, like all megacities, is a city of contrasts, and not all its people benefit from its growth and wealth. Indeed, 60% of the population live in poverty, and the informal sector is increasing. Many of its citizens live in shanty towns, one of which is Dharavi – often referred to as the 'largest shanty town in Asia'. This is untrue as there are larger shanty towns in Delhi, but Dharavi is probably the most organised and successful shanty town in Asia.

Dharavi covers 220 hectares of land near the airport. Figures 5 and 6 show the density and type of housing in Dharavi. It is estimated that 100,000 people live and work in this area. Many of the streets are no more than one or two metres wide, in some places narrowing to less than a metre, but it is estimated that goods worth over $500 m are produced here, with industries in Dharavi being wide-ranging.

However, the future of Dharavi and all the shanty towns in Mumbai is in the balance. The economic growth of the city has slowed down and its quality of life is now one of the lowest in the world. In 2006 it came 150th out of 216 world cities. Officials in Mumbai have come up with a plan called 'Vision Mumbai' to tackle the city's problems and make it into a world class location by 2013.

◄ **Figure 8:** Traffic jams are a constant problem in Mumbai. This huge yellow billboard, promoting the use of public transport, was put up in several high traffic zones, where cars literally inch their way forward. It reads: Of the 367,142 cars in this city, imagine, if the one in front of you wasn't on the road. You'd be one car ahead. If two weren't, you'd be two cars closer to your destination. And if a thousand people decided to leave their cars at home and take a train, a bus, or share a cab, there would be less traffic on this road and you would waste less time reading billboards. Mumbai Traffic Police.

Taking it further

To learn more about industries in Dharavi read 'A deeper look at Dharavi' on your Student CD-ROM.

Vision Mumbai – the future – a sustainable megacity?

Transport: In 2008 Mumbai will open its first metro line – a 15 km line, to be followed by two others with a total length of almost 50 km, by 2011. An elevated highway, known as the 'Sealink', is currently being built along the coast between the northern Mumbai district of Bandra and Nariman Point in the south. Construction will also soon begin on a 25 km bridge that will connect the city centre with towns on the other side of the Bay of Mumbai. And in a bid to earn carbon credits, Mumbai is adding 160 energy-efficient trains to the city's overstretched rail network.

Housing: Since 2004 there has been a massive clean up of the city's housing. More than 200,000 illegal slum dwellers have been moved and 45,000 shanties across the city have been destroyed. Dharavi, due to its size, thriving economy and more permanent nature, has been given its own redevelopment project. New seven-storey apartments will be built in the area to house the slum dwellers. Local industries that are non-polluting will be encouraged to continue and all the established businesses and manufacturing units will be provided with modern technical and economic strategies for sustainable development. The redevelopment is in private hands, with the developers receiving 1.3 m² for commercial development for every m² of housing that they build.

Environment: The city is to become greener, with the creation of 325 new open spaces, which are to be maintained by corporate sponsorship. The municipality will also build an extra 300 public toilets to deal with some of the sanitation problems.

Employment: If the city is to succeed, it must improve its economic growth rate to 8 to 10% a year. It is hoping to create 200,000 new service sector jobs in health care, finance and entertainment. And 200,000 jobs in the new industrial zone, which is based around the port and airport, will be based on computer assembly and the fashion industry. There will also need to be an increase in employment in construction – an estimated 500,000 jobs – to build the' vision'.

By 2013 Mumbai should be a revitalised city, with wide roads, efficient trains and buses, beautiful seafront promenades and gardens. There should also be no shortage of public utilities, such as water, electricity and sanitation. It is important that Mumbai does not fail in its duty to its citizens to improve their city because a city which is a major player in the global economy should provide a healthy living environment.

Figure 9 shows some of the links between India and another global megacity – London.

▼ **Figure 9:** The links between India and London.

Tourism
In 2006, visitors to London from India spent £152 m – more than the £134 m spent by Japanese visitors.
The number of flights from India to London has increased 38% in the last 6 years. London is now the most popular destination for flights from India.

Business
India accounts for the second highest number of inward investment projects into London, after the USA. There are approximately 10,000 Indian-owned businesses in London, employing 49,000 people. 32% of all European investment from India is into London. The software industry accounts for almost 50% of all London-based Indian businesses.

Links between India and London

Academic
Indian student numbers in London have doubled in the last 5 years, from 2,190 in 2001 to 4,320 in 2005. It is estimated that Indian students contributed £60 m to London's economy in the 2005–06 academic year. 75% of Indian students study for postgraduate degrees (M.Sc.s and Ph.D.s). There are also a growing number of collaborative programmes between Indian and London universities.

Film
It is estimated that Indian films produced in London are worth $28 m annually. In 2006, over 40 Indian films were produced in London. The three largest multiplex chains (Odeon, Vue Cinemas and Cineworld) routinely screen Hindi films that appear in the UK's top 15 film lists.

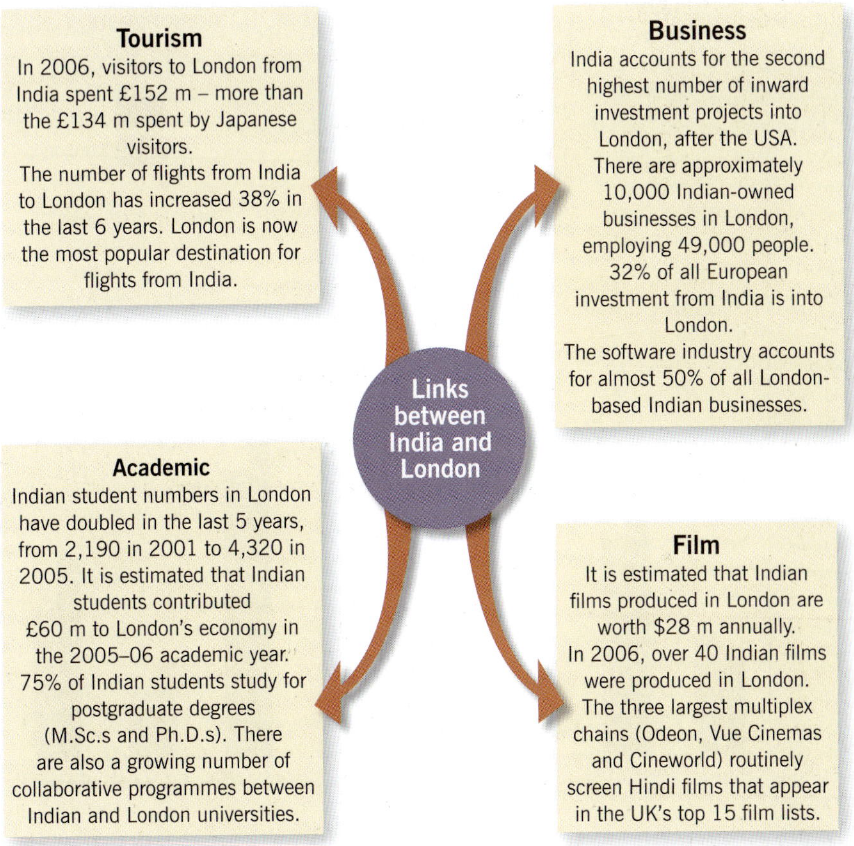

London, a megacity in Europe

London is situated on the River Thames in the south-east of England. It has the highest population of any urban area in the EU, with just over 7.5 million residents in 2005 – 12.5% of the UK population. The population of London has not risen steadily: the peak was 8.6 million residents in 1939, followed by a decline in population which was particularly rapid during the 1960s and 1970s. The population reached a low point in 1988 with 6.7 million. Since then, the population has gradually increased to its present-day number of 7.8 million.

It is also one of the most densely populated places in the EU, with only Paris and Brussels being more densely populated. By looking at the age distribution of the population, shown in Figure 10, it is easy to see that London has a disproportionate number of people (37%) in the age range of 25 to 44, compared with the UK as a whole (28%). In 2004 an estimated 220,000 foreign migrants and 155,000 British migrants came to live in London. However, 350,000 people moved out of London, including 260,000 to other parts of the UK. Finance and tourism are London's prime industries in the twenty-first century. The tourism industry employed 350,000 full-time workers in 2005, and tourists spent around £15 bn. Finance and business services have seen a growth of 550,000 jobs since 1993.

London is one of the three most important business cities in the world, along with New York and Tokyo. Its airports carry three-quarters of all scheduled air passengers in the UK and it generates 14% of the UK's tax revenue. Although it has a thriving economy, like Mumbai, it does have to face the consequences of its success with the problems shared by all large urban areas, such as unemployment, traffic congestion and pollution, as well as a shortage of land and housing. London was developing its spare land at a phenomenal rate. This has been slowed down by the policies of the London Assembly as boroughs have been told to adopt a more sustainable approach to development and to use 'brownfield' rather than 'greenfield' sites.

London's original growth was by spreading outwards, creating rings of suburbs and engulfing the once-separate settlements further out. The many reasons for the growth of suburbs are summarised in Figure 11.

Taking it further

To learn more about sustainable cities read 'How do cities reduce their footprints?' on your Student CD-ROM.

▼ Figure 10: London's age distribution in 2005, compared with the UK as a whole.

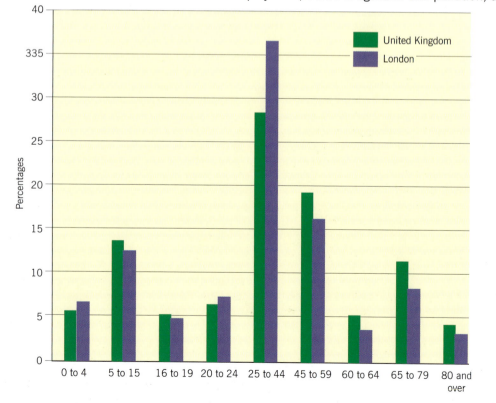

Availability of land
When suburbs first developed, it was felt that there would always be plenty of land around London that could be used. This outward spread has now been stopped, and development is taking place in a more sustainable manner, with brownfield sites being used wherever possible.

Increasing wealth
As the service sectors grew, and salaries increased, more workers could afford to borrow money from the newly developing building societies, to buy their own home.
New Ideal Homesteads, a company which operated in Bexley and Bromley in the 1920s and 1930s, was one of the first property developers to build and sell homes to a new segment of the market that had never owned their homes before – the skilled workers or the clerks.
The first houses built in the suburbs, however, were often rented out by the property developers who built them.

Shorter working hours
Shorter working days meant that people could live further from their work and travel in each day, without making their days unreasonably long. Many people prefer to associate one area with work and another with leisure time.

Suburbanisation

Government funding
In the 1920s the government encouraged local authorities to build housing schemes by giving them funds. Huge schemes were built, such as the 426 homes at Welling (Bexley Urban District Council).

Transport
For suburbs to develop there either has to be an excellent public transport network or a sophisticated road network. In London, the extension of the Underground network outwards and the development of the overground railway (especially in the south) went hand in hand with the development of suburbs.
In Mumbai, 55% of the population live within 15 minutes of their place of work, whereas in London the average journey to work takes 40 minutes.

Households
There has been an increase in the number and size of households as young people marry later but still want the independence of living away from their families; their highly paid jobs in the capital allow them to do this. At the other end of the age scale, older people are no longer living with their families and living longer, and are therefore occupying their houses for longer.

▲ Figure 11: The reasons for the development of the suburbs around London.

Vision London – 'The London Plan' – Seeking a sustainable megacity

The vision that the London Plan wanted to realise is London as an exemplary, sustainable world city for the twenty-first century. In order to do this there will need to be co-operation between the boroughs and a cohesive plan that encompasses and integrates commercial and residential development, the transport and communications infrastructure, and the promotion of vigorous local communities.

The London Plan's objectives
Objective 1: To accommodate London's growth within its boundaries without encroaching on open spaces
Objective 2: To make London a healthier and better city for people to live in
Objective 3: To make London a more prosperous city with strong and diverse long term economic growth
Objective 4: To promote social inclusion and tackle deprivation and discrimination
Objective 5: To improve London's accessibility
Objective 6: To make London an exemplary world city in mitigating and adapting to climate change and a more attractive, well-designed and green city

(The London Plan Summary Document)

North London

- Over 65,000 additional homes by 2016 and almost 300,000 more jobs by 2026 anticipated.
- Opportunity Areas: Euston/Marylebone Road at Paddington, Euston and Kings Cross will be given a coherent transport, open space and tall building strategy.
- Areas for Intensification: Arsenal/Holloway, Mill Hill, Haringey Heartlands/Wood Green, West Hampstead interchange, Holborn and Farringdon/Smithfield.
- Areas for Regeneration: Deprived zones will benefit from their positioning next to Opportunity and Intensification Areas.

North East London

- Priority for development, regeneration and infrastructure improvement. Planned minimum of 102,000 new homes by 2016 and over 250,000 additional jobs by 2026.
- Opportunity Areas: Isle of Dogs, City Fringe, Lower Lea Valley, Royal Docks, London Riverside and Ilford.
- Areas for Regeneration: Containing a significant part of London's largest concentration of deprivation areas, links will be identified to benefit form the growth in nearby Opportunity Areas and from the Olympics and Paralympics legacy.

South East London

- A priority for development, regeneration and infrastructure improvement. Capacity for a minimum of 55,000 additional homes by 2016 and over 100,000 jobs by 2026.

- Opportunity Areas: London bridge/Bankside, Elephant & Castle, Deptford Creek/Greenwich Riverside, Lewisham-Catford-New Cross, Greenwich Peninsula & Charlton Riverside West, Woolwich, Thamesmead & Charlton Riverside East and Bexley Riverside.
- Areas for Intensification: Canada Water/Surrey Quays and The Kidbrooke Area.
- Areas for Regeneration: Enable the deprived boroughs of Southwark, Lewisham and Greenwich links that will enable their residents to benefit from the growth in nearby Opportunity Areas

South West London

- Characterised by strong residential development. 43,000 extra homes by 2016 and 70,000 more jobs by 2026 planned.
- Opportunity Areas: Waterloo, Vauxhall, Nine Elms/Battersea and Croydon.
- Areas for Regeneration: New transport links to Croydon, Merton and Sutton.

West London

- Over 40,000 new homes by 2016 and 140,000 extra jobs by 2026 anticipated.
- Opportunity Areas: Heathrow, Park Royal/Willesden Junction, Wembley and White City.
- Areas for Regeneration: Although a relatively affluent sub-region, there are significant areas of deprivation which should benefit from new transport links, employment and training programmes.

For more details about the specific plans, go to http://www.london.gov.uk/thelondonplan.

▲ **Figure 12:** The London plan.

Taking it further

To learn more about London's problems read 'London – a victim of its own success?' on your Student CD-ROM.

The plan splits London into five sub-regions: West, North, Central, South and East (see Figure 12). Within these sub-regions certain areas have been identified as 'Opportunity Areas', 'Areas for Intensification' and 'Areas for Regeneration'.

- Opportunity Areas will see the development of jobs or homes or a mix of the two. Services will be provided for these areas, including schools, hospitals and good public transport access.
- Areas for Intensification have potential for more intensive use – and for more varied use than at present where they are well served by public transport.
- Areas for Regeneration are areas which at present suffer from social exclusion and economic deprivation. Money will be spent on neighbourhood renewal, better health care, and improved education, employment and housing.

There is much overlap between these policies and all three have the main objectives inbuilt. Figure 12 notes where actual developments for new homes and jobs will be taking place. There are, of course, other parts to the plan, which include the congestion charge and recycling targets. In 2006, six new environmentally friendly buses were tried in London, which compared very favourably on a number of environmental counts with conventional diesel buses. There is an 89% reduction in oxides of nitrogen, 83% reduction in carbon monoxide, 40% reduction in fuel use, 38% reduction in carbon dioxide, and a 30% reduction in perceived sound levels (with noise reduced from 78 dB to 74 dB). The trial was so successful that there should be a fleet of buses like them by 2012, even though the 8,000-strong London bus fleet is already the cleanest in the UK, with around 60% of the fleet achieving EU emission standards.

The congestion charge was introduced in central London in February 2003; in February 2007 it was extended further west (see Figure 13). It costs drivers £8 a day to drive in this part of London. Introducing the scheme has cut down on the number of vehicles in London and therefore reduced air pollution in the city.

Another initiative to help make London a better place to live, and to lessen its carbon footprint, is the plan to increase its recycling rates.

In 2000 recycling rates in London were the worst in the country. In 2003 London was given £21 m, through the London Recycling Fund (and a further £20 m in 2005), to improve recycling rates through local initiatives. This helped to fund 70 projects in the boroughs, including:

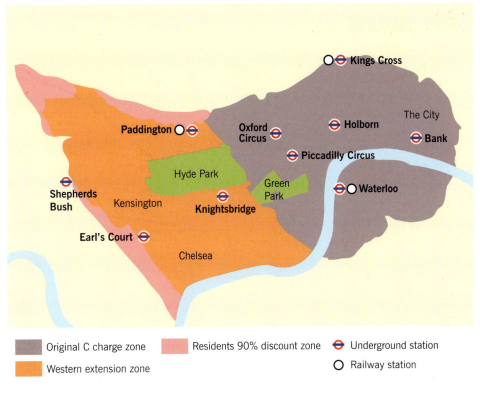

▲ **Figure 13:** The congestion charging zone.

Legend:
- Original C charge zone
- Residents 90% discount zone
- Underground station
- Western extension zone
- Railway station

- Increasing the number of homes covered by kerbside collections
- Increasing the materials that can be recycled through kerbside collections
- Increasing the number of mini recycling centres (including bottle banks, clothes banks and paper banks) across London
- Extending the opening times, the layouts, the materials that can be recycled, and the number of additional recycling banks at civic amenity sites
- Developing recycling initiatives on estates
- Encouraging schools to develop initiatives to get children into the recycling habit as early as possible
- Launching education and publicity initiatives aimed at encouraging more Londoners to recycle more of their waste.

Since the start of the schemes the rates have improved although, as can be seen in the table, some boroughs still have a long way to go to meet the target of 40% set by both the government and the European Union.

Borough	Total recycling rate (%)
Tower Hamlets	12
Kensington and Chelsea	24
Enfield	30
Hounslow	20
Bromley	32
Southwark	18
Newham	14
Havering	20

▲ **Figure 14:** Recycling rates in London in 2005–06.

Summary

Having studied this chapter, you should be able to discuss these ideas and concepts and provide located examples of them:

- Urbanisation and the growth of megacities.
- The causes and processes of rural to urban migration.
- A megacity in an Asian country; some of the problems that it faces and its attempts to be more sustainable.
- A megacity in Europe; some of the problems that it faces and its attempts to be more sustainable.

MCQ

Exam practice

1. a) Which of the cities has:
   The largest population in 2005
   The smallest population
   projected to 2030 (2)

   b) Contrast the growth trends of
   the two Indian cities (Mumbai
   and Delhi) with the two
   Latin American cities (Sao Paulo
   and Mexico City). (4)

   c) Explain why the populations of
   New York and Toyko are now
   stable. (3)

   d) Outline some of the urban
   challenges facing developing
   cities like Mumbai and Delhi between 2010 and 2030. (3)

2. a) Using evidence from the photograph and your own knowledge, describe the typical conditions
   in a developing city slum, and explain why slums form. (10)

   b) Using named examples, examine a range of strategies to make developing cities more
   environmentally and socially sustainable. (15)

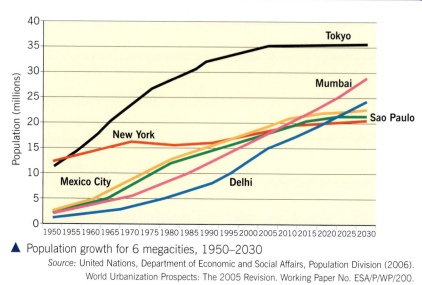

▲ Population growth for 6 megacities, 1950–2030

Source: United Nations, Department of Economic and Social Affairs, Population Division (2006).
World Urbanization Prospects: The 2005 Revision. Working Paper No. ESA/P/WP/200.

▶ A South African slum close to
Johannesburg

CHAPTER 14 What are the social and environmental consequences of globalisation, and can we manage these changes for a better world?

Key terms

Carbon emissions
Exploitation
Fair trade
Fossil fuels
Greenhouse gases
Indigenous people
Landfill sites
Rainforest Alliance
Recycling
Tiger economies

Learning objectives

After studying this chapter, you will be able to discuss these ideas and concepts and provide examples of them:

• Globalisation can bring both positive and negative changes.
• The moral and social consequences of globalisation.
• If the environmental and social costs of globalisation are to be reduced, action needs to be at a variety of scales.
• The validity of green strategies.

This chapter will present a number of ideas, some of which have already been dealt with in the Going Global topic. It can act as a summary, or as a starter for more extensive independent study, and each section ends with a number of questions for you to consider.

Globalisation brings both positive and negative changes

Taking it further

To learn more about the debate surrounding globalisation read 'Globalisation – the cases for and against' on your Student CD-ROM.

There have been many positive economic changes brought about by globalisation – from the growth of the Tiger economies to the high standard of education in western society which enables the citizens to work in highly paid office jobs. But the changes have not all been positive. Cities in the UK that were based on manufacturing industry, such as Manchester and Sheffield, lost many of their jobs when the factories were moved to countries where production costs were lower. Some of the older workers have never worked again, although many have retrained. The cities themselves are still being renewed and redeveloped into cities for the future. In the lower-income countries to which manufacturing had been moved, there developed an income gap between the rich citizens who own the factories and the poor who worked in them.

Look at the chapters on 'Unequal spaces' (Chapters 23 to 26) and 'Rebranding places' (Chapters 27 to 30), then develop your ideas with further research in these areas:

• How can we make the world a more equal place?
• Are cash donations or aid the best way to help the poorest people in the world?

The moral and social consequences of globalisation and the viability of green strategies

The growth of global networks has led to the rapid industrialisation of countries such as China. However, does this rapid industrialisation benefit all the people who are involved with it? The owners of the factories and the services that benefit from the multiplier effect are happy with this rapid industrialisation but what about the workers? Many Chinese factory workers live in conditions that are worse than the conditions endured by nineteenth-century British factory workers. Their situation is discussed in Chapter 10.

Revisit Chapter 10 and consider further the information on living and working conditions for Chinese workers:

- Is it morally correct that these workers are denied the same rights as their urban counterparts because they have migrated from the countryside?
- Is the life of these workers better than the life they left behind in the countryside?
- Should the exploitation of these workers be allowed to continue?
- Are our actions in buying the goods they produce contributing to these conditions?

The growing demand for rainforest timber has led to conflicts because the homelands of indigenous people are being destroyed. Oil extraction has caused the same problem in other rainforest areas.

Take these ideas further by finding out actual places where this has occurred:

- In buying timber or using petrol, are we adding to these problems?
- Can we, by our actions, make a difference?

Many foodstuffs are grown on farms where the workers are not paid a fair wage. Some large companies are now refusing to buy produce from these farms that exploit their labourers. McDonald's, for example (see Chapter 9), buys its coffee from the Rainforest Alliance.

Revisit Chapter 9 and further research the idea of fair trade coffee through the Rainforest Alliance:

- How can governments or individuals ensure that workers on farms are paid a fair wage for the food products that they produce?

The social and cultural impacts of globalisation are profound. A world in which consumer products are increasingly dominated by western – usually American – tastes and fashions, combined with an aggressive commercialism in which everything is packaged and 'sold', is not a world that pleases everyone. Rural migrants from western China who arrive in the growing coastal megacities in the East are faced by housing shortages, poor working conditions, social isolation and discrimination, amongst other challenges. Not all Chinese migrants leave the land willingly. Government policies have supported larger landowners by reallocating land to them, meaning that some peasants have no access to the land, leaving them with no alternative but to migrate. The pull factor is, of course, employment, and the income which can be sent home to distant families in the form of remittances. Major cultural differences confront these migrants, and adaptation to urban life is not easy. China is not alone in experiencing rapid urban growth fuelled by changes in the countryside and industrial development in the cities.

It is estimated that in India 100 to 300 new families come to Mumbai every day, and most end up in a slum colony or just erect a shanty on the nearest available footpath.

Reducing the environmental and social costs of globalisation and the viability of green strategies

The environmental and social costs of globalisation are many and varied. They range from the issue of consumer waste and all the packaging that ends up in landfill sites, to rainforest deforestation. The most obvious impact at a global level is the difficulty of managing continuing economic growth, which is the engine of globalisation, whilst also making an attempt to manage the natural environment sustainability. Many commentators point to the rapid expansion of the new superpowers, specifically India and China, as posing a particularly serious threat. Not surprisingly, many of the citizens of these countries aspire to western lifestyles with their high levels of personal consumption. They want cars, iPods and computers. The management of the world's major corporations would very much like to provide them with these goods, thus maintaining their profits and the dividends of their shareholders who, for the most part, are the wealthiest inhabitants of the wealthiest countries. In 2008 the giant Indian corporation Tata Motors launched its £1,500 car on the Indian market and plans exist for similarly cheap vehicles to be launched in China. The prospect of two giant 'new' car-owning societies emerging startles many observers, already concerned about the prospects for oil supplies and the environmental impact of existing emissions, let alone future levels. This is a critical debate because, for some, the reduction of the social and environmental impacts by using green strategies will not be possible whilst the 'rules' that currently govern the world economy are in place – the rules which encourage more and more consumption. Many of these issues must be dealt with at a range of scales, from the actions of the individual to the actions of global groups of countries.

Taking it further

To learn more about the challenges facing us all read 'Is it all unravelling?' on your Student CD-ROM.

Issue	Result	Individual action	Government / EU action
The growth of waste and packaging in our world of high consumer demand.	Increasing use of landfill sites.	Recycle as much waste as possible. Each Council has a different system for households, but schools and industry must be more aware of their waste.	New EU legislation (the WEE directive) makes it increasingly expensive for local authorities to dispose of waste by landfill.
Paper and plastics go to China for recycling.	Ships produce greenhouse gases to move the waste to be recycled.	Do not use carrier bags or reuse the same carrier on many occasions. Some supermarkets, such as Tesco, offer green points to people who do this.	Governments need to deal with recycling of waste themselves rather than shipping it to other countries to be dealt with.
Oil pollution in major shipping lanes as goods are transported around the world.	Pollution of coastal areas and the damage to the sea ecology.	Buy goods that are more locally produced, if possible.	Increase fines on ships that deliberately pollute by washing out their tanks in the sea.
Global demand for timber (and the growing of palm oil as fuel).	Deforestation of large areas of the rainforest, air miles and carbon emissions to transport the timber.	Buy wood products that are made from locally produced woods rather than rainforest timber. Or buy from sustainable rainforest sources.	Control imports of hardwood timbers to cut down on the supply.
The problem of carbon emissions from transport as goods are moved around the world.	Increase in greenhouse gases.	Buy locally sourced products that have needed fewer food miles.	Large supermarket chains to label where their food is from to enable customers to make more informed decisions about the food that they buy.
The production of energy-using fossil fuels.	The release of greenhouse gases into the atmosphere.	Being aware of where and how goods are produced and buying from sustainable sources.	Tax breaks given to companies in the UK who use renewable energy sources, such as wind turbines.

▲ Figure 1: The environmental and social costs of globalisation and the strategies that have been implemented.

Study the suggestions in the table. You may wish to research some of these ideas more fully on your own:

- Are the ideas expressed the only environmental and social costs of globalisation, or are others more important?
- Are the ideas for individual or government actions realistic?
- Find out if any of the ideas have been implemented and whether they were successful.
- Remember that to produce tomatoes in the UK in December, greenhouses need to be heated. How does this compare with the air miles used to transport them from a climate where they can be grown outdoors?

Summary

After studying this chapter you will have learnt about:

- The positive and negative changes due to globalisation.
- The moral and social consequences of globalisation.
- How the environmental and social costs of globalisation are to be reduced by the actions at a variety of scales.
- The validity of green strategies.
    - How to independently research topics.

MCQ

Exam practice

1.

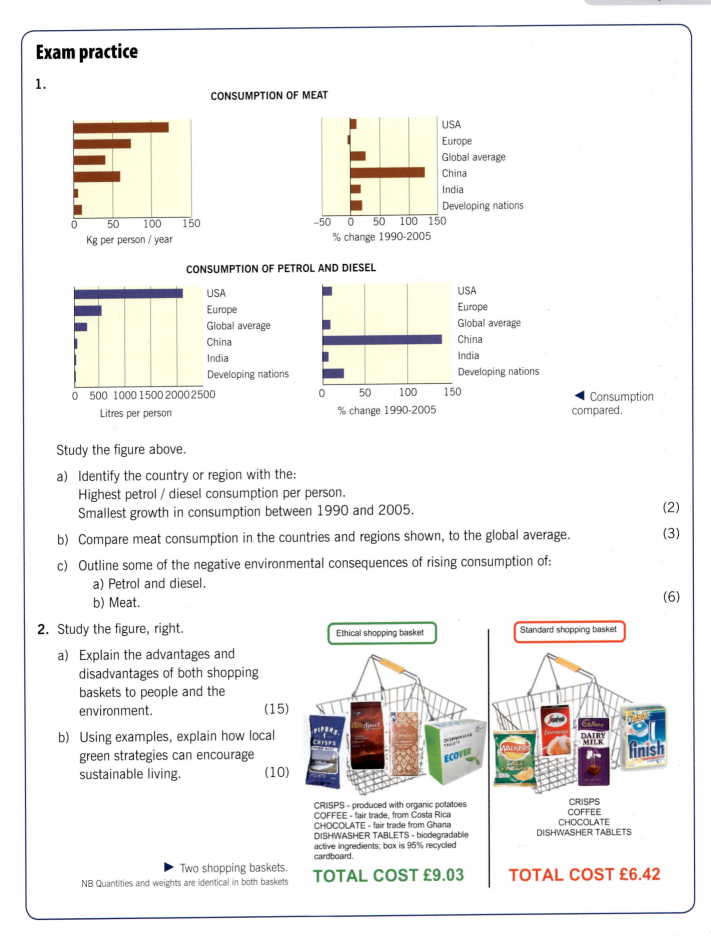

CONSUMPTION OF MEAT

USA
Europe
Global average
China
India
Developing nations

Kg per person / year

% change 1990-2005

CONSUMPTION OF PETROL AND DIESEL

USA
Europe
Global average
China
India
Developing nations

Litres per person

% change 1990-2005

◀ Consumption compared.

Study the figure above.

a) Identify the country or region with the:
Highest petrol / diesel consumption per person.
Smallest growth in consumption between 1990 and 2005. (2)

b) Compare meat consumption in the countries and regions shown, to the global average. (3)

c) Outline some of the negative environmental consequences of rising consumption of:
a) Petrol and diesel.
b) Meat. (6)

2. Study the figure, right.

a) Explain the advantages and disadvantages of both shopping baskets to people and the environment. (15)

b) Using examples, explain how local green strategies can encourage sustainable living. (10)

Ethical shopping basket

Standard shopping basket

CRISPS - produced with organic potatoes
COFFEE - fair trade, from Costa Rica
CHOCOLATE - fair trade from Ghana
DISHWASHER TABLETS - biodegradable active ingredients; box is 95% recycled cardboard.

CRISPS
COFFEE
CHOCOLATE
DISHWASHER TABLETS

TOTAL COST £9.03

TOTAL COST £6.42

▶ Two shopping baskets.
NB Quantities and weights are identical in both baskets

CHAPTER 15 What are extreme weather conditions, and how and why do they lead to extreme weather events?

Key terms

Air masses
Anticyclone
Blizzards
Depression
Drought
Flooding
Heat wave
Recurrence interval
Synoptic chart
Temperate storm
Tornado
Tropical cyclone

Learning objectives

After studying this chapter, you will be able to discuss these ideas and concepts and provide located examples of them:

- What extreme weather conditions are, and how they can be recognised as posing a threat.
- How to recognise extreme weather events, both in nature and on maps and charts.
- The wide variety of extreme weather events, and how they are distributed both globally and locally.
- The atmospheric processes that lead to the development of extreme weather conditions.
- The evolution of extreme weather events.

Extreme weather

There are many different types of extreme weather phenomena. The definition of 'extreme', however, is quite problematic. It can be seen either as an event that is unusual – and thus defined by the frequency of its occurrence – or as an event that is extreme in terms of its severity.

◀ **Figure 1:** Extreme weather events can be highly destructive, but they also inspire feelings of awe and wonder at the power of nature.

The first category would include events that are not, in themselves, especially threatening to human activity, such as Sunday 10 February 2008, being the warmest February day in southern England since records began. Paradoxically, in climates as moderate as Britain's, extremes of this sort are not that rare. In the past we have often heard about the 'wettest March day', 'driest autumn', 'coldest August Bank Holiday', and so on. Few of these events are ever severe, and thus are not threatening to life and property. However, an increasing frequency of such events, when analysed as a whole, might indicate a changing pattern to the weather and thus a changing climate. And recently, such changes have frequently been linked to global warming:

> Yet in the UK alone, in the past 14 months we have experienced the hottest July, the hottest April and the wettest June since records began. We have seen the hottest autumn and the hottest spring, and the second-hottest winter. We have also seen the hottest single month, and – by a considerable margin – the hottest single 12-month period.
>
> Now we are on the brink of seeing the soggiest British summer as a whole – defined as June, July and August – since records were first kept for the United Kingdom in 1914. By Friday morning of last week, the average rainfall in Britain since the beginning of June was 356.6mm – just over 14 inches – and nudging up to the record of 358.4mm, set in 1956. It is increasingly likely a new record will be set if there is any significant rainfall between now and Saturday.
>
> Even if there is none, summer 2007 has already passed the second-wettest summer mark (which previously was 1985, with a rainfall of 342.7mm). And the three months from May to July have easily broken the record for rainfall for that period.
>
> The significance of these records is that they are actually occurring in the real world – rather than in the forecasts generated by computer mathematical models of the global climate.

(Michael McCarthy, *The Independent*, 28 August 2007)

The frequency with which an event occurs is an important concept when analysing extreme weather events. Frequency can be monitored using 'recurrence intervals'. These are based on the probability that the given event will be equalled or exceeded in any given year. Common sense would tell us that the more extreme the event, the less frequent it is going to be. For example, the table, on page 130, shows that there is a 1 in 10 chance that 5.04 inches of rain will fall in a 24-hour period in Mecklenburg County (North Carolina, USA) during any given year, whereas there is a 1 in 50 chance that 6.60 inches of rain will fall in a 24-hour period. Thus, a rainfall total of 5.04 inches in a 24-hour period has a 10-year recurrence interval, whereas 6.60 inches in a consecutive 24-hour period is said to have a 50-year recurrence interval.

Recurrence interval, in years	Duration, in hours						
	0.5	1	2	3	6	12	24
1	1.05	1.34	1.60	1.77	2.09	2.51	2.86
2	1.29	1.57	1.94	2.15	2.54	3.00	3.48
5	1.60	2.07	2.46	2.77	3.24	3.87	4.39
10	1.85	2.38	2.92	3.18	3.71	4.39	5.04
25	2.18	2.77	3.31	3.60	4.38	5.00	5.88
50	2.40	3.09	3.76	3.97	4.78	5.71	6.60
100	2.73	3.39	4.09	4.44	5.40	6.22	7.09

▶ **Figure 2:** Rainfall estimates (in inches) or selected durations and recurrence intervals in Mecklenburg County (after Hershfield 1961).

Extreme weather events that are hazardous, in that they pose a threat, have long been features that both frighten and attract human beings. If the evening weather forecast said it would rain frogs you would think the forecasters to be mad. But raining fish or frogs have been reported, from Biblical times onwards. On 8 August 2000 a shower of dead (but still edible) sprats rained down on the port of Great Yarmouth after a thunderstorm. The raining fish were caused by a waterspout, a type of tornado out at sea, which sucks up water just as tornadoes suck up earth and debris. When the waterspout touches the land it begins to lose energy and thus the water and its contents fall to the ground. In other parts of the world it has rained frogs, toads and tadpoles. These are stories which make the local, but rarely the national, press.

Tropical cyclones

Tropical cyclones have several different popular names, including 'hurricanes' and 'typhoons'. They are intense low pressure systems that are generated in the tropics and rarely impact outside this region. Of course 'hurricane-speed' winds (Force 11 on the Beaufort Scale) can occur in other regions of the earth but, when this happens, they are not generated by real hurricanes.

The distribution of real tropical cyclones is quite limited because they need very specific conditions for their formation:

- Warm water at 27 °C, to provide the heat that generates rising air currents
- A minimum water depth of 60 metres to provide enough latent heat to drive the whole system
- A rapid outflow of air at the tropopause, where air moving quickly at high altitude sets up the conditions for air to rise from below
- The rotation provided by the Coriolis force, which is the angle of deflection produced by the spin of the earth. At the Equator this doesn't operate but it becomes more significant as one moves away, thus tropical cyclones can only be generated at least 5° away from the Equator.

Tropical cyclones are very energetic systems. Scientists estimate that a tropical cyclone releases heat energy at the rate of 50 to 200 exajoules (10^{18} J) per day. For comparison, this rate of energy release is equivalent to 70 times the global energy consumption of humans, or to exploding a 10-megaton nuclear weapon every 20 minutes.

Key terms

Tropical cyclones are intense low pressure systems generated in the tropics by warm water.

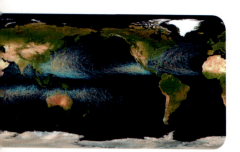

▲ **Figure 3:** The cumulative tracks of all tropical cyclones between 1985 and 2005. The Pacific Ocean west of the International Date Line sees more tropical cyclones than any other basin, while there is almost no activity in the Atlantic Ocean south of the Equator.

Case study: The life and death of Katrina

Hurricane Katrina formed as a tropical depression, 300 km south east of the Bahamas on 23 August 2005. The depression was upgraded to 'tropical storm' status on the morning of 24 August, and at this point it was given the name *Katrina*, the eleventh hurricane of the 2005 'season'. The storm continued to move erratically towards Florida, and became a hurricane only 2 hours before it made landfall in southern Florida, near North Miami Beach, on the morning of 25 August.

The storm weakened over the land, but rapidly intensified after entering the Gulf because of its movement over the warm water. Sea water temperatures were at least two degrees warmer than usual and Katrina passed over an area known as the 'loop current' – an exceptionally

▲ **Figure 4:** The pathway of Katrina. The colours indicate its severity, from blue (Category 1) to red (Category 5).

warm area of water, even in normal circumstances. On 27 August, the storm reached Category 3 intensity on the Saffir–Simpson Hurricane Scale. Feeding on the unusually warm water, the storm doubled in size, and rapidly intensified, reaching Category 5 status on the morning of 28 August. It reached its peak strength at 1:00 p.m. that day, with maximum winds of 280 km/hr and a minimum central pressure of 902 mb. This made Katrina the fourth most intense Atlantic hurricane on record at the time, only to be surpassed by Hurricanes Rita (897 mb) and Wilma (882 mb) later in the same season.

Having tracked westwards across the Gulf, weakening pressure over the mainland allowed Katrina to turn northwards, where it made its second landfall at Buras-Triumph, Louisiana, at 6:10 a.m. on 29 August as a Category 3 hurricane, with sustained winds of 205 km/hr. At landfall, hurricane-force winds extended outward 190 km from the centre and the storm's central pressure was now 920 mb. After moving over south-eastern Louisiana and Breton Sound, it made its third landfall near the Louisiana/Mississippi border, with 195 km/hr sustained winds, still at Category 3 intensity.

Katrina maintained strength well into Mississippi, finally losing hurricane strength more than 240 km inland near Meridian, Mississippi. It was downgraded to a 'tropical depression' near Clarksville, Tennessee, but its remnants were last distinguishable in the eastern Great Lakes region on 31 August, when it was absorbed by a frontal boundary. The resulting extratropical storm moved rapidly to the north-east and affected eastern Canada.

Temperate storms

The temperate zones only account for 7% of the world's land surface but they are the most populated areas of the planet, with around 40% of the total population. This is probably a consequence of the mildness of the climate, which prevents conditions from becoming too harsh, plus a reliable and moderate supply of rain and, as a result, some of the most fertile soils on the planet. But storms do occur, and when they happen they make headlines. They are often associated with low pressure systems known as depressions. Depressions are formed in mid-latitudes where contrasting air masses meet each other.

An air mass is a large body of air with similar temperature and moisture properties throughout. The best source regions for air masses are large flat areas where air can be stagnant long enough to take on the characteristics of the surface below. As an air mass moves away from its source region, it is modified as it encounters different conditions. If warmed from below, the air might become unstable, rising rapidly and producing heavy showers. Air that tracks northwards, however, is usually stable, having passed over cooler sea and land, thus producing grey skies of stratus cloud and drizzle, rather than heavy rain.

Key terms

Temperate storms are often generated by mid-latitude low pressure systems, otherwise known as 'depressions'.

	Tropical Continental (Tc)		Polar Continental (Pc)		Tropical Maritime (Tm)		Polar Maritime (Pm)	Arctic Maritime (Am)	Returning Polar Maritime (rPm)
	Summer	Winter	Long Sea Track	Short Sea Track	Exposed	Sheltered			
Temp.	Very warm or hot	Average	Cold	Very cold	Near sea temp	Warm	Rather cold	Cold (colder than Pm)	Warm (warmer than Pm)
Humidity	Relatively dry	Rather moist	Moist in lowest layers	Very dry	Very moist	Moist	Moist	Fairly moist (not as moist as Pm)	Fairly moist (not as moist as Pm)
Stability	Generally stable	Stable	Unstable	Stable	Stable	Stable aloft	Unstable	Unstable	Unstable
Weather	Clear, occasional thundery showers	Clear	Rain or snow showers	Clear	Low cloud, drizzle	Broken cloud, dry	Variable cloud, showers	Showers (mainly coastal)	Showers (mainly coastal)
Visibility	Moderate or poor	Moderate or poor	Good	Moderate or poor	Often poor with coastal fog	Moderate	Good	Very good	Very good

▲ **Figure 5:** Characteristics of the six main types of air mass.

The classic depression is formed where the maritime tropical air originating from the Caribbean and the much colder polar maritime air from the North Atlantic meet under an accelerating jet stream over the Atlantic. If the contrast in temperature, pressure and humidity between the two air masses is considerable, then wind speeds will be high and the turbulence associated with the passage of the fronts is considerable. Depressions appear on a synoptic chart as a set of closed curved isobars, with winds circulating anticlockwise in the northern hemisphere and clockwise in the southern hemisphere, due to the rotation of the earth. The warm and cold fronts associated with depressions bring with them characteristically unsettled weather. Depressions vary between 300 and 3,000 km in diameter, and they are described as 'deep' when pressure at their centre is very low, or 'shallow' when they are less well developed.

Tropical storms and cyclones draw their energy from the evaporation of sea water and, to a lesser extent, from the temperature difference between the air and this water and so only develop over the sea. Temperate latitude depressions, on the other hand, are based on horizontal temperature variations in the air. So, a depression can grow in strength away from the sea (although energy is lost through friction). Storms are mainly oceanic phenomena. Storms follow each other on the track at a rate of roughly 1 every 24 hours in winter, but not all of them reach land. To see the many that remain at sea we need to use a 'synoptic chart'.

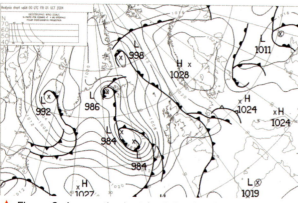

▲ **Figure 6:** A synoptic chart for 1 October 2004.

The synoptic chart is one of the most useful methods of visualising what the weather is doing over a large area. It is a map showing surface pressure, areas of high and low pressure, and weather fronts. Isobars join points of equal pressure and are typically spaced at 4 mb intervals. Cold fronts are marked with triangles; warm fronts with semi-circles, both 'pointing' in the direction of movement.

Figure 6 is a synoptic chart, showing a deep depression to the west of Ireland. Depressions generally travel from west to east and this storm will shortly impact upon the Irish coast. When deep depressions do hit land, they can be very destructive indeed, with high wind speeds and heavy rain triggering flood events.

Anticyclones

Anticyclones are high pressure systems that have widely spaced isobars and, as a result, wind speeds are low. They are associated with descending air and as the air is sinking, it is usually dry, leading to clear skies in both summer and winter.

Anticyclones are much larger than depressions, and they can lead to many days or even weeks of settled and calm weather. Anticyclones often block the path of depressions, either slowing them down, or forcing them round the outside of the high pressure system. They are then called 'blocking highs'. In these circumstances, a number of extreme weather conditions can occur. In winter, if a blocking high is established over the UK then we might experience prolonged cold weather, blizzards and bitterly cold winds; usually polar continental in origin. In the winter of 1962/63 such a system brought a prolonged period of these conditions to most of the UK:

- Pressure rose to reach 1050 mb as the block established itself on 23 Dec 1962.
- Glasgow had a white Christmas, and the heavy snow brought by an Arctic air mass later affected much of southern England on Boxing Day.
- Harbours and rivers froze. The Thames froze for the first time in many centuries.
- January temperatures were 5 °C below normal, and fell to −16 °C at night.
- More snow fell in February. A 36-hour blizzard caused heavy, drifting snow in most parts of the country.
- 6 March was the first day of the year without any frost anywhere in the country.

Key terms

Anticyclones are very large areas of high pressure. They tend to bring settled weather conditions that persist for some time.

Examiners' tip

Don't use terms like 'good' and 'bad' about weather events unless you specify who or what it is 'good' or 'bad' for.

Case study: 2003 – an extreme summer?

In July 2003 an anticyclonic system moved northwards from west Africa. It made its way over north Africa, warming itself from the hot air of the Sahara, before losing momentum above the western European landmass, where it firmly anchored itself. Over France, it not only held back and diverted the rain-bearing depressions from the Atlantic Ocean that normally cool Europe but it also funnelled in more hot air from the Sahara. The preceding spring had been exceptionally dry, so that soil and ground temperatures were higher than usual, reducing latent cooling and therefore amplifying the high temperatures. From Manchester to Madrid, temperatures rose to the mid- to upper 30s throughout the week, with several continental cities topping 40 °C.

On 4 August, maximum temperatures of 35 °C or greater were experienced at around two-thirds of France's 180 weather stations, with 15% having temperatures exceeding 40 °C. Temperatures in the west of Germany hit a record 40.8 °C degrees that day, after setting a new night-time record of 26.7 °C.

The blistering heat, coupled with severe drought, led to forest fires in many countries. On 17 August a cold frontal passage signalled the end of the heatwave for much of Europe, although strong thunderstorms associated with the front brought severe weather to parts of southern France and Spain. The storms produced widespread flooding.

Although heat waves are rarely given so much attention, they can claim more lives each year than floods, tornadoes and hurricanes combined. Heatwaves are a silent killer, mostly affecting the elderly, the very young, or the chronically ill. It was estimated that, in France alone, the 2003 heatwave caused more than 14,000 extra deaths.

Thunderstorms and tornadoes

▲ Figure 7: A distant thunderstorm.

Thunderstorms and tornadoes affect relatively small areas when compared with hurricanes and winter storms. The typical thunderstorm is 40 km in diameter and lasts an average of 30 minutes. Despite their small size, all thunderstorms are potentially dangerous. They are caused by rapid updraughts of air, which occur either along a front (where air of contrasting temperatures and humidity meet) or because of intense heating of the ground, leading to convection. In either case they are associated with large cumulonimbus clouds. Of the estimated 100,000 thunderstorms that occur each year in the USA, about 10% are classified as 'severe'. The greatest threat posed by thunderstorms is the flash floods that accompany them, although lightning and sudden downbursts of air can be extremely dangerous too.

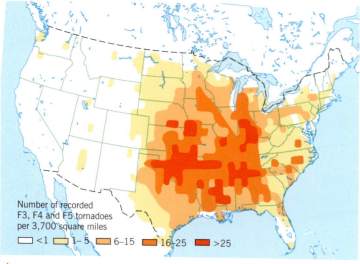

Number of recorded F3, F4 and F5 tornadoes per 3,700 square miles

☐ <1 ☐ 1–5 ☐ 6–15 ☐ 16–25 ☐ >25

▲ Figure 8: Tornado activity in the USA.

Tornadoes are amongst the most destructive and most fascinating of all extreme weather events. There are several websites devoted to the enthusiasts who spend much of their time chasing storms in the hope of witnessing tornado activity.

- A tornado is a violently rotating column of air, extending from a thunderstorm to the ground.
- Tornadoes cause an average of 70 fatalities and 1,500 injuries in the USA each year. Similar numbers are killed by lightning each year.
- The strongest tornadoes have rotating winds of more than 350 km/hr.
- Tornadoes can be over 1 km wide and have pathways of over 100 km.
- Although widely associated with 'tornado alley' in the USA (see Figure 8), tornadoes are not unknown in the UK, one of the most famous being in December 2006 when up to 150 houses and many cars were damaged when a tornado hit the Kensal Rise area of London.

Fieldwork

Aim:

To carry out an investigation into local weather and the way in which extreme weather conditions might be predicted.

1. Keep a weather diary for at least a fortnight to record weather in your local area.
2. Take measurements of weather conditions in your local environment.
3. Using synoptic charts and your own knowledge, attempt to forecast future weather conditions.

4. Assess the possibility of extreme events occurring in the next few days. Decide whether or not you would issue a 'severe weather warning' for your area.

Risk assessment

This is a low-risk investigation. Be careful when you are taking photographs that might include people. It is important to ask permission before photographing individuals.

Health and safety

Always tell an adult when and where you are going to do your fieldwork.

Fieldwork (continued)

Data presentation

Draw up a table of predictions based on daily measurements and observations, and compare them with a similar table of actual weather conditions.

Weather log

	Mon	Tues	Wed	Thurs	Fri
Temperature	10 °C				
Precipitation	none				
Air pressure	998				
Cloud types	Cirrus and cumulus				
Humidity	85%				
Wind speed	10-15 knots				
Wind direction	south west				
Cloud cover	Variable 1/8 in morning 5/8 later				
Sunshine hours	About 6 hrs				

This log can be used to fit your needs. Record available information on the log, using your own measurements from a school weather station or from the TV weather report or radio. Measurements should be made at the same time each day. Look at the weather each day, and see how the previous day's weather was different.

Try to forecast the next day's weather, using the following basic guidelines:

- Air pressure – If air pressure is falling, this means a low pressure area is approaching. Low pressure can bring rain or snow, or at least an increase in cloudiness. If the pressure is rising, high pressure is approaching. Fair weather should follow.
- Cloud types – Small cumulus clouds mean fair weather. Stratus clouds that appear to be getting thicker could bring rain or snow. Cirrus clouds that look like feathers are associated with fair weather, but may be associated with the approach of a front. Cumulus clouds that are growing tall means a thunderstorm may occur.
- Wind direction – Wind coming out of the north often occurs after a cold front has passed, bringing cooler temperatures and clear but colder weather. A south wind will bring warmer temperatures, and a chance that rain or snow may be approaching.

Score the accuracy of your predictions using a pre-determined set of standards. Simple statistical tests could be used to measure their accuracy. For example, each forecast could be scored with three points for a direct 'hit', two points for a 'near miss' and one point for a 'miss'. The group should agree the various categories before the exercise begins and the results should be examined by comparison with Met. Office data. The most important part of the exercise is the examination of why the forecasts are not accurate. What went wrong? Bad forecasting or the unpredictability of the systems?

Conclusion

At the end of your study period, take an overview of the accuracy of your forecasts and try to explain why they were not always accurate. Remember that you need to establish what you consider to be a fair test of accuracy.

Evaluation

Other than just taking more data over a longer period, consider how you might usefully extend your investigation. Think about how useful local data might be in predicting national trends and how very small changes in meteorological conditions can lead to very large variations in weather from one day to the next, and from one place to another.

Summary

This chapter has focused on the definition of extreme weather events, what they are and how they are distributed, globally and locally. Having studied this chapter, you should now be able to discuss these ideas and concepts and provide located examples of them:

- What extreme weather conditions are and how they can be recognised as posing a threat.
- How to recognise extreme weather events, both in nature and on maps and charts.
- The wide variety of extreme weather events and how they are distributed both globally and locally.
- The atmospheric processes that lead to the development of extreme weather conditions.
    - The evolution of extreme weather events.

MCQ

To try an exam question using what you have learned in this chapter, turn to page 161.

CHAPTER 16 What are the impacts of extreme weather on people, the economy and the environment?

Key terms

Catastrophes
Economic costs
Primary impacts
Secondary impacts
Social costs
Storm surge
Tertiary impacts
Vulnerability

Learning objectives

After studying this chapter, you will be able to discuss these ideas and concepts and provide located examples of them:

* Why extreme weather events have different impacts, both because of their severity and because of the type of place affected.
* Why extreme events have a primary impact when they occur, but also a secondary (and even a tertiary) impact.
* That impacts vary, both in severity and in their nature, affecting people differently according to their economic and social status, as well as their location.

▲ Figure 1: Extreme weather events affect people. Lives are lost and lives are damaged beyond repair. Very often these events affect some groups of people much more than others. This photograph was taken in New Orleans, a few days after the impact of Hurricane Katrina.

Impacts and how to assess them

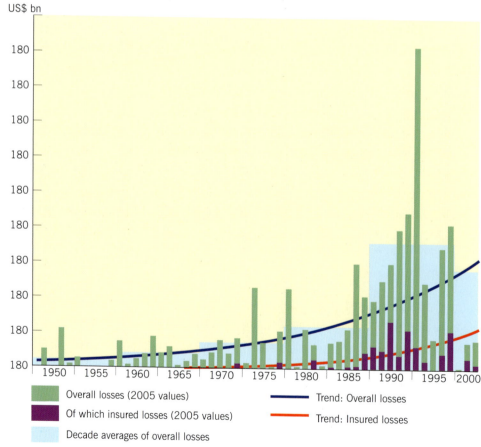

US$ bn

Overall losses (2005 values)
Of which insured losses (2005 values)
Decade averages of overall losses
Trend: Overall losses
Trend: Insured losses

▲ Figure 2: The costs of weather-related extreme events.

One way of assessing impacts is to measure the economic costs that result. These include the losses in economic activity and the insurance costs that result from such events. Figure 2 shows clearly that the costs of extreme weather events have risen in the past few decades. There are two distinct reasons for this – changes in the events themselves and, much more importantly, changes in the vulnerability of the population to such events. The rising trend in Figure 2 can be explained by:

- A significant increase in the number of extreme weather events – from an annual average of 13 in the 1950s to 72 in the 1990s.
- A rise in global population from 2.5 billion to 6.5 billion in the same period.
- A rise in the population in urban areas, making them more vulnerable.
- An increase in the value of both private property and the public infrastructure, as well as greater ownership of consumer goods, has increased the cost of disasters.
- A greater awareness of the potential losses increasing insurance cover.
- Better reporting of events, especially from remote areas.

In general terms, the impact can be assessed according to one of four distinct categories:

1. Loss of life and physical injury
2. Economic losses and insurance costs
3. Social impacts, including the disruption to family and community life
4. Environmental losses and costs.

Poverty itself also plays a role, since poverty leads to poor building structure, increased population density in urban areas, and lack of communication and infrastructure.

Human intervention in natural processes can also increase vulnerability. Developing and inhabiting lands susceptible to hazards – for example, building on floodplains subject to floods or on a coastline subject to hurricanes and floods – will expose people to a greater extent.

Human activities can increase the severity or frequency of a natural hazard. For example, overgrazing or deforestation leads to more severe erosion (floods, landslides), extracting groundwater leads to subsidence, and constructing roads on unstable slopes leads to landslides. Even contributing to global warming will lead to more severe storms.

'Vulnerability' refers not only to the possible physical effects of a natural hazard, but also to the way the hazard affects human life and property. Vulnerability to a given hazard depends on:

- Proximity to a possible hazardous event
- Population density in the area affected by the event
- Scientific understanding of the hazard
- Public education and awareness of the hazard
- Income levels
- Existence or non-existence of early-warning systems and lines of communication
- Availability and readiness of emergency infrastructure
- Construction styles and building codes
- Cultural factors that influence public response to warnings
- The resilience of communities and how well they respond collectively.

In general, lower-income countries are more vulnerable to natural hazards than high-income countries because of a lack of education, infrastructure, building codes and predictive systems.

Key terms

The impacts of an extreme event can be sub-divided according to when they occurred and whether they were directly related to the event itself or related to a consequence of the event.

Key terms

Vulnerability is how exposed human beings are to the impacts (of hazards).

Assessing the impacts of Hurricane Katrina

Hurricane Katrina devastated 233,000 km² of the southern USA on 29 August 2005, and was a reminder that it is not just the 'poor' countries who are vulnerable. The 'rich' countries are too, even if their losses are counted more in money than in lives lost. The extensive media coverage that Katrina received showed to the rest of the world that no one country has an exclusive monopoly on poor people, opportunistic looters, or inefficient government.

The storm surge that breached the levees and caused most of the city of New Orleans to flood was largely due to the application of the wrong technology. The 500 km of levees were built to withstand a Category 3 storm, but not one of intensity 4 or 5. Katrina was a Category 5 storm.

Loss of life: Estimates for loss of life due to Hurricane Katrina vary, but are widely reported to be around 1,500 people.

Primary losses due to the hurricane winds were not high. Perhaps 50 to 100 deaths were caused by falling masonry, collapsing buildings and other damage caused by the high winds.

Secondary losses were very significant, as the flood surge saw water levels rise to 5 metres in much of downtown New Orleans. Estimates put the numbers at about 1,400. At least 80% of New Orleans was under water on 31 August, when the levees failed along Lake Pontchartrain.

Tertiary losses are controversial. The health care system of New Orleans was devastated by the flood damage, and deaths certainly resulted from that. For example, in the immediate aftermath, when people took refuge in the Superdome, there were 4 deaths from heart attacks, perhaps induced by the conditions and the stress of losing a home and relatives. Many other lives were so deeply affected by the loss of property and loved ones that the costs are still mounting.

Economic costs: The total losses from Katrina have been estimated in the region of $150 bn, a staggering seven times the previous highest recorded losses in the USA, which were from Hurricane Andrew in 1992 (see table). Most of these losses were not a direct result of the high winds but a consequence of the extensive flood damage and the tertiary losses incurred through the closure of businesses and the loss of economic activity. These included:

- The disruption to the oil industry in the Gulf of Mexico, which reduced production by 95% in the first few days after the hurricane.
- $34 bn of insurance losses in loss of property and costs of reconstruction.
- The closure of the Port of New Orleans and the resultant loss of trade.
- The loss of tax revenue. Since the local economy was unable to operate local taxes were not paid and government revenue was reduced.

Key terms

A storm surge is a rise in water levels above the normal level, because of the combined effects of wind and low pressure.

Taking it further

To learn more about losses read 'Primary, secondary and tertiary effects' on your Student CD-ROM.

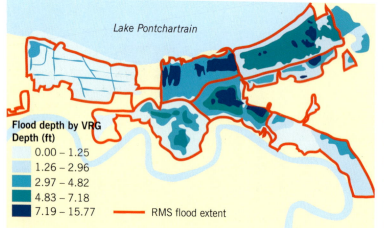

Lake Pontchartrain

Flood depth by VRG Depth (ft)
- 0.00 – 1.25
- 1.26 – 2.96
- 2.97 – 4.82
- 4.83 – 7.18
- 7.19 – 15.77
- —— RMS flood extent

▲ **Figure 3:** The impact of Katrina. The water breached the levees alongside Lake Pontchartrain.

Rank	Year	Event	Insured loss ($ bn at 2005 values)
1	2005	Hurricane Katrina	150.5
2	1992	Hurricane Andrew	21.2
3	2001	World Trade Center (9/11)	20.5
4	1994	Northridge Earthquake (California)	16.3
5	2004	Hurricane Charley	7.7
6	2004	Hurricane Ivan	7.2
7	1989	Hurricane Hugo	6.5
8	2004	Hurricane Frances	4.6
9	2004	Hurricane Jeanne	3.7
10	1998	Hurricane Georges	3.4

◀ **Figure 4:** 'Top ten' economic catastrophes in the USA.

An alternative view: Economic impact is often measured in terms of GDP. So figures are often quoted whereby a hazard event reduces the GDP, or more likely, reduces the likely growth of that GDP over a year. Many forecasts of the impact of Katrina were made. For example:

> A UCLA Anderson School of Business forecast released last week reports that Hurricanes Katrina and Rita will have a minimal impact on the US economy. The forecast predicts that Hurricane Katrina will reduce the US gross domestic product by 1.5%.

But this report, and many others, go on to point out that the reconstruction work needed might actually boost the economy, making some (if not all) disasters a 'good thing'. This strange idea is based on an oddity of national accounting. If a firm loses equipment and a factory burns down, then it is a loss. All companies will allow for the fact that their machinery and equipment gets older every year and includes a figure for this depreciation. National accounting does not do this. The loss of resources, manmade or natural, is not counted, but the work generated to repair and replace those resources is. (The loss of human life is not accounted, either.)

With this bizarre logic, it can be seen that natural disasters, such as Katrina, and unnatural disasters, such as 9/11, can be seen as good for the economy.

Social costs: The social costs of Katrina were especially severe for the poor, largely African-American community, who lived in the districts most affected.

- New Orleans is a city in which 28% of residents live below the poverty line, 12% are aged 65 or older, only 75% graduated from high school, and 27% of households do not have cars. Many of these people were not insured and lost all their possessions. And the loss of some possessions, such as photographs and diaries, is not measurable in financial terms.
- In addition, 77% of New Orleans residents were born in Louisiana and have lived most of their lives there. These statistics alone go far to explain why tens of thousands of the 500,000 residents of New Orleans did not evacuate; in so many ways they were more rooted in place than the average American.
- Lives changed, houses were destroyed and local communities broken up.
- Contaminated water supplies created fear of water-borne disease.
- Very many thousands of domestic pets were drowned.

Environmental costs: Oil spills led to groundwater being contaminated. Long-abandoned wetlands which acted as a potential sponge to soak up extreme events were 'reclaimed' by the river. Offshore islands that protected the coast were destroyed by Katrina, making it more exposed to future events.

Key terms

GDP is the total value of goods and services produced within a country.

Key terms

Economic losses are financial and can be assessed in terms of money lost, whereas social costs involve the disruption of ordinary lives and impact on people's contentment and happiness.

Examiners' tip

Remember that social and economic costs are quite closely related and the same 'loss' may be both economic and social.

Tropical cyclones cause storm surges and river flooding

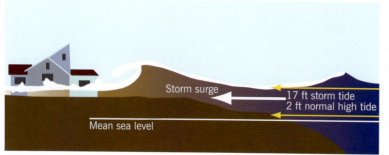

Storm surge
17 ft storm tide
2 ft normal high tide
Mean sea level

▲ Figure 5: A storm surge.

Hurricanes frequently lead to flooding through storm surges and river flooding. Storm surges occur with low pressure systems, typically tropical cyclones, when high winds cause the water to pile up. Low pressure at the centre of a weather system also has a small secondary effect. It is this combined effect of low pressure and persistent wind over a shallow water body which is the most common cause of storm surge flooding problems.

The Katrina storm surge impacted most heavily along the coast to the east of New Orleans but as a result, the wind would come back from the north as the storm passed. This forced large volumes of water from Lake Pontchartrain against the levees that protected the city, most of which was built below sea-level. It was also forecast that the storm surge in Lake Pontchartrain would reach 4 to 5 metres, with waves reaching 2 metres above the storm surge. Despite this challenging surge, the levees should have held, but poor design, poor maintenance and years of indifference by the authorities eventually led to their destruction.

Heavy rain and river flooding

Intense rainfall is not directly related to the wind speed of tropical cyclones. In fact, some of the greatest rainfall amounts occur from weaker storms that drift slowly or stall over an area.

When it comes to hurricanes, wind speeds do not tell the whole story. Hurricanes produce storm surges, can trigger tornadoes, and often, the most deadly of all, cause inland flooding. In the USA, 60% of the people who die in such extreme weather events die because of inland flooding, the flooding caused by intense rain and subsequent river flooding.

Inland flooding can be a major threat to communities hundreds of kilometres from the coast, as intense rain falls from these huge tropical air masses long after they have stopped being 'hurricanes'.

Hurricane Allison (2001) produced extremely heavy rainfall and catastrophic floods in the Houston, Texas, area. Allison then acquired sub-tropical 'storm' characteristics and continued to produce heavy rainfall and flooding as it tracked from Louisiana eastward to North Carolina, and then northward along the east coast to Massachusetts. Forty-one deaths were directly related to the heavy rain, flooding and the tornadoes it triggered. Damage estimates reported by the Federal Emergency Management Agency (FEMA) were near $5 bn in the Houston metropolitan area alone.

Hurricane Floyd (1999) brought similar very heavy rain (over 400 mm) and, as a result, record flooding to the eastern USA. The rains caused widespread flooding over a period of several weeks; nearly every river basin in the eastern part of North Carolina exceeded 500-year flood levels. Of the 56 people who perished, 50 drowned due to inland flooding. Four weeks later, Hurricane Irene passed over the same area, adding another 150 mm of rainfall to ground that was still saturated after Floyd, thus provoking more floods.

▲ Figure 6: Widespread flooding caused by Hurricane Floyd in 1999

The impact of tornadoes

Tornadoes are much more local events than hurricanes and thus their impact is more restricted geographically. However, their violence makes the degree of that impact very severe. Although tornadoes are associated with the USA and, especially, 'tornado alley', tornadoes are not unknown in Britain.

Britain has more tornadoes per square mile than any other country in the world. On 7 December 2006, a tornado hit Kensal Rise in London. Winds of up to 192 km/hr caused extensive damage to an area of the country rarely associated with extreme weather phenomena. An even larger tornado had struck Birmingham in 2005.

▲ **Figure 7:** A tornado in formation – rapidly spiralling air about to make the contact between ground and cloud.

Researching the impact of tornadoes should involve a consideration of the following possible effects:

- Costs and losses to agricultural and livestock producers – loss of livestock, crops, trees and timber resources, damage to houses, barns, farm machinery, and fences
- Urban, residential, and commercial impacts – damage to and destruction of buildings, cars, trucks, trains, airplanes, etc., disruptions to local utilities and services (power, communications, drinking water, transportation), loss of trees and landscaping
- Health – injuries, fatalities, mental and physical stress associated with loss of family, friends, and property
- Secondary and tertiary economic effects – revenue loss from lost production in business and industry, negative impact of economic multiplier.

Researching extreme weather impacts

Using a framework like the one below, assess the impact of an extreme weather event by analysing it in terms of:

- The types of costs involved
- How they impacted over time.

Don't forget that secondary impacts are those things triggered by the event itself, such as the flooding of New Orleans, and that tertiary impacts are the long-term impacts of both the event itself and its secondary effects.

Framework for researching extreme weather impacts

	Primary Impact	Secondary Impact	Tertiary Impact
Death and injury			
Economic losses			
Social costs			
Environmental impact			

The impact of the 2003 European heatwave

The summer (June to September) of 2003 was 3.4 °C warmer in Europe than the average for the period 1960–1990. This made it an event that would recur once every 450 years (if we do not allow for global warming). In other words by the standards of the period leading up to our recent run of 'hot' years, this was an exceptional event. This extreme event was in reality even more unusual because it followed an unusually dry spring. As Figure 8 shows, there was a very strong relationship between the extreme heat and the death rate, with France suffering most.

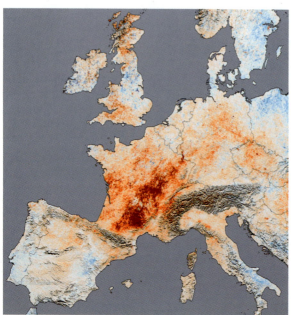

▲ **Figure 8:** Red colours indicate the area of much higher than average temperatures

	Fatalities
France	14,800
Spain	2,000
Portugal	1,300
Italy	4,000
Germany	3,500
United Kingdom	900
Netherlands	500

The impact was considerable, affecting an unusually wide area of Europe from France to Romania, covering more than 4 million km2 (see the assessment below).

AN ASSESSMENT OF THE IMPACT OF THE EUROPEAN HEATWAVE OF 2003

Death and injury

- 20,000 deaths, mostly in France (see Figure 8)
- Increased deaths and illness because of consumption of spoilt food
- Increased road traffic accidents with freak weather, poor road surfaces affected by heat, and reduction in sleep because of heat

Economic losses

- Loss of crops due to heat and water shortages
- Losses due to forest fires destroying property
- Interruption to shipping because of reduced water levels in rivers
- Reduction in output with lower efficiency of workforce and absenteeism
- Reduction in electricity generation because of low water levels for cooling (six power plants were shut down in France)
- Reduction in income in tourist destinations such as theme parks because it was 'too hot to go out'

Social costs

- Rescue services have 75% increase in 'call outs' for acts of aggression in heatwave periods
- Increased crime, especially in urban areas

Environmental impact

- Changing vegetation patterns – 10% of Portugal's forest was destroyed by fire
- Changes in vegetation induced by higher ozone levels
- Longer term changes to freshwater ecosystems
- Reduction in species richness.

Fieldwork investigation

Aim:

To investigate local awareness and attitudes to the risks of extreme weather events, in an area that is familiar to you.

1. Use local records to establish a history of any extreme events in the past 50 years.
2. Identify those events and develop a timeline of their impact.
3. Conduct interviews and questionnaires in the local area to establish the level of awareness of those past events and the popular view of the risk of future events. Questionnaires should be gathered using a stratified sampling technique. For example, by using the environment agency flood maps, equal numbers of questionnaires should be gathered from people living in high-risk, medium-risk and low-risk areas. In conducting the questionnaire (see results framework below) two preliminary questions should be asked:
   (a) How long have you lived at your current address?
   (b) Identify three major problems facing your town/community.
4. Assess the impact of subsequent hazards, such as flooding, on the local economy and environment.

Risk assessment

This is a low-risk exercise, but do be respectful and thoughtful when gathering questionnaires. Not all local residents either want to answer questions or to have photographs taken.

Health and safety

Always work in pairs or in groups, not alone. All interviews and questionnaires should involve at least two of you.

Data presentation

Draw up tables to show differences between the real risk of extreme events and the perceived risk. Ratings should be made on a five-point scale, with higher numbers indicating higher levels of frequency, likelihood or severity. Calculate the average responses (mean) for the three different groups.

Comparative maps could be drawn, using official flood-risk information with an overlay of perceived risk.

Conclusion

Make a judgement whether you feel that the local community over-estimates or under-estimates the risk posed by extreme weather events and how this relates to where people live.

Evaluation

Consider ways in which you could extend your investigation without simply gathering more of the same type of data. Is there any evidence that people have moved into or out of the area because of their risk perception?

Hazard awareness, likelihood and severity: Questionnaire results

	Mean	Comment
How frequently do you think about the possibility of a flood? Very frequently Frequently Occasionally Very occasionally Hardly ever		
How do you rate the likelihood of a flood in the next 10 years? Very high risk Moderate risk Low risk Very low risk		
How do you rate the likelihood of injury to yourself or your family? Very high risk Moderate risk Low risk Very low risk		
How do you rate the likelihood of damage to your property? Very high risk Moderate risk Low risk Very low risk		
How severe would be the consequences of a flood for residents of your town? Very severe Severe Moderate Limited Very limited		
How severe would be the consequences of a flood for you and your family? Very severe Severe Moderate Limited Very limited		

Summary

Now that you have worked through this chapter you have a clear idea of how to assess the impact of hazards and why they vary. By using Hurricane Katrina's impact on New Orleans in 2005 and the European heatwave of 2003, you will be able to discuss these ideas and concepts and provide located examples of them:

- Why extreme weather events have different impacts, both because of their severity and because of the type of place affected.
- Why extreme events have a primary impact when they occur, but also a secondary (and even a tertiary) impact.
- That impacts vary, both in severity and in their nature, affecting people according to their location, economic and social status.

MCQ

To try an exam question using what you have learned in this chapter, turn to page 161.

CHAPTER 17 How are people and places increasingly at risk from and vulnerable to extreme weather?

Key terms

Flash floods
Global warming
Greenhouse gases
Hydrographs
Significance

Learning objectives

After studying this chapter, you will be able to discuss these ideas and concepts and provide located examples of them:

- The frequency of extreme weather events in the UK and elsewhere and whether this frequency is increasing.
- The increasing threat posed by those hazardous events because of human behaviour and natural changes.
- The increasing flood risk posed by increased storm activity.
- The changing nature of drainage basins also contributes towards higher flood risks.

The frequency of extreme weather events

It is often suggested that extreme weather events are becoming more common and that the reason for this is global warming, caused by human activity. This chapter does not debate the causes of global warming but it is important to determine whether extreme weather events are actually becoming more frequent and if they are, whether the rise is significant, whether the change is long term (or just a 'blip'), and whether these events are related to global warming.

▲ **Figure 1:** The impact of the flash flood in Big Thompson Canyon, Colorado in the summer of 1976.

Key terms

Global warming is the trend of rising global temperatures since the 1960s.

Hurricanes

There is no consensus at all about the frequency of hurricanes. Some experts contend that the number of hurricanes has increased in recent years, whilst others reject that view. Another group suggests that although there may be little evidence for an increased number of hurricanes there is evidence that they are becoming stronger. Yet another group has found that there is evidence that stronger hurricanes are less likely to make landfall (in the USA) and thus they will do less damage. According to the 2007 Fourth Assessment Report of the Intergovernmental Panel on Climate Change (IPCC-AR4), it is 'more likely than not' that there is a human contribution to the observed trend of hurricane intensification since the 1970s. In the future, 'it is likely that future tropical cyclones (typhoons and hurricanes) will become more intense, with larger peak wind speeds and more heavy precipitation' associated with ongoing increases of tropical sea surface temperatures. According to the IPCC-AR4, on a global scale, there is 'no clear trend' in the frequency of tropical cyclones. However, as shown on Figure 2, the frequency of tropical storms has increased dramatically in the North Atlantic. Reasons for this increase are currently subject to a fierce debate among climate scientists. At least two recent scientific studies suggest a significant statistical link between the increased frequency and global warming, but research to identify how this link works is still going on, and is highly controversial.

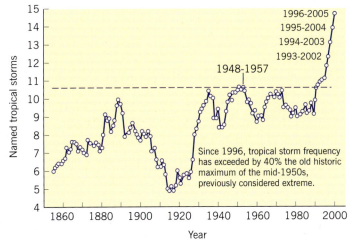

▲ **Figure 2:** The increasing frequency of North Atlantic tropical storms.

Tornadoes

One of the main difficulties with tornado records is that a tornado, or evidence of a tornado, must have been observed. Unlike rainfall or temperature, which may be measured by instruments, tornadoes are brief, highly localised and very unpredictable. If a tornado occurs in a place with few or no people, it is not likely to be documented at all. Unfortunately, this affects much of what we know today. 'Tornado alley' was very sparsely populated until the twentieth century, and so it is possible that many significant tornadoes may never have made it into the historical record.

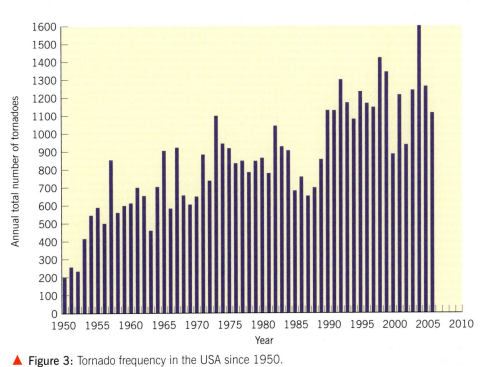

▲ **Figure 3:** Tornado frequency in the USA since 1950.

In the film, An Inconvenient Truth, Al Gore added the 2004 USA tornado season into his collection of weather phenomena apparently related to climate change: 'Also in 2004, the all-time record for tornadoes in the United States was broken'.

However, the evidence here is not much clearer than it is for hurricane frequency and intensity. Figure 3 shows an apparent upward trend since 1950 but improvements in recording techniques and the use of satellite imagery has added a new dimension to meteorology and added considerably to the chance of these very local and quite brief events being recorded. They remain unusual, for even in tornado alley the 'average' frequency of a tornado hitting any particular square kilometre would be about once every thousand years.

It is important to add that this problem with the records means nothing, one way of the other, about the global warming debate. It simply means that tornado frequency has probably not changed significantly.

Key terms

Greenhouse gases include water vapour, carbon dioxide and methane. The contribution of humans to the rising quantities of carbon dioxide and methane is, for many, a prime cause of global warming.

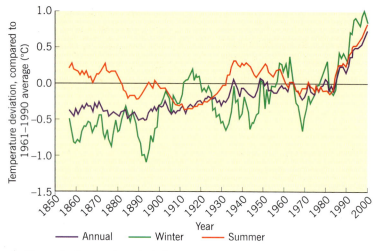

▲ Figure 4: Temperature deviations in Europe since 1850.

Drought, heatwaves and summer storms

As Figure 4 shows, the temperature increase in Europe over the last 150 years is about 0.95 °C, which is higher than the global average. The warmest year in Europe was 2000; the next 7 warmest years occurred in the last 14 years. If you look carefully at Figure 4, it is also quite obvious that if the data stopped in 1980 the 'trend' would be so slight as to be undetectable. In other words, the interesting changes have happened in the last 30 years.

In the past 3 decades, hot summer days (those with temperatures above 25 °C) and heatwaves have become more frequent. The most severe changes have been observed in western and southern parts of Europe. At the same time, the number of frost days has decreased even more, due to a greater warming in winter than in summer.

The rainfall pattern is more varied than that of temperature, showing marked increases in some regions but significant decreases elsewhere. Related to increasing temperatures, however, there is evidence of more violent thunderstorms and the resultant flash floods.

Examiners' tip

Remember that global warming can be measured, and is accepted as a fact by most experts. The reasons for global warming are more controversial, and several theories exist. It may very well have several causes.

► Figure 5: A cartoon showing that some people might enjoy heatwaves.

The causes of rising frequency

Climate change does pose some threats for us in Europe, as it does for the rest of the world. To say that 'climate is changing' is not controversial. To say that 'the changes are significant and amount to a trend' is more debatable. Records are incomplete and quite recent in origin, so spotting trends in them is not easy. This weakness allows those people who dispute the human causes of global warming to dispute the evidence of climate change itself.

Any shift in average climate will almost inevitably result in a change in the frequency of extreme events. For less adaptable societies in the developing world, a shorter return period of extreme weather events may not allow them to fully recover from the effects of one event before the next one strikes.

Every region of the world experiences record-breaking climate extremes from time to time. In 1989, for example, the 'Big Wet' in eastern Australia brought torrential downpours and the worst flooding in two centuries. Many people in England will remember the storm of October 1987. Early this century, a trend towards increased drought in the North American Midwest culminated in the 'Dust Bowl' decade of the 1930s, after which conditions eased. During the 1970s and 1980s annual rainfall over the Sahel zone of northern Africa dropped 25% below the average, leading to severe desiccation and famine.

The rising impact of extreme climatic events

Year	Number of events	Victims	Total losses Original values (US$ m)	Insured losses	Major events
1994	680	13,000	89,000	21,000	Earthquake Northridge
1995	615	20,800	172,000	16,000	Earthquake Kobe, floods North Korea
...					
2000	890	10,300	38,000	9,600	Floods UK, Typhoon Saomai
2001	720	25,000	40,000	12,000	Tropical Storm Allison, hailstorm USA
2002	700	11,000	60,000	14,000	Floods Europe
2003	700	109,000	65,000	16,000	Heatwave Europe, earthquake Bam/Iran
2004	650	235,000	150,000	47,000	Hurricanes Atlantic, typhoons Japan, tsunami
2005	670	101,000	220,000	99,000	Hurricanes Atlantic, earthquake Pakistan
2006	850	20,000	50,000	15,000	Earthquake Yogyakarta/Indonesia
2007	950	15,000	75,000	30,000	Winter Storm Kyrill, floods UK

◀ Figure 6: The losses from extreme events in recent years.
Source: www.munichre.com

The risk of a disaster increases according to changes in the vulnerability of a population and changes in its capacity to cope. These can be shown using the disaster 'risk equation'.

$$R = \frac{H \times V}{C}$$

R – Risk V – Vulnerability
H – Hazard C – Capacity to cope

There are a number of reasons why the vulnerability of populations has increased and their capacity to cope has decreased. The sections below consider these reasons in greater detail.

A rise in global population: There has been a rise in global population from 2.5 billion to 6.5 billion between 1950 and 2008. The existence of more people produces a greater impact of the personal tragedies and economic losses that extreme events provoke. The most significant aspect in terms of extreme weather events has been the growth of population in areas that were previously only lightly populated – some of them because of the potential hazard risk.

Key terms

Significance can be measured and assessed statistically to show the chances of a trend or relationship occurring by chance.

Taking it further

A useful link is the BBC website: www.bbc.co.uk/weather/features/understanding/extreme_climate.shtml.

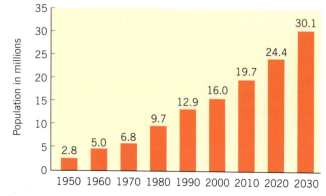

▲ Figure 7: The past, present and predicted population of Florida.
Source: www.flsuspop.org

In Florida for example, the threat from hurricanes and tropical storms was recognised by the original Native Americans, who stayed well away from the coastline. The 1900 United States Census identified only four cities in Florida with more than 5,000 inhabitants. The total population of the state was recorded as 528,542. Rapid development for tourism and retirement changed that and will, by most forecasts, go on fuelling rapid growth.

A rise in urban population: There has also been a rise in the concentration of the population in urban areas, which makes that population more vulnerable. Over 50% of humanity now live in cities, and it is forecast that the proportion will rise to nearly 70% by 2050. These concentrations of people are inevitably more exposed to severe climatic events, especially since so many cities are situated on low-lying land, close to oceans and major rivers. In cities such as Manila, Jakarta, Mexico City and Lagos, the urban poor, living under terrible conditions of squalor, crime and insecurity, now make up 30 to 40% of the population – a figure that will increase in the next few decades.

With budgets cut by austerity programmes imposed by the IMF and World Bank, city governments cannot always provide the basic services needed by this swelling urban mass, such as water, electricity, and infrastructure. Nor are they in a very strong position to protect exposed environments from the risks associated with extreme weather events.

There is very powerful evidence from New Orleans – in a country that prides itself on being wealthy – that the disaster of Katrina was not an 'equal opportunity event'.

• Low-income residents had fewer choices about how to prepare for the imminent arrival of Katrina.
• Since the storm was at the end of the month many low-income residents of New Orleans lacked the economic resources to pay for evacuation.
• Furthermore, low-income New Orleanians are those who are least likely to own vehicles, making voluntary evacuation more costly and logistically more difficult.
• These residents were also more reliant upon television and radio for news of the storm, and alarm from these channels only became heightened in the last 48 hours before the storm arrived.
• Although most of these residents joined the flow of traffic out of the city on Sunday, many remained in their homes, hoping for the best, and others headed to the Superdome rather than taking the few city buses available to out-of-town shelters. Those going to the Superdome believed that these shelters would provide sufficient protection until the storm had passed but they hadn't considered the flooding that occurred when several levees were breached.
• The people hit hardest by the flooding were those from the neighbourhoods of federally subsidised housing, where poverty was most concentrated.
• Not coincidentally, they were least able to leave the city without assistance.

It is very likely that events of this magnitude will recur as the world becomes more urbanised.

Increasing cost of disasters: The rising value of property and growing numbers of expensive consumer goods has led to an increase in the cost of disasters. Historically, the cliché has been that such events 'cost lots of money but few lives' in the rich world but 'lots of lives and not so much money' in the poor world. This is partly explained by rising levels of material wealth in the rich countries.

Rising affluence in the new superpowers, such as China (see table) and India, will inevitably lead to an increase in the financial losses caused by extreme weather events.

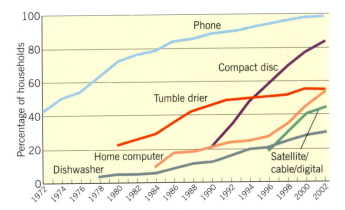

▲ **Figure 8:** Rising household ownership of consumer durables in the UK between 1972 and 2002.

Source: www.statistics.gov.uk

	1990	1995	1999	2000	2001	2002
Motorbike	1.9	6.3	15.1	18.8	20.4	22.2
Washing machine	78.4	89.0	91.4	90.5	92.2	92.9
Fridge	42.3	66.2	77.7	80.1	81.9	87.4
Colour TV	59.0	89.8	111.6	116.6	120.5	126.4
Video		18.2	21.7	20.1	19.9	18.4
Hi-Fi		10.5	19.7	22.2	23.8	25.2
Camera	19.2	30.6	38.1	38.4	39.8	44.1
Air conditioner	0.3	8.1	24.5	30.8	35.8	51.1
Shower		30.1	45.4	49.1	52.0	62.4
VCD/DVD player			24.7	37.5	42.6	52.6
Computer			5.9	9.7	13.3	20.6
Mobile phone			7.1	19.5	34.0	62.9
Car			0.3	0.5	0.6	0.9

◀ **Figure 9:** Consumer durable ownership in China 1990–2002 (number owned per 100 urban households).

Source: www.chinability.com

Awareness of loss: There seems to be a greater awareness of the potential loss and thus rising insurance cover for those losses. It is also argued that disaster losses are greater in the rich countries because levels of insurance are higher. Even in rich countries the insurance position is not as simple as it might seem.

In general in the USA and much of Europe, homeowners' insurance policies cover damage caused by wind and wind-driven rain, but contain a provision that excludes coverage for flood damage. In America's Gulf region, some (about 15% in Mississippi and up to 40% in New Orleans) but not most homeowners carried separate flood insurance, which is underwritten by the federal government. Immediately following Katrina, the insurance industry was quick to deny responsibility for covering most of the damage its policy holders were suffering, wasting little time spreading the message that most damage was flood related. Unsurprisingly, those who did not have the 'extra' flood insurance policies were the poorest people in the city who lived in the most vulnerable area.

Key terms

Flash floods occur when there is a very sudden increase in the discharge of a river, usually as a result of a storm event.

Flash floods

Like tornadoes, flash floods are localised events that can cause very considerable damage – but usually within a fairly small area. They are usually the secondary impact of an extreme weather event, such as a convectional storm. If the amount of rainfall far exceeds the averages, the channels are unable to cope with the increased runoff, and flooding results. Flash floods can also result from a prolonged period of heavy rain, leading to saturation of the ground, which is then unable to absorb any more rainfall.

Flash floods can occur in any environment, but they are especially dangerous in regions that are either arid or semi-arid. Every year people die and property is destroyed when stream beds that are only wet on a few occasions each year are suddenly – and often very unexpectedly – filled with water. Sometimes the heavy rainfall takes place so far away that no rainclouds are visible as a sudden flood sweeps down from the mountains.

"….Actually… We're trying to find our house…."

▲ **Figure 10:** Flash floods can lead to a very rapid rise in water levels.

▲ **Figure 11:** Flash flood warning in Death Valley, California.

Case study: Big Thompson Canyon flood

A devastating example of a flash flood was the Big Thompson Canyon flood in Colorado, in August 1976. Big Thompson Canyon is a narrow canyon, typical of the river basins in this region of the Rockies. Very steep rock forms the canyon walls, with little soil or vegetation to absorb runoff from storms. In some places, the canyon walls are almost vertical. The river drops more than 1,000 m and exits the canyon into the rolling plains. Highway 34 stretches the length of the canyon and is dotted with homes, restaurants and other businesses.

▲ **Figure 12:** The flood in Big Thompson Canyon on 1 August 1976.

Case study: Big Thompson Canyon flood (continued)

31 July: afternoon	About 3,000 tourists and locals start to gather in the canyon, preparing to take part in Colorado's 'centennial party' in this popular hiking and camping area.
31 July: afternoon	A weak but very wet air stream begins to cross the mountains from the east.
31 July: early evening	The rain begins. Usually, fast moving air from the west at 3,000 metres is enough to keep thunderstorms out of the area, but not on this occasion.
31 July: evening	As darkness falls, 360 mm of rain falls over a 3-hour period – a year's rainfall in an evening.
31 July: evening	The canyon fills with water, turning the river from a 50 cm trickle into a 6 metre wall of water, travelling at speeds of up to 8 metres per second. Boulders weighing up to 275 tonnes are moved by the sheer force of the water, which sweeps everything before it.
31 July: evening	Peak discharge is reached very quickly, after about one hour, reaching 900 m³/sec at the end of the canyon – a 'one in three hundred years' event. (The peak discharge would fill an Olympic swimming pool every 2.8 seconds.)
1 August: morning	After a night of appalling tragedies, the clean-up begins in the early hours. 144 people have died, some of whose bodies will never be recovered.

Figure 13: A timeline of the Big Thompson disaster of 1976.

'I will always remember that day . . .'

I was a junior in college. Three buddies and I worked at a popular restaurant that rested nearly on the edge of the dammed up lake. That summer we had decided to live in Estes Park rather than in the canyon, as we had the previous summer. I had that Saturday afternoon off, and had driven east along Highway 34 to Fort Collins. Driving back west to Estes, I had noticed how crowded the canyon was – I knew it was a huge weekend in Estes Park because of the centennial and bicentennial celebrations. After working at 'The Yum Yum Hut' for about an hour, my boss, Mr Pabst, looked out and said that 'one heck of a storm' was coming. It rained so hard that we could not even see the motel some 60 feet away. Then there was a deadly pause for about half an hour and we stepped outside, as no one was at the restaurant. My boss commented that it was strange that the clouds were quickly reversing tracks and moving to the west. Once again – tremendous rain. At about 8:30 p.m. we closed, but we listened to a short-wave radio broadcast in the canyon in which people were screaming for ropes. We really had no idea what was going on. At about 9:30 I was driving home up on Olympia Lane, just on the east edge of Estes Park, and I came to a sudden stop. There was a 20-foot-deep, 30-foot-wide hole in the middle of the road. I knew then that this was a strange incident. The next morning, Sunday, I got called into work in the morning shift – many of the morning workers were unable to get to work. I distinctly remember an Estes Park policeman coming in and I asked what kind of damage there was in the canyon. He sort of rolled his eyes and said, 'Bad!'. I asked him what he meant, and he said 'Lots of death'. He went on to say a temporary morgue was set up in Loveland. We all felt shock at that point. As the morning rolled on, more reports came in. This was huge – national news! I suddenly came to the shocking realisation that I had to get a hold of my parents. Many tourists had said that the national news reported that all this tragedy had occurred in Estes Park. They would be worried sick. I drove 25 miles to find a phone line. I was able to get through and discovered they had just (30 seconds earlier) turned on the television and heard the news. They suffered only 30 seconds of fear. I will always remember that day.

(Anonymous)

Tornado warnings

Meteorologists rely on radar to provide information on the developing storms that might lead to tornado activity. In the USA the National Weather Service has 'Doppler' radars across the country, which can detect air movement towards or away from the radar. Early detection of increasing rotation high up within a thunderstorm can allow life-saving warnings to be issued before the tornado forms. NOAA advise people living in areas at risk to purchase special 'Weather radios' to hear their 24-hour local radio service. Four types of warning can be issued:

• Tornado watch: Tornadoes are possible in your area. Remain alert for approaching storms.
• Tornado warning: A tornado has been sighted or indicated by weather radar. If a tornado warning is issued for your area and the sky becomes threatening, move to your pre-designated place of safety.
• Severe thunderstorm watch: Severe thunderstorms are possible in your area.
• Severe thunderstorm warning: Severe thunderstorms are occurring.

The population are also advised to look for a number of warning signs themselves: dark, often greenish sky, wall cloud, large hailstones, or a loud roar.

Flood warning

During the flooding in the summer of 2007, BBC Berkshire launched an 'interactive floodmap' to help local residents by giving them information about the floods and where to get help. There are similar websites offering flood advice and warnings in most countries. They frequently offer advice about how to prepare for a flood, how to assess the risk of flooding in your local area, and what to do in the event of a flood. However, these sites do not generally debate the issue of flood plain development itself and the increased risks that have come about by planning decisions. The current planning position is laid out as follows:

Applications likely to require particular consideration of flood risk issues include those for development:

• within a river flood plain or washland shown on the indicative flood plain map prepared by the Environment Agency;
• within a coastal flood plain, including that adjacent to the tidal length of a river, shown on the indicative flood plain map prepared by the Environment Agency;
• within or adjacent to any watercourse, particularly where there might be potential for flash flooding;
• adjacent to or including any flood bank or other flood control structure;
• situated in an area where the Agency have indicated that there may be drainage problems;
• likely to involve the culverting or diverting of any watercourse; or
• of such a size or nature relative to the receiving watercourse/drainage system that there could be a significant increase in surface water runoff from the area.

Source: www.odpm.gov.uk

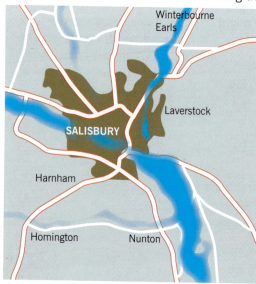
▲ **Figure 3:** The flood risk for part of Salisbury in Wiltshire.

Taking it further

In the UK, the Environment Agency gives full details of current flood alerts on its website: www.environment-agency.gov.uk/subjects/flood/floodwarning/.

Hard engineering

Hard engineering solutions to extreme weather risks involve physical adaptation of the environment, often changing it quite radically. Commonly used techniques include:

• Building dams to store water and regulate discharge
• Building levees and embankments to increase channel capacity
• Building flood walls to protect settlements
• Channelling a river, making it deeper, increasing velocity so reducing flood risk
• Flood relief reservoirs and channels
• River barriers, such as the Thames Barrier.

▲ Figure 4: New Orleans is located in a saucer-shaped depression, much of which is below sea level.

An example of hard engineering

Levees have long been one of the best known methods of flood protection. Natural levees are formed along rivers when they flood, as they deposit coarser sediment closer to the channel. Building these up effectively increases channel capacity. Of course the sediment in rivers has to go somewhere, and if levees prevent flooding then some of that sediment is going to be deposited in the channel, reducing the channel capacity. Ultimately this would lead to the levees being built higher and higher, raising the river higher and higher above its floodplain and making the flood risk more and more extreme.

The levees 'protecting' New Orleans are extensive, and consist of earth banks with, in some places, flood walls above them. They were built to withstand the type of storm surges and water heights resulting from a Category 3 hurricane. Katrina was a Category 5 hurricane offshore and a Category 4 hurricane by the time it made landfall. All the same, the number of failures (over fifty different breaches) were not all explicable in terms of the size of the storm. Many failed because of bad design, such as being built on structurally weak peat foundations, or because they had been badly maintained.

For example, although the depth for the steel sheet foundations for the flood walls was supposed be 5 metres, after the Katrina breaches a forensic engineering team showed that at one point near the 17th Street Canal breach, the piling extends just 3 metres below sea level, not nearly deep enough to withstand the pressure without collapsing.

In the view of many, the loss of life in New Orleans was a failure of management, of engineering and of the political will necessary to address these issues.

▼ Figure 5: The failed 17th Street Canal flood wall.

▲ **Figure 6:** The in-filled 'canal' and partially restored Kissimmee.

Rank	State	Growth (%) over 10 years
1.	Nevada	66.3
2.	Arizona	40.0
3.	Colorado	30.6
4.	Utah	29.6
5.	Idaho	28.5
6.	Georgia	26.4
7.	Florida	23.5
8.	Texas	22.8
9.	North Carolina	21.4
10.	Washington	21.1
11.	Oregon	20.4
12.	New Mexico	20.1

▲ **Figure 7:** The fastest-growing US states.

Soft engineering

Soft engineering solutions involve adapting the natural environment, with minimal change to the environment itself. In recent years soft engineering solutions have been pursued in river basins where previous hard engineering projects have been judged as unsuccessful. One well-known example of this is the restoration of the Kissimmee River in Florida, which would provide an excellent research project on the complex issues surrounding river management.

Managing drought and heatwaves

Droughts and heatwaves are often related events, although not necessarily so. In the summer of 2003 it was the exceptional heatwave rather than drought that caused serious difficulties in much of mainland Europe. Of course, increased heat leads to increased evaporation and thus water losses, and in years to come drought will probably accompany heatwaves.

Of all the threats posed by climate change, drought is perhaps the hardest to plan for because it involves very significant changes to patterns of human activity. In the past, drought has been treated, rather like other extreme weather events, with short-term solutions rather than advance planning.

These short-term solutions might involve hosepipe bans, public campaigns to moderate demand, and restrictions on taking water from rivers for irrigation. But if our climate is changing – and if hot summers like that of 2003 are to become more frequent – then we will need to plan ahead to prevent the impacts of such events from being as severe, for example, by enforcing the installation of water meters.

Elsewhere in the world, drought is an increasingly worrying trend. In the south-west USA there is a mismatch between a rising population and a drying climate. Water demand is often excessive and wasteful.

The most rapidly growing states of the USA are in the South West (see Figure 7). Precipitation here is often low (often less than 400 mm per annum) and summer temperatures high. Evidence is emerging that the climate is drying. 2002 was Colorado's driest year for 108 years.

Management of water resources needs to take into account a number of issues.

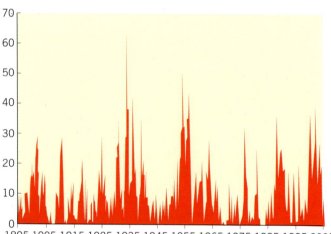

▲ **Figure 8:** Drought in the USA since 1895: percentage area of the country 'in severe and extreme drought'.

Most of the water supply for the South West comes from melting snow during the spring and early summer. However, changes in storm tracks, in the proportion of precipitation that falls as snow, and in seasonality, can result in earlier snow melt, diminished snowpack, increased evaporative losses, and lower runoff. Even the most optimistic climate models for the second half of this century suggest that 30 to 70% of the snowpack will disappear as climate changes. This translates to reduced river levels and less water being available for storage in the network of western reservoirs.

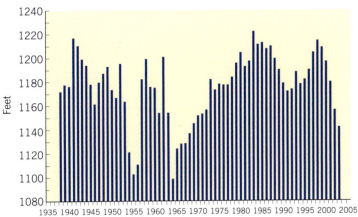

▲ Figure 9: August water levels in Lake Mead.

The largest river basin in the South West is the Colorado River Basin. When filled to capacity, its reservoirs can store 75 million megalitres of water. This amounts to about a four-year supply at current consumption rates. Lake Mead, formed when the Hoover Dam was built across the Colorado River in 1935, is the largest of the reservoirs. But its levels have fallen significantly in recent years (see Figure 9). The Colorado River Basin is already two degrees warmer than it was in 1976 and it would be foolhardy to imagine that the next 50 years will resemble the last 50.

Cities such as Las Vegas are not only growing fast but are also amongst the heaviest water consumers in the world. Golf courses, swimming pools and extravagant water shows create world-record-breaking levels of consumption of up to 900 litres of water per person per day for households in Las Vegas. Historically, agriculture in the south-west USA has adapted to drought, with very low numbers of livestock farmed extensively, but in some regions the growth of animal-fattening farms has placed a further strain on water resources. Most of the region's water comes from rivers such as the Colorado. That is now fully used. The other source is groundwater. Unfortunately the largest aquifer, the Ogallala aquifer, is a 'fossil' aquifer, an enormous underground reserve that was created in the last Ice Age. As such, it is a non-renewable resource, and water levels are falling in most of the region.

▲ Figure 10: An irrigated golf course on the fringes of Las Vegas.

To date, the 'management' of this mismatch between demand and supply has largely involved seeking new supplies of water and applying some short-term restrictions, including:

• In Salt Lake City, if you spray, you pay. Residents who do not conserve water could face up to $30 more a month in water fees than their neighbours.
• The city of Phoenix saves over 750 million litres of water each year by delaying planting and purposefully under-seeding golf-course fairways. City officials have also ordered the shutting off of fountains and misting systems and installed more efficient plumbing fixtures.
• Residents living on a canyon or near an open space are asked to plant fire-resistant shrubbery, which typically requires very little water.
• In El Paso, water restrictions allow outdoor watering for only 2 hours, on one designated day a week, before 9 a.m. and after 7 p.m.

- Personal vehicles may be washed at the owner's home – on the designated watering day only – with a bucket or a hose equipped with a positive shut-off nozzle, but not between the hours of 10 a.m. and 6 p.m., and not on Mondays.

More radical solutions are not yet on the agenda of most political leaders – although they are on the academic agenda. In Europe an increasing awareness of the risks of drought, stimulated in part by the 2003 heatwave, has led to the development of sophisticated techniques for monitoring drought, such as soil moisture content maps and detailed climate data, such as that available from the European Drought Centre (www.geo.uio.no/edc/).

In other parts of the world, such as Australia, management has looked beyond short-term demand-saving schemes to longer-term planning for coping with the prolonged droughts that may become more common and, of course, coping with a semi-arid climate. Policies include:

- Introducing drought-tolerant crops, some of which will be especially bred to withstand the new drier conditions.
- Using GPS and precision farming systems to identify the best places for sowing seeds and finding those places with accuracy.
- Reducing livestock numbers, replanting trees and reducing ploughing.
- 'Recapturing' water in both urban and rural areas.

Fieldwork

Aim:

To investigate ways of managing and responding to extreme weather events and show how some strategies are more acceptable than others to the general public.

1. Decide which extreme weather events pose a risk to your local environment.
2. Using local records from newspapers, try to calculate the frequency of these events and their recurrence intervals.
3. Examine ways in which these risks have been managed, by conducting interviews with the local authority and using the internet to look at risk-assessment research that they might have conducted.
4. Design and distribute a questionnaire to the public to examine whether there is awareness of both the risks and the policies in place to deal with them.

Risk assessment

This is a low-risk activity, although questionnaires involve some contact and not everyone is willing to answer questions. It is strongly advised that these be conducted by at least two students working together.

Health and safety

Make sure that a responsible adult knows where you are and when you are going to conduct your fieldwork.

Data presentation

A number of statistical tools can be used to assess the level of concern and awareness about potential threats, and also awareness about the policies in place to deal with them. It might also be possible to show differences in awareness according to age, length of time living in the area, geographic proximity to the 'risk' area and other socio-economic variables. These could be shown in tables or graphs.

Conclusion

It is probable that you'll find that awareness is very different from reality. In some cases risks might be exaggerated and in others, they may be underestimated. There will be significant variations according to length of residence.

Evaluation

Think about how you might extend your investigation by looking at other areas of higher (or lower) risk, and assess whether these areas show significant differences in public awareness of risk and in judgement of the management schemes in place.

Summary

Having studied this chapter, and, in particular the case studies of management of the New Orleans floods after Hurricane Katrina and the drought in the South West of the USA, you will now be able to discuss these ideas and concepts and provide located examples of them:

- Different ways of managing extreme weather events and evaluating the success of these management strategies.
- Short-term and long-term strategies for responding to the threat of extreme weather events.
- The use of technology to improve the forecasting of events so as to help communities to be prepared for them.
    - The management of drought, through changes to the physical environment and through social, economic and political responses.

MCQ

Exam practice

Study the figures, right.

(a) Briefly describe the sequence of weather shown, and say why it led to an extreme weather event. [10]

(b) Using your fieldwork and research experience, describe how you would record some of the results shown in the figure below, and how they might help you to analyse the immediate impact of an extreme weather event in your local area. [15]

(c) With reference to **any** extreme weather hazard suggest reasons why its impacts can vary in their intensity in different parts of the world. [10]

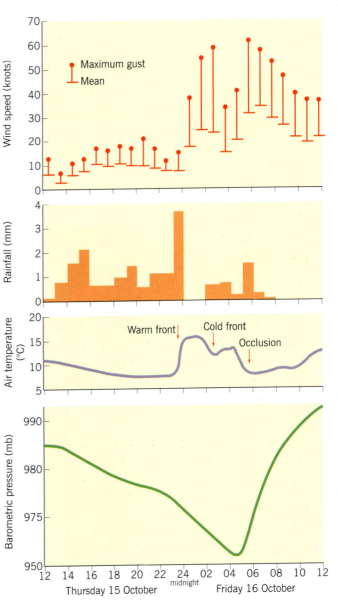

CHAPTER 19 Why is the coastal zone so favoured for development?

Key terms

Cretaceous
Geomorphology
Jurassic
Lithology
Succession
Triassic

Learning objectives

After studying this chapter, you will be able to discuss these ideas and concepts and provide located examples of them:

- The variety of different coastal environments and their vulnerability.
- The range of factors that have encouraged population growth in more accessible coastal environments.
- The economic potential of coastal locations for fishing, recreation and tourism, and for industrial and port development.

Defining the coastal zone

People have always lived by – and used – the coast. The coastal zone is one of the world's most densely populated areas, yet it is also an area of considerable environmental value which can be vulnerable to human activity and to natural processes. This interface between land and sea provides agricultural land and fisheries, ports and harbours, leisure and recreation, and locations for docks, shipbuilding, trade, and the oil industry. Figure 2 lists some coastal features, their uses and examples of their locations.

▶ **Figure 1:** An aerial view of the coastline of Plymouth, Devon. Notice how many different activities are taking place.

Coastal feature	Human activity	Examples
Upland coastlines with sheltered inlets and natural harbours	Ports and harbours for fishing, sailing	Hong Kong, Portsmouth, Poole
Estuaries and their hinterlands	Large industrial and port development	Rotterdam, Shanghai
Coastal ecosystems	Fragile environments and food resources	The Sundarbans in India, Spurn Head
Beaches and dunes	Recreation and tourism	Florida, Blackpool, Camber Sands
River floodplains, deltas and inshore areas	Farming and fishing, nature conservation	Cairo – Nile delta, Louisiana, USA
Cliffs, stacks and other geological features	Attractive coastal scenery	Dorset's Jurassic Coast

▲ Figure 2: Some coastal features and their uses.

The coastal zone includes quite a wide band of sea and land. The land is affected by the tides for some distance inland; the River Thames, for example, is tidal as far as Teddington Lock, 90 km upstream of where its estuary meets the sea, and has a tidal rise and fall of 7 metres at London Bridge. On the seaward side, the low water mark indicates the lowest point that is exposed to the air at low tide but offshore features such as tidal flats may also be exposed at this time. Figure 3 shows the names of the different parts of the coastal zone.

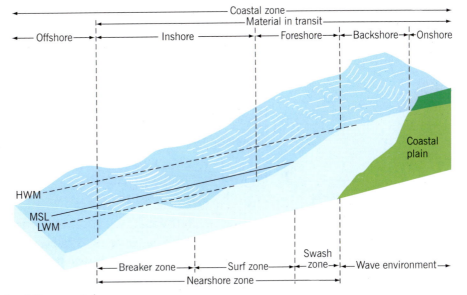

▲ Figure 3: The subdivisions of the coastal zone.

The coastal climate, anywhere in the world, differs from the climate further inland. This is because water's specific heat capacity is much higher than land's: water takes more heat energy (and therefore more time) to warm up, but it also takes much longer to cool down than land. Land temperatures therefore change much more rapidly than sea temperatures and have a much greater range (depending on the latitude). Local climates are strongly influenced by their proximity to the sea, so that coasts are generally kept warmer than inland areas in winter and kept cooler than them in summer. Coastal climates are more equable, that is, they do not vary as much as the climate further inland.

Coasts also tend to be flatter and possess more fertile land, often because here rivers flow across their floodplains and out to sea. Such land has always attracted settlement, which is why many of these areas are now densely built upon. The coastal zone also contains some of the world's most fragile and valuable ecosystems, such as mangrove swamps and saltmarshes.

The majority of the world's major cities are located at the coast, and many continue to attract in-migration. Many cities began as small settlements around harbours and estuaries which provided natural shelter for sailing ships and suitable land for docks.

These settlements have become large cities as all the functions necessary to support the shipping trade – warehousing, processing, and commerce – have developed and the docks have grown to accommodate larger ships. The suitability of some ports has changed over time as the nature of shipping has changed. London Docks, for example, thrived for centuries but, when goods started to be shipped in containers, the docks were unable to take the new larger ships, and new docks had to be developed downstream at Tilbury.

The principal UK container ports are at Felixstowe, Southampton, Thamesport (located on the River Medway where it flows into the Thames estuary), Tilbury and Liverpool. These handle nearly all the UK's deep-sea container ships and some 'short-sea' shipping (that is, short journeys). Containers handled at other ports like Hull, Tees, Immingham, and Belfast are nearly all short-sea or coastal movements. Felixstowe is by far the UK's busiest port (but is not as big as Rotterdam, Hamburg or Antwerp).

Rotterdam – the world's busiest port – is noted for its oil trading. Some ports have specialised in the import of crude oil, refining, and export of fuels. Other coastal sites have been developed as oil terminals, bringing oil onshore, such as those serving the North Sea platforms as at Cruden Bay in Scotland. There are also gas terminals, like those at Easington (just north of Spurn Head in Yorkshire) or Bacton in Norfolk. Nuclear power stations are also usually located near the sea, as at Dungeness in Kent. Coastal location gives access to cooling water, but sparsely populated coastal areas are also chosen for safety reasons.

While some ports handle the large volume of exported and imported goods, others such as Southampton handle the major ocean-going liners for holiday cruises, or the ferries that connect the UK with the rest of Europe, including Ireland. Smaller harbours and purpose-built marinas provide moorings for yachts and other pleasure boats. Cowes, for example, on the Isle of Wight hosts a major annual regatta. Other coastal settlements grew around the fishing industry, although now, as fish stocks have been depleted by over-fishing, the industry has declined. One such port, Grimsby, is undergoing regeneration to provide a modern fish-processing business park, a new fish market, and a seafood institute offering degree-level courses.

Mudflats provide a rich habitat for shellfish, such as cockles, providing a good harvest for people – and an essential food source for wading birds and wildfowl. Mudflats are in the inter-tidal zone, covered by the sea at high tide and uncovered at low tide, and formed by the deposition of silts, clays and organic matter. The Wash and Morecombe Bay are the largest areas of inter-tidal mudflats in the UK.

In south-east Asia, mangrove swamps are being cleared to make way for prawn fisheries, which are being developed in response to the growing popularity of prawns around the world. The fisheries are an important income source for the local people but their development is often environmentally damaging. Tropical environments are also increasingly pressured by the demands of tourism.

Coral reefs are particularly vulnerable: people use reefs as sources of food, for marine souvenirs and aquarium fish, and as sites for sub-aqua diving and reef walking. Tourism and recreation can have a severe impact as walking on coral reefs kills the organisms. Coral reefs are also vulnerable to pollution from sewage and industry, and oil from shipping, and from sea-level rise and rising water temperatures, due to global warming.

Taking it further

Look up maps of seaports and energy installations in Britain in a school atlas and note the volumes of trade and the locations of oil refineries, gas terminals, nuclear and other power stations. Find a map of fishing around the British Isles, and notice the difference in terms of types and quantities caught.

Key terms

Succession is a sequence of vegetation changes through which an ecosystem evolves.

Taking it further

To learn more about succession read 'Sorting out succession' on your Student CD-ROM.

Case study: Estuaries, inter-tidal mudflats and saltmarshes

Estuaries are the flooded lower courses of river valleys where the mixing of sea and freshwater takes place. Non-tidal currents are caused by the mixing of fresh and salt water because they have different densities. Estuaries provide sheltered environments where deposition of fine river sediment occurs, and the incoming tide moves sediment into the estuary, building up extensive tidal flats and salt marshes. The processes operating in estuaries are mainly controlled by the interaction of tidal and non-tidal currents.

Mudflats and salt marshes form in the more sheltered parts of estuaries, such as behind spits, as the high tide carries in sediment and deposits it where the velocity decreases; vegetation then helps to trap the sediment forming inter-tidal mudflats. These are water-logged, thus excluding oxygen, and have a high pH due their salt content. Only plants that can tolerate being covered by salt water – 'halophytes' – can survive. The first plants to colonise new mud flats, the algae, eel grass and *Salicornia*, can survive being submerged for most of the day.

More mud and silt is trapped by these plants, raising the level of the mudflats so that their surface is exposed for longer periods between tides. This encourages different vegetation to invade, with *Spartina* often becoming a dominant species. As the succession continues, a sward zone develops which may only be inundated for about an hour at high tide. This may be very saline as sea water evaporates from hollows in the mud, sometimes forming saltpans where very little vegetation can survive.

As each tide ebbs (retreats), water drains into creeks that dissect the mudflats. The upper sward zone may only be covered by the highest tides, so *Juncus* and rushes can grow. Further inland, non-halophytic species are able to colonise because, without tidal inundation, the salt levels are reduced. Mudflats and salt marshes are very fertile ecosystems and they are important feeding grounds for the many wildfowl and waders who eat the molluscs and worms that inhabit the mud.

Case study: Mangrove swamps and coral reefs

Mangroves are composed of low trees and shrubs, with dense root systems that grow in swampy muddy waters in the marginal tidal zones between tropical sea and land. They are adapted to tidal areas as their thick waxy leaves are able to conserve water by reducing transpiration during low tides, and their anchor roots support them in the mudflats. The plants are salt-tolerant halophytes and prefer the brackish water.

Much like coral reefs, mangrove swamps suffer threats from land-based development causing pollution and siltation. Half the world's mangrove swamps have been lost in the last 50 years. The forests are used for building and fuel wood and have been cleared in places to make way for prawn fisheries. It is estimated that 1 million hectares are lost each year.

The clearance of mangroves leads to the destruction of breeding grounds for fish and also removes a natural line of defence against storm surges and tsunamis. Sometimes they are found together with coral reefs, the mangroves filtering out sediment that would harm the coral and the reef absorbing wave energy that would damage the mangroves. This is described as a 'symbiotic' relationship.

The world's largest coral reef is the Great Barrier Reef in Australia, which is 1,500 km long, but actually comprises 2,900 different reefs. Coral reefs are often small and separated from each other, and they are found in three different forms: fringing reefs, barrier reefs and atolls. Charles Darwin (of evolution theory fame) recognised these three forms and suggested that they represented different stages in a sequence, as shown in Figure 4.

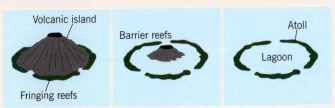

◀ **Figure 4:** The evolution of coral reefs and atolls according to Darwinian theory. The volcanic rock is gradually eroded, leaving the reefs.

Case study: Mangrove swamps and coral reefs (continued)

Different physical environments create different coral communities so reefs show vertical and horizontal zonation. Single-celled algae (zooxanthellae) provide sugar and nutrients to coral cells, while the coral polyps give them shelter and a source of carbon dioxide – another symbiotic relationship. Coral reefs are one of the most productive ecosystems, with a rapid growth rate due to nutrient inputs from sources such as river runoff, ocean up-welling and very efficient recycling. But sudden large inputs of sediment can damage reefs as the corals filter the water for their food.

A living reef that grows faster than it is eroded provides a natural barrier along coasts, dissipating wave energy and creating a low-energy environment near the shore where sea grass and mangrove swamps can flourish. But it is a very fragile ecosystem, so any over-exploitation can affect the entire community structure.

Taking it further

To investigate landforms around the British coastline read 'Drawing coastal landforms' on your Student CD-ROM.

Natural processes create a variety of valuable coastal environments, which can be put under pressure when they are developed. Sand dunes, for example, are depositional landforms created onshore in the coastal zone. Over time they are inhabited by plants and animals that create a whole series of specialised ecosystems (a succession). But they are popular destinations for recreation and can be damaged. The largest sand dune system in Europe, the 100 metre-high Dune du Pyla in south-west France, for example, has become a victim of its own success. Steps have had to be constructed for all the people who want to climb to the top, to prevent them from eroding the dune away.

Case study: The development of sand dunes

The conditions required for sand dunes to form are wide, low-gradient beaches, strong onshore winds, a supply of sand (20% from the foreshore, 80% from the backshore), and obstacles, such as driftwood or vegetation, to trap the sand. At low tide, sand is dried and blown further onshore until it is beyond the reach of the sea. The sand grains are moved mainly by the process of 'saltation' which is an aeolian (wind-driven) process. Onshore winds roll and saltate sand particles up the beach, where they collect behind boulders, driftwood, vegetation and litter, beyond the high tide line.

Mounds of sand begin to build up to form 'embryo dunes' at the back of the foreshore. The onshore winds continue blowing the sand grains inland so a continuous dune belt develops called the 'fore dune' (or 'yellow dune'). The fore dune is 'mobile' because the sand is still being moved. Behind the fore dune, the dunes become more vegetated and less mobile; these are described as 'fixed dunes' (or 'grey dunes'). Behind them are the oldest dunes, covered with mature soil and vegetation; these are the 'wasting dunes'. In places there may be 'blow-outs' – hollows in the dunes caused by vegetation being damaged and destroyed by:

- Excessive grazing by rabbits, goats or horses
- Other recreational activities such as barbecues
- Past uses such as defence training or sand extraction.
- Trampling by visitors
- Accidental fires

Taking it further

To learn more about sand dunes read 'The sand dune ecosystem' on your Student CD-ROM.

Tourism pressure on sandy beaches has been a feature of the coastal zone ever since the first trains enabled easy access. Blackpool Pleasure Beach is the UK's most visited tourist attraction, and other seaside resorts in the top twenty attractions are at Southend, Southport, Clacton and Great Yarmouth. Many seaside resorts boast piers as central attractions. Several stretches of coastline are popular with walkers, and one, the Pembrokeshire Coast, is a National Park to protect its stunning scenery and rich wildlife. Organisations such as English Heritage and the National Trust work to conserve the British coastline, recognising its ecological, heritage and aesthetic value.

Beach huts, such as at Mudeford Spit at Hengistbury Head in Dorset have become very popular, and can sell for very high prices. Seaside or riverside locations are very popular locations and redundant wharves and warehouses have been redeveloped as luxury apartments.

The attraction of warmer and more reliable weather has made foreign destinations more popular than many British resorts. The Spanish 'Costas' have developed since the 1970s and package holidays and cheap flights have enabled many people to enjoy the sun, sand and sangria they offer. More recently, longer haul destinations such as Florida, the Caribbean or Hawaii have become more accessible.

The geology of the coastline is the dominant factor in determining its shape and the striking landscapes that attract tourists, whether they come to study the coastal features or simply to admire the view. Coastal resorts such as Lyme Regis, famous for the fossils to be found in its cliffs, have grown to accommodate tourism.

Many stunning coastal landscapes are the result of the combination of marine weathering and erosion processes and the geological formation of the land. The vulnerability of the coastline to erosion is determined by the type of rock, its lithology and structure, and the angle and direction in which it lies. Together these factors will determine cliff development (Figure 6).

▲ **Figure 5:** Dramatic scenery by the sea: holiday apartments on the Spanish coast.

◀ **Figure 6:** Cliff morphology and geological structure.

a Uniform horizontal strata produce steep cliffs

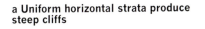

— — Bedding planes

b Rocks dip gently seawards with near-vertical joints

Joints opened by weathering and pressure release

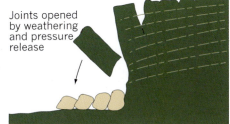

c Steep seaward dip

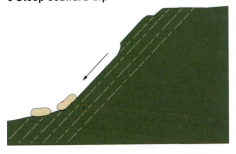

d Rocks dip inland producing a stable, steep cliff profile

e Rocks dip inland but with well-developed joints at right angles to bedding planes

Joints act as slide planes

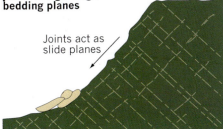

f Slope-over-wall cliffs

Periglacial slope

Periglacial solifluction deposit (head)

Marine cliff

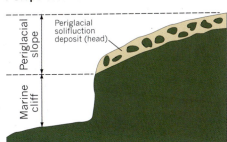

▲ **Figure 7:** An impressive arch in the chalk cliffs at Selwicks Bay, Flamborough.

In Figure 7, the bedding planes of the chalk can be clearly seen. They are the horizontal lines in the rocks which show how the chalk deposits – originally the remains of many cretaceous micro-organisms – were deposited in layers at the bottom of the sea. These bedding planes, and other faults (cracks) within rocks, form lines of weakness which are vulnerable to weathering processes.

Some types of rock are much more easily eroded than others. On the Holderness Coast in Yorkshire, the cliffs are made of glacial till. (This used to be called 'boulder clay' which described it well, as it is a mix of materials – from huge boulders to very fine clays – which were deposited by the ice as it retreated over 13,000 years ago). This material is unconsolidated and very easily eroded so this coastline is rapidly retreating, often by several metres per year. At Land's End, by comparison, the hard granite cliffs are much more resistant to erosion, receding by barely a millimetre a year. Limestone produces some of the most dramatic coastal landscapes, with stumps and stacks, arches and caves, such as at Flamborough Head in Yorkshire (Figure 7) or the Needles on the Isle of Wight.

In the past, coastal rocks were easily accessible for quarrying. Ironstone, for example, was extracted in the nineteenth century from behind the cliffs at Hengistbury Head in Dorset. In Devon, shingle was removed from the shingle banks just offshore of the village of Hallsands. But these banks had protected the coastline from marine erosion, and when a bad storm struck on 26 January 1917, half the village was swept away by the waves.

Now coastal geomorphologists have a better understanding of coastal processes and we have learned to value our coastline, so such mistakes are less likely to be made. Geological features produce some of the most stunning landscapes – that at Lulworth Cove in Dorset is part of a UN World Heritage Site protecting 95 miles of Cretaceous, Jurassic, and Triassic coastline in Dorset and East Devon (see Figure 8). Parts of this coast and countryside have also been designated Areas of Outstanding Natural Beauty (AONB) or Sites of Special Scientific Interest (SSSI), recognising their geological, ecological and aesthetic value.

► **Figure 8:** Durdle Door – one of the more dramatic features on the Dorset coastline.

Fieldwork exercise: Coastal land use

Aim:
To carry out a land use survey of a coastal resort.

Method:
1. Decide on your survey area — the sea front may be sufficient.
2. Obtain a good large-scale street map and make several larger copies of it (photocopies will do) to prepare your base map.
3. Visit the entire study area and mark in the ground level use of every building and structure (an extension of this research might be to survey also the use of other storeys).
4. Take photographs to illustrate the range of land uses you find.
5. Obtain maps of past land use - these should be available online or in a local reference library. Old newspapers and census data will also be useful. You may be able to use satellite images too but note the date of any satellite image that you use as some are several years out of date.

Data interpretation:
The best way to interpret all the information you collect is to draw a series of maps. Start with your survey results and devise a key to categorise the different types of land use. Then, using one of your photocopied street maps, shade your map accordingly. You can establish previous land use at convenient dates from the old maps and other archive material you have obtained from the library and internet by colouring another base map using the same categories.

Data analysis:
It may be possible to make a quantitative assessment of the area devoted to each type of land use. For this you will need a small grid — you could draw one, preferably to a scale that fits your map such as square metres, onto a sheet of acetate (use a permanent OHT pen, non-permanent pen will smudge too easily). Place the grid over your land use map and count the number of grid squares for each land use category. From this you could work out percentages of the total area of land in use and draw pie charts or proportional bar graphs to compare land use at different points in time.

Alternatively, you could describe what is shown on your maps — possibly there may be clusters of similar types of use, or some uses may be more central than others — to complete a qualitative analysis. Your photographs will be useful here: annotate them to draw attention to significant features, perhaps the age of the building or how long the business has been established, or the quality of the building.

Summary

This chapter has identified many of the human activities that take place in the coastal zone. It has examined the nature of some of the fragile ecosystems found in this zone, notably mudflats and saltmarshes, sand dunes, mangrove swamps and coral reefs, showing how human activities can threaten these ecosystems. The geology of the coastline and the consequent landforms have also been studied, together with some of the opportunities and threats that these present for people.

Having studied this chapter, you should now be able to discuss these ideas and concepts and provide located examples of them:

• The variety of different coastal environments and their vulnerability.
• The range of factors that have encouraged population growth in more accessible coastal environments.
   • The economic potential of coastal locations for fishing, recreation and tourism, and for industrial and port development.

MCQ

To try an exam question using what you have learned in this chapter, turn to page 201.

CHAPTER 20 How do various coastal developments create competition and conflict? How can these pressures be resolved?

Learning objectives

After studying this chapter, you will be able to discuss these ideas and concepts and provide located examples of them:
- Competition for space in the coastal zone puts pressure on coastal environments, and distinctive patterns of land use develop as a consequence of this competition.
- There are economic benefits and environmental costs to coastal development, which influence the success of development and involve the views of different stakeholders and their conflicting needs.
- Conservation is both one of the competing stakeholders and a mechanism for managing potential conflict.

Competition for space

There is a wide variety of environments in the coastal zone, including rocky cliffs, sandy beaches, dense forests, deep inlets and extensive mud flats. Each attracts a range of different users, some of whom may be in conflict. Different stakeholders use different parts of the coastal zone. Competing land uses in the backshore zone include shipping ports and fishing harbours, marinas, housing, industry, quarrying, commerce, retailing, agriculture, nature reserves, tourism and recreation.

Figure 2 shows how a 'conflict matrix' of these land uses might look. You can see that commerce is the most compatible land use, but as this involves functions like administration and finance many, if not all, of the other stakeholders need to use these services. Quarrying, on the other hand, is the least compatible.

◀ Figure 1: This rocky shoreline has been covered in oil, following a spill from a tanker. The birds that feed upon the shellfish to be found in the rock pools have also been covered in the oil, and many of them will die.

x indicates that uses are not compatible	Shipping ports	Fishing harbours	Marinas	Housing	Industry	Quarrying	Commerce	Retailing	Agriculture	Nature reserves	Tourism	Recreation
Shipping ports	▨		x	x				x	x	x		x
Fishing harbours		▨				x			x	x	x	x
Marinas	x		▨		x	x			x	x		
Housing	x			▨	x	x			x	x	x	x
Industry			x	x	▨				x	x	x	x
Quarrying		x	x	x		▨	x	x	x	x	x	x
Commerce						x	▨		x	x		
Retailing	x					x		▨	x	x		
Agriculture	x	x	x	x	x	x	x	x	▨			
Nature reserves	x	x	x	x	x	x	x	x		▨	x	
Tourism		x		x	x	x				x	▨	
Recreation	x	x		x	x	x						▨

▲ Figure 2: A conflict matrix of backshore zone users.

Perhaps the most vulnerable land use is that involving nature reserves, which might include coastline that has significant aesthetic, historical, archaeological, or geological value. Ecosystems and the specific flora and fauna that inhabit them are the most fragile environments, and there is a range of conservation legislation designed to protect them. Nature can be cruel when tsunamis or storm surges occur (see Chapter 21) but sometimes accidents can happen and stretches of coastline can be badly damaged, especially when oil tankers run aground.

Taking it further

Other notable oil tanker spills have included the Torrey Canyon and the Amoco Cadiz. Research the details and consequences of these and other such events.

Case study: The *Exxon Valdez* oil spill

On 24 March 1989, an oil tanker, the *Exxon Valdez*, ran aground in Prince William Sound in Alaska. It was carrying 1.2 million barrels of crude oil, of which 240,000 were spilled (one barrel is approximately 160 litres). Within a week, the oil had spread out over 2,300 km² of water and affected 1,750 km of coast. Eventually it spread out over 25,000 km² of offshore and coastal waters, home to 600,000 sea birds. At the time there was a lot of media coverage, with emotive pictures of dead and dying birds covered in oil. It is thought that between 100,000 and 300,000 birds did die. The way in which the oil was spilled and then spread meant that its impact varied. In small amounts, the sea can break up the oil (a process known as emulsifying) and some of the oil evaporates – probably about a third in this instance. Also, chemicals were used to clean up the oil – nitrogen fertiliser was used to speed up the biodegradation by micro-organisms. In retrospect, the impact of this event on the fragile tundra ecosystem is still debated by marine scientists; but in time the coastline does recover from such accidents.

Pollution is one of the most damaging threats to wildlife. In many parts of the world effluent from industry, raw sewage from urban settlement, agricultural chemicals and the increased sediment from land disturbance can severely damage or even destroy coastal ecosystems. In tropical regions, mangrove forests are at risk from the development of prawn fisheries, and coral reefs are vulnerable to a range of human activities and their consequences, including tourism and urban runoff. In temperate regions, coastal ecosystems are threatened by agriculture and fisheries, as well as urban development.

Case study: Damage to coral reefs

Coral reefs are threatened by sediment in runoff, which is increased by deforestation, mining and building work. As most reefs are located in developing regions, such as south east Asia, the pressure for land clearance and urban development is significant.

Rapid urbanisation, when the provision of infrastructure often lags behind the development of housing, can also cause an increase in raw sewage output. This increases the nutrient content of coastal waters, encouraging the growth of plankton which in turn leads to a population explosion in the crown-of-thorns starfish which graze on the coral. Other direct anthropogenic (human-induced) impacts on coral include its removal (for souvenirs or to make cement), blast fishing, where dynamite is used to stun the fish making them easier to catch, and ships' anchors dragging on to the reefs.

Global warming is also threatening the coral. Tropical reefs grow where sea temperatures are between 20 °C and 30 °C, but as the oceans are heated, the corals are damaged and this is thought to be a cause of bleaching and death. Rising sea levels may also outstrip the corals' rate of growth, submerging them below their preferred depth of up to 40 metres.

Case study: The proposed Severn Barrage

The current pressure to establish sustainable energy resources has renewed interest in the proposal to build a barrage across the Severn Estuary (see Figure 3), and in January 2008 the government set up a feasibility study. The barrage could supply up to 5% of the UK's energy demand by harnessing the power of the tides, using a hydro-electric dam. The Severn Estuary is a particularly effective location because it has a tidal range of 13 metres – the second highest in the world.

The estuary supports important habitats and has a unique ecology. The construction of a barrage would have significant impacts on wildlife, flood protection, navigation, and the landscape. The estuary contains mudflats, saltmarshes, rocky islands and food that support some 65,000 birds in winter. The Royal Society for the Protection of Birds (RSPB) says that a barrage could put at risk thousands of waders and wildfowl, as well as migratory fish species, such as salmon and sea trout.

The proposed barrage may contravene current legal protection as the species and habitats are subject to EU 'Habitats and Birds Directives' and the 'Ramsar Convention' (see Figure 10 on page 177). It would also affect shipping access to upstream ports, and water quality would be affected because sediment transfer could be interrupted. Areas of the mudflats that are exposed as the tide goes out would be inundated for longer, as the water is held back. This will not only restrict times for feeding for the waders and wildfowl but will also change the habitat of the bivalves, shrimps and worms upon which they feed.

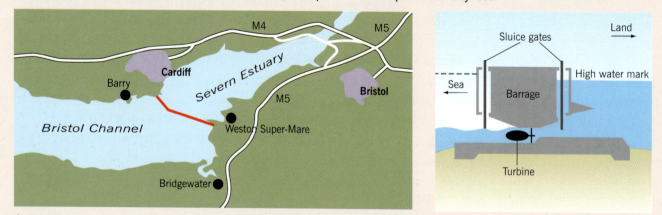

▲ **Figure 3:** The location of the proposed Severn barrage (left) and how tidal power works (right). As the tide comes in, sea water passes through the barrage to the landward side. At high tide, the sluice gates are shut, trapping water in the estuary. After the tide has receded on the seaward side of the barrage, the sluice gates are opened. The water flows through the barrage, driving the turbines and generating power. Power could be generated by the incoming tide as well, but this can affect the efficiency and economics of the project.

Land use in the coastal zone

The shoreline distorts typical patterns of urban land use. Classic patterns of urban structure place the Central Business District (CBD), with the main business and retail functions, at the centre, surrounded by rings of neighbourhoods of different quality and wedges of industry, transport, and high-class residences.

The CBD of a coastal settlement is generally found on or running inland from the coast, with major business, tourist accommodation and high-class residential property built along the sea front, either side of the core.

Case study: Brighton and Hove

The main road from London (A23) runs right through the city centre, parallel to the railway, past the museum and art gallery, theatre and Royal Pavilion to the sea front (and the Palace Pier continues on the same line out to sea). There has been a settlement here for at least 1,000 years, but Brighton grew as a health resort in the eighteenth century and became a popular destination for day trippers from London when the railway was built in 1841.

To the east, along Marine Parade, there are hotels and expensive housing, leading to the Brighton Marina Village, constructed in the 1990s and being expanded with the addition of over 800 new high-rise apartments. Behind this is a golf course, adjacent to agricultural land marking the boundary of the urban area.

To the west along the sea front, past the crumbling remains of West Pier which was destroyed by fire, there is the Brighton Conference Centre and the principal hotels, such as the Grand, making the most of the sea view. The frontage between the two piers contains bars, restaurants, nightclubs and amusement arcades; behind them are 'the Lanes', an area of retail, leisure and residential property, along a cluster of narrow alleyways following the street pattern of the original fishing village. Further west, Brighton merges into Hove, where there are Georgian houses that were built in a grid of streets running north from the sea front.

Behind this packed coastline is a series of housing estates, bounded by a main east–west highway, the A27, which in any inland city would be part of an outer ring road but here just marks the northern boundary of the built-up coastal settlement.

▲ Figure 4: A map of Brighton for tourists, showing some of the attractions of the onshore zone.

Some coastal towns and cities are so short of space that they are having to build out to sea. Brighton's marina is a modest example. Much more extensive examples are found in Hong Kong, where the new Chek Lap Kok airport was built on 12 km² of reclaimed land between two islands, and in the Netherlands, where whole islands of new land (polders) have been built. The Netherlands is one of the most densely populated countries in the world, and to gain extra land a barrage was built across the Zuider Zee (now called the Ijsselmeer) and 2,500 km² of polders were constructed, primarily for agricultural use.

Key terms

Polder: Dutch term for a flat tract of land that has been reclaimed from the sea, lakes or rivers by building dykes and draining. Polders are maintained by pumping.

▲ **Figure 5:** The Ijsselmeer, showing the location of the polders.

▶ **Figure 6:** Building Dubai out into the Arabian Gulf.

There is significant pressure on some sections of urbanised coastline for waterside residential property. One way of producing more coastline is to build artificial islands, as is being done in Dubai, on the north-eastern tip of the Arabian Peninsula. Dubai is one of the fastest-growing cities in the world, and is currently spreading out into the Arabian Gulf by building four giant reclaimed island archipelagos, which form the shapes of three palm trees and a map of the world.

Major cities are often located at the mouths of rivers, such as Rotterdam at the mouth of the Rhine, or Marseilles at the mouth of the Rhone. Here industrial land uses may compete with residential and commercial uses. In some places, past industry and port facilities have been redeveloped, bringing derelict marine, commercial and industrial buildings back into use and accommodating new stakeholders.

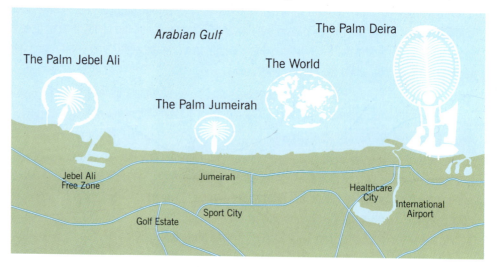

Rural coastlines and shingle beaches

Rural coastline is also contested. For centuries, farmers have drained marshes and fens, areas that would have been regularly flooded in the past. The Somerset Levels used to be inundated by the high tides from the Severn Estuary, turning settlements like Glastonbury into islands; they have been comprehensively drained in the last 200 years to produce valuable arable and pastoral land. In this way, unique ecosystems have been irrevocably altered.

Case study: Albert Dock, Merseyside

Redevelopment was undertaken on the Albert Dock in the early 1980s, under the Merseyside Urban Development Corporation. Within this, the Albert Dock Company was set up to bring about the redevelopment of the dock to create a cosmopolitan quarter as the flagship for the regeneration of all Liverpool's docklands. It is now a very popular heritage attraction, with many speciality shops and coster carts, bars, restaurants and cafés alongside the major attractions, including the Merseyside Maritime Museum, the Beatles Story, Tate Liverpool and Granada TV Studios.

Initially, the area was very popular with visitors but, perhaps suffering competition from other such regeneration schemes, visitor numbers declined by the end of the century, demonstrating that regeneration is an ongoing process, not a one-off scheme. The whole area received a boost, however, when Liverpool was named European Capital of Culture for 2008.

Shingle beaches fringe much of the British coast and are threatened by development pressures, yet they often act as an effective natural form of flood defence and form a unique habitat which is home to a range of rare insects, bees, plants, and birds such as gulls, terns and waders. Shingle beaches are defined as those with sediments between 2 mm and 200 mm in diameter, deposited above the high water mark. Such beaches are continually losing and gaining pebbles, as storms shift the sediment. The stones heat up by day and cool at night, and water drains easily through them creating desert-like conditions. They are colonised by vegetation that is specially adapted to the harsh, dry and salty conditions, such as bright yellow biting stonecrop, purple and yellow bittersweet, red valerian, and sea holly.

Most shingle beaches are in eastern England and along the Channel coast, and the largest is at Dungeness in Kent. They are valuable economically, socially, and environmentally, but almost half are in poor and declining condition. They are threatened by the industry, quarrying, power stations, and housing that encroach on the shingle and, ironically, one of the greatest threats is coastal defence works, which alter the sediment transfer patterns. There is also pressure from recreational uses like walking and off-road driving, and the invasion of alien plants escaping from dumped garden waste. Rising sea-level is adding to all of these problems.

▲ Figure 7: Shingle being collected before being moved to the other side of Dungeness.

Taking it further

To learn more about shingle beaches read 'Shingle foreshore communities' on your Student CD-ROM.

Case study: Dungeness, Kent

Dungeness is a 38 km stretch of coastline in Kent and East Sussex around two sides of a triangular-shaped cuspate foreland. It contains a classic sequence of shingle beaches, totalling about 1,600 hectares of exposed shingle – one of the largest expanses of shingle in the world. The foreland has evolved since the last ice age as sediment, mostly flint eroded from chalk, was transported eastwards by longshore drift, as the sea level rose. Flint is a hard, silica-rich rock which occurs as seams within the Upper Cretaceous chalk of southern England. The area now occupied by Romney Marsh was once a wide, open coastal inlet, which gradually filled with fluvial sediment and was dammed first by spits and then by the mass of shingle, creating the cuspate foreland. Erosion of the western edge continues today but beach material is now constantly replenished with shingle from the eastern side to protect the nuclear power station (see Figure 8).

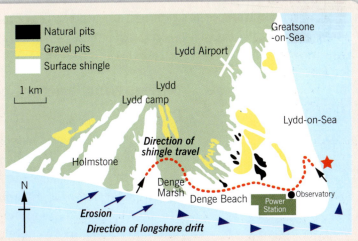

▲ Figure 8: Dungeness, showing the marine processes operating and some of the main land uses. The red star shows where shingle is continuously being excavated, before being transported by a fleet of lorries from the east to the west (as shown by the dotted line) to replenish the eroding south-western shoreline.

Case study: Dungeness, Kent (continued)

Dungeness has been a contested environment for centuries, because of its location. Now there is a small village here, plus two nuclear power stations, the world's smallest public railway, and an important ecological site. Dungeness village is a dispersed collection of dwellings rather than a village, with huts, wooden sheds, corrugated iron constructions and some brick-built homes apparently randomly located over the shingle. Many of the homes are lived in by fishermen.

▲ Figure 9: The nuclear power stations and one of the lighthouses on Dungeness.

The foreland is of international importance because of its geomorphology, plant and invertebrate communities and birdlife, and has been designated an NNR, SPA and SAC (see Figure 10), and it is proposed as a wetland of international importance under the Ramsar Convention. The area supports over 600 different plants, as well as rare moths, bees, beetles and spiders, some unique to the area.

There are many different stakeholders with social, economic and environmental interests on Dungeness including:

- Wildlife enthusiasts, such as the RSPB and visitors to the Dungeness Bird Observatory, and the increasing number of people running light-traps for moths and recording their results.
- Historians preserving structures, such as the Old Lighthouse which is a Grade II listed building. Two of Dungeness's five lighthouses still survive but only one is now in use, an important reference point for vessels navigating the Dover Straits.
- The Dungeness Lifeboat Station, still needed because of the many ships that run aground or flounder in the Straits.
- Artists displaying their work at the Dungeness Gallery or visitors to the shingle garden of filmmaker Derek Jarman.
- Dungeness B nuclear power station (Dungeness A was decommissioned in 2006) is still supplying electricity – and against this economic interest is the pressure group 'Kent Against a Radioactive Environment'.
- An army cadet camp is based at Lydd and 'the ranges' are used for military training.
- Railways enthusiasts work to maintain the Romney, Hythe and Dymchurch railway, one of the smallest railway lines in the world.
- The Dungeness Residents' Association and the Dungeness (UK) Community Website represent the interests and concerns of local people.
- Dungeness Fish, a family-owned fresh fish supplier has been established in the area for over 150 years.
- Sand and gravel extraction for construction materials provides local employment, but there is concern now that too much has been extracted, affecting groundwater levels and quality (with the risk of saltwater incursion).

Taking it further

To learn more about Dungeness read 'The art of Dungeness' on your Student CD-ROM.

Resolving land use conflicts

Application for planning permission must be made to the local authority for all significant development in the UK. This will be decided upon by the local planning committee to whom any objections can be presented. If a dispute is not settled at this stage, an appeal can be lodged with the Secretary of State for the Environment and a full public enquiry may be held for larger schemes. Two mechanisms are commonly used to assess the advantages and impacts of proposed and existing development; these are cost-benefit analysis (CBA) and environmental impact assessment (EIA). They can be applied at any scale and, in their simplest form, are useful research and fieldwork tools. Local authorities are responsible for strategic planning in their areas and must prepare a Local Development Framework. The coastal zone will be governed by this mechanism but is also subject to specific management strategies overseen by the Department for the Environment, Farming and Rural Affairs who advise the planning authorities.

Conservation in the coastal zone

Specific controls are needed to protect the ecology and the fabric of the coastline because coastal land is used more intensively and many stretches of coast have geological or geomorphological significance or historical or cultural value. There is a range of conservation measures designed to protect the coastline and these are summarised in the table below. There are also charitable organisations such as the National Trust or the RSPB who manage parts of our coastline. National Trust land, which is marked on OS maps, covers over 1,100 km of coastline in Britain – nearly 10% of the total. All the foreshore and inter-tidal areas are actually owned by the Crown but fortunately the Monarch allows unimpeded access!

In the UK there are several statutory organisations with responsibility for conservation. These are:

- Natural England (including the former English Nature and the Countryside Agency)
- The Countryside Council for Wales
- Scottish Natural Heritage
- The Department for Environment (Northern Ireland).

In addition there are European Union Directives concerned with conservation, the International Union for the Conservation of Nature (IUCN), and the United Nations Educational, Scientific and Cultural Organisation (UNESCO) who designate 'World Heritage' sites such as the Jurassic Coast.

▼ Figure 10: Types of conservation area.

Designation	What the designation does	Coastal examples
Area of Outstanding Natural Beauty (AONB)	Gives special protection to especially attractive landscapes, including coastal areas.	North Norfolk, Cornwall and Northumberland.
Environmentally Sensitive Area (ESA)	Encourages the adoption of environmentally friendly farming practices.	The many estuaries of the Essex Coast containing saltmarshes and grazing marsh are within an ESA.
Geological Conservation Review (GCR)	Identifies sites of national and international importance for the earth sciences.	Laggan Bay on the Isle of Mull, where basaltic lava formations may be found.
Heritage Coast	Protects scenically attractive and heavily used coastlines from the pressure of tourism, housing and industrial development.	North Devon coast, protecting the popular sandy beaches.
Local Nature Reserve (LNR)	Conserves places in England with wildlife or geological features that are of special interest locally.	Drigg Dunes and Gullery at Ravenglass in Cumbria.
Marine Nature Reserve (MNR)	Like National Nature Reserves but covers territorial waters.	Strangford Lough, which was designated as Northern Ireland's first MNR.
National Nature Reserve (NNR)	Identifies and protects both geological and biological interests.	Holkham NNR in Norfolk protects a maze of creeks and saltings, and miles of dunes and sand spits.
National Park	Conserves and enhances natural landscape and provides opportunity for outdoor recreation while promoting the well-being of local communities.	The Pembrokeshire Coast National Park covers 412 km of cliffs, beaches, estuaries and inland hills.
Ramsar Convention	Enables sustainable conservation of wetland habitats by international agreement.	The Sundarbans mangrove forest in India and Bangladesh.
Site of Special Scientific Interest (SSSI)	Protects areas of biological, geological and geomorphological importance.	Slapton Sands in Devon is a shingle bar damming a former estuary and enclosing a freshwater lagoon.
Special Area of Conservation (SAC) – an EU 'Habitats Directive'	Protects wildlife areas.	The Dee Estuary in Cheshire.
Special Protection Area (SPA) – an EU 'Birds Directive'	Conserves the habitats of rare, vulnerable and migratory birds.	The Ribble and Alt Estuaries SPA, on the coast of Lancashire and Merseyside.
World Heritage Convention – a UNESCO designation	Identifies a wide range of significant cultural, historical and natural sites.	The Giant's Causeway in Northern Ireland; Liverpool's 'Maritime Mercantile City'.

Case study: The Jurassic Coast

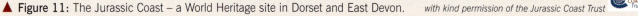

▲ **Figure 11:** The Jurassic Coast – a World Heritage site in Dorset and East Devon.　*with kind permission of the Jurassic Coast Trust*

The Jurassic Coast is England's first natural World Heritage Site. The designation covers 150 km of coastline from East Devon to Dorset, and is designed to protect a geologically significant area. The rocks along this stretch of coast are described as 'a walk though time' as they span three geological periods – the Triassic, Jurassic and Cretaceous – which cover the time from 250 to 65 million years ago. These cliffs are noted for their numerous fossils, such as ammonites, which are gradually uncovered as the coastline erodes.

The World Heritage Site extends from the cliff top to the low water mark, between Exmouth in east Devon and the southern point of Studland Bay in Dorset. It does not include the developed frontages of the towns of Swanage, Weymouth, Lyme Regis, Seaton, Sidmouth, Portland Port and West Bay, all of which have developed as coastal resorts based on fishing villages.

Virtually all of the land in the World Heritage Site has legal protection under UK and European conservation laws.

- There are fourteen SSSIs, and many of the fields inland from the cliffs are designated as SSSIs for their flora and fauna.
- The Axmouth to Lyme Regis Undercliffs and Durlston Country Park are additionally recognised as an NNR.
- The SSSIs encompass sixty-six GCR sites.
- The vegetated sea cliffs are a rare habitat recognised and protected in many places by SAC status.
- The Fleet Lagoon behind Chesil Beach and the Exe Estuary are protected as Ramsar sites.
- Most of the World Heritage Site also lies within the East Devon AONB and the Dorset AONB. These two designated areas are nationally important landscapes.

The erosion of this coastline is part of the justification for World Heritage status, not because of the danger of losing it, but because it is a living geomorphological classroom and contains such good examples of landslides, beaches, lagoons, bays, headlands and sea stacks. There is also significant botanical and zoological value in the plants that colonise this constantly changing environment and the bees, wasps and beetles that make their homes in the freshly disturbed soft rocks. The greatest threat to the Jurassic Coast would be the extension of coastal defences – though the towns, of course, need to be protected.

Fieldwork exercise: Evaluating conservation

Aim:

To evaluate the conservation value of a stretch of coastline.

Method:

1. Carry out a visual assessment of natural environmental quality using a detailed tally sheet. The factors to be included in your tally sheet will depend upon the site you are surveying: the table shows some suggestions. Your results become more valid as you increase the number of locations that you survey so you should have at least twenty (A, B, C, etc).

Location		A	B	etc.
Managed grassland	Short			
	Tall			
Natural grassland	Short			
	Tall			
Woodland	Single species			
	Mixed species			
Herb layer (wild flowers)	Many species			
	One or two			
	None			
Boundaries	Fence			
	Stone wall			
	Hedgerow			
	None			
Buildings	Some			
	None			
Traffic	Path			
	Road			

2. You should also take photographs of every location and annotated sketches are very valuable too.

3. Take note of, and where possible photograph, measures being taken to conserve the area. These will include way-marked paths, fencing to protect more fragile habitats, and information boards (called 'interpretative media') to educate the public.

Data interpretation and analysis:

This is a more qualitative exercise so your analysis will be more descriptive. First you should work meticulously through the data individually but then you must look for patterns and trends, general themes that link different aspects of the survey area to enable you to make an overall judgement. It may be possible to carry out a SWOT analysis of the area after you have interpreted the detailed data, identifying the Strengths, Weaknesses, Opportunities and Threats of conservation in your study area.

Conclusion and evaluation:

It is unlikely that a clear-cut conclusion will be made as you are dealing with more qualitative data so a good summary of the investigation would discuss both the strengths and weaknesses of the conservation area, drawing upon the details of the SWOT analysis, while the evaluation would build upon the opportunities and threats identified.

Extensions:

This type of field exercise can be carried out in any type of coastal environment, regardless of its conservation status or whether it is predominantly rural or urban. Conservation of the built environment is equally valuable where buildings are historic and form part of our cultural heritage.

Summary

This chapter has examined the competition for space in the coastal zone, the potential for conflict between different stakeholders, and the damage to coastal environments that human activities may cause. A range of both rural and urban land uses have been reviewed with case studies of Dubai, Dungeness, Brighton and the Severn Estuary. Finally, conservation measures have been identified with particular reference to the south coast of England.

Having studied this chapter, you should now be able to discuss these ideas and concepts and provide located examples of them:

- Competition for space in the coastal zone puts pressure on coastal environments, and distinctive patterns of land use develop as a consequence of this competition.
- There are economic benefits and environmental costs to coastal development, which influence the success of development and involve the views of different stakeholders and their conflicting needs.
  - Conservation is both one of the competing stakeholders and a mechanism for managing potential conflict.

MCQ

To try an exam question using what you have learned in this chapter, turn to page 201.

CHAPTER 21 How is coastal development increasingly at risk from and vulnerable to physical processes?

Key terms

Backwash
Barrier beach
Cuspate foreland
Erosion
Eustatic change
Fetch
Isostatic change
Mass movement
Rollback
Sediment cell
Spit
Swash
Tombolo
Weathering

Learning objectives

After studying this chapter, you will be able to discuss these ideas and concepts and provide located examples of them:
- The increasing risks faced by coastal development on vulnerable coasts, due to rapid coastal erosion and flooding.
- The impact of rising sea levels in areas of dense population and high-value property and important industrial and commercial developments.
- The particular dangers faced by people living in coastal zones that may be subject to tsunamis and storm surges.

Coastal erosion

The erosion of the Holderness coast in Yorkshire is a classic case study for geography students. The coast is retreating at an average of 1.8 metres per year as the waves approach from the north east and cut into the glacial till cliffs, removing the material and transporting it south to the Humber Estuary and thence towards North Norfolk to settle in the Wash. In time, all of the glacial deposits will be removed and the coast will follow the line of the harder limestone ridge that currently forms the Yorkshire Wolds.

Defending this coastline is a losing battle, and the concept of 'rollback', which involves moving settlement further inland, is increasingly seen as the most sustainable and economic way of living with the inevitability of coastal erosion. On the Holderness coast, this has already started with a feasibility study of rolling back the caravan and holiday industry.

◄ **Figure 1:** The collapse of the cliff near Scarborough on the North Yorkshire coast that destroyed the Holbeck Hall Hotel in 1993. The owners of the hotel sued Scarborough Council, on the grounds that they had failed to defend this stretch of coast adequately.

There are two sets of weathering processes at work on the coastline: marine processes that attack the foot of the cliff, and sub-aerial processes that erode the cliff-face – the part of the cliff that rises above the section in contact with the sea. Sub-aerial processes include the types of weathering that are normally found on land, such as freeze thaw, hydration and biological weathering, as well as salt weathering. Marine processes include abrasion, attrition, solution and hydraulic pressure.

Figure 2 is a concept map showing how these processes interrelate. Where cliffs are formed from harder rocks, features such as wave-cut platforms, caves, blowholes, stacks and stumps are produced.

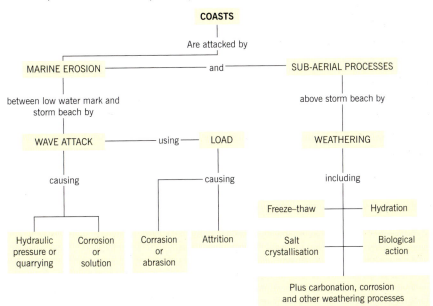

Marine and sub-aerial weathering exploits structural weaknesses in the structure and lithology of the rock. In softer sands and clays, mass movement processes may be more important. Mass movement (or mass wasting) is the downslope movement of material, such as rocks, loose stones and soil, by gravity and is often lubricated by water. Such processes are classified according to the speed of movement and the moisture content of the material, so different processes are dominant in different environments.

In softer sands and clays, mass movement features, such as rotational slumps or mud flows, may dominate the landscape. These forms of mass movement are found, for example, along the Holderness coast and in Christchurch Bay on the Dorset/Hampshire border, where the cliffs are formed from a mix of clays, sands and gravel (see Figure 3).

▶ Figure 3: Cliff slumping at Barton-on-Sea in Christchurch Bay.

Key terms

'Weathering' is the breakdown of rocks at or near the earth's surface where they are situated, whereas 'erosion' is the wearing away of the land surface and the removal of debris by wind, water or ice. So weathering provides material that may be removed by gravity and the agents of erosion – wind, water and ice.

Examiners' tip

A concept map is a useful revision technique. It is a good way of sorting out terms and processes and showing how they link to each other, and it reinforces your understanding of key terms.

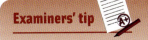

◀ Figure 2: A concept map summarising sub-aerial processes.

Taking it further

Over a sufficient timescale, maps will reveal the rate of coastal erosion. Old postcards and photographs can also show significant changes, not just in the natural coastline but in the use and defence of the coast. Old maps, photos and postcards can be found in coastal towns' local reference libraries (and increasingly online, if you cannot visit a coastal settlement).

Taking it further

The energy input to coastal systems comes from three sources: waves, currents and tides. Waves are transformed as they enter the shallow water of the coastal zone, producing currents of varying strengths and directions. They are responsible for the movement of coastal sediment. To learn more about waves and for an exercise on sorting out the two types of wave read 'Making waves' and 'Spilling or plunging waves' on your Student CD-ROM.

Factors that affect the rate of coastal erosion include:

- The shape of the coastline
- The width of the beach (wider beaches absorb more energy and protect the cliff foot)
- The length and direction of fetch
- Where the wave breaks (the point of maximum impact)
- The height or steepness of the wave (deeper waves are more destructive)
- Wave energy
- Rock resistance (its relative hardness)
- Structure (faults and bedding planes) and dip (angle) of rocks
- Human activity.

Waves are caused by the transfer of energy from wind to the sea water – it is the form of the wave that moves forward, not the water. The height and power of the waves depend upon the strength of the wind and the fetch – the distance across the sea over which the wind blows to generate the waves. As waves reach the shore, and water depth decreases, the wave energy is concentrated in a narrowing zone, changing the form of the wave until it collapses and water is thrown on to the beach, releasing the wave energy. Water is thrown up the beach in the movement called 'swash' and it drains back as 'backwash'.

Coastal sediment is moved by the waves. Wave forms that are 'constructive' have a stronger swash than backwash, leading to net transport of sediment up the beach. Others waves are 'destructive', resulting in the removal of sediment from the beach, as the backwash is the stronger movement.

The coastal sediment system

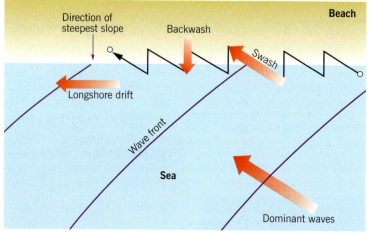

▲ Figure 4: The process of longshore drift, by which sediment is moved along the shoreline by waves approaching at an angle.

The material removed from some parts of the coast is carried along the coastline and deposited elsewhere. Sediments such as sand and shingle are moved along the coastline by 'longshore drift' (see Figure 4). Where waves approach the coastline at an angle, the swash moves sediment up the beach in the direction of the wave – at the same angle. But the backwash is caused by gravity and normally moves straight back down to the sea – at right angles to the coast line. This causes the beach material to be moved along the coastline in a zig-zag movement. Obstacles such as rocky outcrops or groynes will trap sediment and prevent it from travelling further along the coast. Spits may form in places where the coastline cuts inland abruptly, such as at an estuary.

The process of marine deposition causes sediment to build up along shorelines in low-energy environments. These are locations that are sheltered from the largest waves and the strongest currents. Deposition also occurs when rivers, which transport sediment, reach the open sea. At this point, the river velocity slows, its energy is reduced and it is no longer able to carry its load, which at this point comprises fine silt and clay.

The features created by deposition along coastlines, which include barrier beaches, tombolos, spits and cuspate forelands, can be divided into three types:

- Spits and related features
- Beaches and sand dunes
- Mudflats and salt marshes.

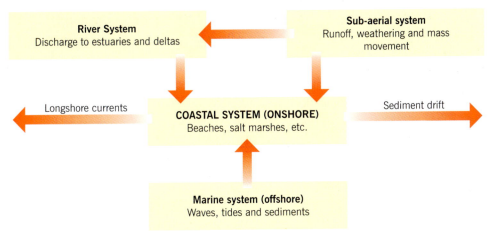

The way in which sediment is moved between the various stores in the coastal zone is illustrated in Figure 5. The longshore transport of material redistributes sediment within the coastal system so that sediment is gained from eroding sections of coastline, called 'sources', and lost to sections experiencing deposition, called 'sinks'.

The whole section of coastline from source to sink is called a 'sediment cell'. The amount of sediment gained from the sources and lost to the sinks can be quantified, and a sediment budget can de derived that can highlight variations in the amount of source and sink sediments. It is an invaluable tool for assessing the causes of coastal change, such as the effect of artificial structures on beach erosion, so these cells are increasingly used as a basis for coastal management schemes.

There are three sources of sediment:

- Coastal cliff erosion provides a small amount. The harder rock cliffs of the western coastline of Britain erode very slowly, so very little sediment is produced, whereas the glacial till of the Holderness coast retreats by nearly 2 metres per year, and 30% of this sediment is held on its beaches.
- Most sediment comes from the fluvial (river) erosion of the land and from wave transport from the sea floor. This is the most important source, accounting for over 90% of global marine sediment.
- The offshore zone also supplies some sediment to the coastline as waves move sediment towards the coast, mainly in depths of less than 20 metres.

The main sediment sinks include:

- The accumulation of material at the back of beaches, which is blown inland to form sand dunes beyond the reach of storm waves.
- Most estuaries and inlets are filled with fluvial or coastal sediment – the Wash, for example.
- Sediment is lost to the offshore zone during storm conditions, although this is usually moved back onshore in fair weather.

Key terms

Barrier beach: an accumulation of sand and shingle lying parallel to the shoreline that encloses a marsh or lagoon on the landward side.
Spit: a long, narrow and sometimes curved accumulation of sand and shingle extending the shoreline where it changes direction.

◀ **Figure 5:** The main components and transfers of the coastal sediment system.

Key terms

Tombolo: an accumulation of sand and shingle which joins an island to the mainland.
Cuspate foreland: a triangular accumulation of sediment such as sand and shingle.

Key terms

A sediment cell is a length of coastline and its associated nearshore area, within which the movement of coarse sediment (sand and shingle) is largely self-contained.

Taking it further

The study of coastal sediment provides information about coastal processes. The main types are muds, sands and pebbles (shingle). Small-scale differences in the pattern of waves cause sediment sorting according to grain size, because more energy is needed to transport larger or heavier material.

Taking it further

To learn more about the Boxing Day Tsunami read 'Tsunami timeline' on your Student CD-ROM.

The first sign of a tsunami is sometimes a small rise in the water level, followed by a deeply receding water level. This can be a remarkable sight – and it may attract people towards the danger. The incoming wave then approaches the shore, rather like an incoming tide but much more rapidly. (A tsunami, in fact, is nothing to do with the tides, so the popular term 'tidal wave' is inappropriate.) The maximum vertical height of the water in relation to sea level is referred to as 'run-up' and the maximum horizontal distance is referred to as 'inundation'.

Case study: The Boxing Day Tsunami

The tsunami on 26 December 2004 that devastated Aceh in Indonesia, parts of Thailand and Sri Lanka, southern India and many islands in the Indian Ocean, killed nearly 300,000 people (two-thirds of whom were women) and left millions homeless. A destructive plate boundary lies 240 km off the coast of Sumatra, marked by a 1,200 km trench called the Andaman–Sumatran subduction zone. Here the Indian/Australian tectonic plate is being forced beneath part of the Eurasian plate. Movement along this junction caused an earthquake, measuring 9.3 on the Richter scale, creating a series of waves measuring up to 20 metres high.

In the aftermath of this disaster, one aspect became obvious: unlike in the Pacific, there was no tsunami warning system operating in the Indian Ocean, and such a system could have saved countless lives.

Case study: Louisiana's wetlands

America's wetland, on the Louisiana coast, is one of the most productive expanses of coastal wetlands in North America, but it is being lost at the rate of at least 60 km^2 a year. In the last 50 years, more than 2,500 km^2 of land has been lost. This area, which covers the Mississippi Delta, is of world ecological significance. The wetland provides rich fishing grounds (95% of all marine life in the Gulf of Mexico spends part of its life cycle here), and it provides winter habitats for more than five million waterfowl and migratory birds.

Offshore oil and gas exploration and development began in the 1940s and the first pipeline canal was dug through the coastal wetlands. Canals now carry more than 24,000 miles of pipeline across Louisiana's shore, anchored on its barrier islands. Those running north–south exacerbate wetland loss because they allow salt water and stronger tides into the marshes, and the east–west canals and levees trap excess salt water on the marshes and swamps.

The wetlands provide protection from hurricanes and storm surges for more than 2 million people living in the coastal zone, including the city of New Orleans. Many goods are transported worldwide via the Gulf Intra-coastal Water Way that was built through the wetlands in the early 1900s. The navigation corridors and port facilities for commerce and national defence are valued at more than $15 bn annually, but erosion of the wetland threatens the transport network and energy installations.

A combination of human and natural causes is contributing to the rapid land loss that makes the marshes more vulnerable to hurricanes and storm surges. Major causes of erosion include subsidence, sea level rise, sediment reduction, the levee system, oil and gas development, salt water intrusion, storms, and barrier island degradation.

Scientists have identified two main reasons for the rapid loss of land:
1. Building canals through the marshes has altered drainage patterns and facilitates the intrusion of salt water into Louisiana's fresh and brackish water marshes. Salt water weakens and kills many of the marsh grasses which bind the sediment. Fresh water withdrawal adds to this problem.
2. Dams and levees built along the Mississippi River – to provide flood protection for its cities and to channel the river for better navigation – have reduced the volume of water and of sediment reaching the coast. The nutrients and sediments that had replenished and rebuilt the wetlands, balancing the natural subsidence of the area, are now funnelled out into the Gulf of Mexico and off the continental shelf.

The features created by deposition along coastlines, which include barrier beaches, tombolos, spits and cuspate forelands, can be divided into three types:

- Spits and related features
- Beaches and sand dunes
- Mudflats and salt marshes.

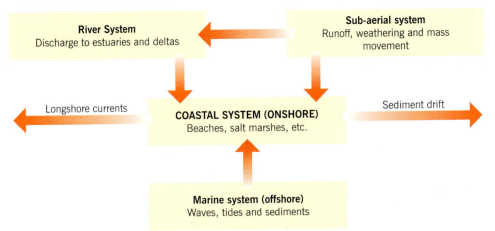

Figure 5: The main components and transfers of the coastal sediment system.

The way in which sediment is moved between the various stores in the coastal zone is illustrated in Figure 5. The longshore transport of material redistributes sediment within the coastal system so that sediment is gained from eroding sections of coastline, called 'sources', and lost to sections experiencing deposition, called 'sinks'.

The whole section of coastline from source to sink is called a 'sediment cell'. The amount of sediment gained from the sources and lost to the sinks can be quantified, and a sediment budget can de derived that can highlight variations in the amount of source and sink sediments. It is an invaluable tool for assessing the causes of coastal change, such as the effect of artificial structures on beach erosion, so these cells are increasingly used as a basis for coastal management schemes.

There are three sources of sediment:

- Coastal cliff erosion provides a small amount. The harder rock cliffs of the western coastline of Britain erode very slowly, so very little sediment is produced, whereas the glacial till of the Holderness coast retreats by nearly 2 metres per year, and 30% of this sediment is held on its beaches.
- Most sediment comes from the fluvial (river) erosion of the land and from wave transport from the sea floor. This is the most important source, accounting for over 90% of global marine sediment.
- The offshore zone also supplies some sediment to the coastline as waves move sediment towards the coast, mainly in depths of less than 20 metres.

The main sediment sinks include:

- The accumulation of material at the back of beaches, which is blown inland to form sand dunes beyond the reach of storm waves.
- Most estuaries and inlets are filled with fluvial or coastal sediment – the Wash, for example.
- Sediment is lost to the offshore zone during storm conditions, although this is usually moved back onshore in fair weather.

Key terms

Barrier beach: an accumulation of sand and shingle lying parallel to the shoreline that encloses a marsh or lagoon on the landward side.
Spit: a long, narrow and sometimes curved accumulation of sand and shingle extending the shoreline where it changes direction.

Key terms

Tombolo: an accumulation of sand and shingle which joins an island to the mainland.
Cuspate foreland: a triangular accumulation of sediment such as sand and shingle.

Key terms

A sediment cell is a length of coastline and its associated nearshore area, within which the movement of coarse sediment (sand and shingle) is largely self-contained.

Taking it further

The study of coastal sediment provides information about coastal processes. The main types are muds, sands and pebbles (shingle). Small-scale differences in the pattern of waves cause sediment sorting according to grain size, because more energy is needed to transport larger or heavier material.

Case study: Managing coastal sediment transfer

Bournemouth is a major leisure resort in Dorset with extensive conference facilities to encourage business tourism. The large sandy beach is an attractive asset for both functions, but it is vulnerable to erosion as wave energy is quite strong here. The beach was originally formed of sands eroded from the local cliffs but when the sea wall and promenade were built between 1907 and 1911, the supply of sand was cut off, and the beach started to shrink. The response was to build groynes to trap the sand as it was transported eastwards by longshore drift. But this strategy deprived the coastline east of Bournemouth of its sedimentary input.

At Hengistbury Head, about five miles east of Bournemouth, erosion was increased as it lost its supply of sediment, so groynes were built there too. One long groyne extends out to sea just in front of Mudeford Spit, which has also been defended with a series of groynes. While the sea defences erected at Bournemouth and at Hengistbury Head have significantly slowed the erosion in those places, it is difficult to see how equilibrium in the sediment budget can now be restored within this area without introducing a different strategy. There is now concern, following a breach across Barn Field on the western edge of Hengistbury, that in time the Head could become an island.

Changes in sea level

All coastal processes are affected by sea level changes. Sea levels are currently rising as ice-sheets and glaciers are melting because of global warming. (The melting of sea ice, including icebergs, makes no difference to sea level because it merely displaces its own liquid volume in the ocean.) Global warming is also causing the thermal expansion of seawater and this also contributes to sea level rise. An increase or decrease in the volume of water in ocean basins is called 'eustatic' change. In the past, eustatic change created drowned river valleys (called rias) and fjords.

Sea levels are estimated to have risen by about 15 cm in the last hundred years, and predictions suggest a rise of a further 30 cm by 2100. If sea levels continue to rise, islands such as the Maldives will be inundated, major deltas could disappear, and low-lying coastal areas of the UK and the Netherlands will be severely eroded. In the Indian part of the Sundarbans, the island of Lohachara has already been abandoned to the sea – the first inhabited place to be lost to rising sea levels. Salt water will also pollute ground water supplies as it percolates through permeable rocks in the coastline.

Sea levels also vary due to local ('isostatic') changes caused by tectonic movements of the earth's crust. These occur especially near plate margins, where land may be rising or falling. Parts of the crust that were glaciated during the ice ages are also experiencing 'isostatic recoil' – rising of the land after the weight of ice has gone. Southern Finland, for example, is rising by 2.6 mm per year through isostatic recoil.

While rising land will counter the effect of rising sea level in a few places, for most stretches of coastline the threat is of inundation. In some parts of the world, high-value property and important industrial and commercial developments are seriously at risk of flooding. Elsewhere, many poorer people live in poverty on land that is already being lost to the rising tides.

Case study: The Sundarbans, India and Bangladesh

◀ **Figure 6:** The location of the Sundarbans (left) and the Indian section of the swamps.

The sea is eroding the Sundarbans, threatening an ecological disaster. The Sundarbans forest – one of the largest mangrove forests in the world – lies on the delta of the Ganges, Brahmaputra and Meghna rivers in the Bay of Bengal, one-third in India and two-thirds in Bangladesh. Satellite imagery shows that the sea level has risen at an average rate of 3.1 cm a year in the past 20 years, much higher than the global average of 2 mm a year. A further rise of 1 metre in sea level would inundate 1,000 km² and, at the current rate, this looks very likely in the next 50 years.

Four islands in the Indian section, Bedford, Lohachara, Kabasgadi and Suparibhanga, have so far been lost to the sea, making 6,000 families homeless. Two more islands, Ghoramara and Mousuni, will soon be inundated. A total of 54 of the 102 islands in the Indian Sundarbans are still habitable, but the entire island system is facing rapid coastal erosion, flooding and salinisation of drinking water. By 2020, the rising sea level and soil erosion threaten to displace more than 30,000 people.

The authorities also need to address a range of other issues:
- The growth of the prawn monoculture.
- Erosion caused by the barraging of rivers and the diversion or blocking of upstream water.
- The use of mangrove wood to feed a gas plant in the Gosaba and Choto Mollakhali islands.
- The silting up of West Bengal's largest port, Haldia.

The Sundarbans is a network of tidal waterways, mudflats and small islands of salt-tolerant mangroves. The area is valuable for its exceptional biodiversity, with a wide range of fauna, including 260 bird species, the Bengal tiger and other threatened species such as the estuarine crocodile and the Indian python. Part of the 20,000 km² forest was designated a World Heritage Site in 1987. The forest is also South Asia's largest carbon sink, absorbing carbon dioxide and helping to counter global warming.

The region is ecologically significant because of the combination of processes operating there – monsoon rains, flooding, delta formation, tidal influence and plant colonisation. The diverse marine life, including river sharks, red crabs, shrimps and snakes, are all uniquely adapted to the saline water and, if they are harmed, it will drastically affect the food chain and the fishing industry.

Sagar, the largest island, has already lost 30 km². Embankments have been constructed to ring the coastal inlands but they are often damaged by high tides and some have collapsed. There are other pressures:
- About 2,500 km² are set aside as a tiger reserve, but poaching of the Bengal tiger continues.
- Land reclamation for human settlement has involved extensive tree-felling which has halved the mangrove cover in the Indian section. This depletion, however, only increases the threat of flooding upstream in Calcutta.
- Since the first settlements in 1770, the population of the Indian Sundarbans has risen 200% to nearly 4.3 million, threatening the aquatic ecosystem.

Storm surges

Storms are caused by atmospheric depressions (low pressure systems). At sea they generate larger waves because higher wind energy is transferred to the water. Depressions also increase the height of the surface of the sea – a drop in atmospheric pressure causing the sea surface to rise by about one centimetre per millibar – which can cause a significant increase in sea level. If such a rise coincides with a spring tide and an onshore wind, which can pile up the water towards the coastline, a 'storm surge' will occur, raising the incoming waves above the normal high water mark and causing coastal flooding. The Bay of Bengal is particularly vulnerable to cyclones, the regional name for hurricanes, which funnel up the Bay between Burma (Myanmar) and India and cause damaging storm surges far inland in Bangladesh.

In England and Wales, the Environment Agency is responsible for flood warning and defence. The Agency has an advanced warning system in place which aims to give homes a minimum of 2 hours notice before imminent flooding. In April 2000 the Agency established a National Flood Warning Centre in Surrey to provide a focus for improving forecasting, warnings and communications to help people in flood-risk areas.

Sea levels are expected to rise by between 26 and 86 cm above the current level in south east England by the 2080s, and extreme sea levels are expected to occur up to twenty times more frequently than now. So the chances of another serious storm surge (like the one in 1953 – see the case study on page 187) will increase, presenting a challenging task for the authorities who protect coastal communities against flooding.

London's defence is vital. The city contains many buildings of significant historical and cultural value – and some of the most expensive real estate in the world. Tide levels in the Thames are steadily increasing, owing to a combination of factors including higher mean sea levels, greater storms, increasing tide amplitude, the tilting of the British Isles (with the south eastern corner tipping downwards), and the slow downward settlement of London on its bed of clay. Consequently, tide levels in the Thames estuary are rising, relative to the land, by about 60 cm per century.

In the lower part of the Thames, defences include a number of moveable gates, maintained and operated by the Environment Agency, the largest of which is the Thames Barrier. Other defences include gates at the entrances to the old Royal Docks, and the Barking, Dartford Creek and Fobbing Horse Barriers.

Tsunamis

A tsunami is a series of very large waves generated by a disturbance on the ocean floor, such as an earthquake, volcanic activity or a landslide, as opposed to 'normal' waves generated by wind. These waves can threaten life in coastal settlements and cause severe damage to property. Tsunamis generally appear as an advancing tide without a developed wave face, and they produce rapid flooding of low-lying coastal areas.

Taking it further

Find a map of the Thames estuary and locate these defences. Find out the maximum height of flood they can withstand and assess their effectiveness by relating this information to a contour map of the area.

Case study: The 1953 floods and the response

▲ Figure 7: The height of the storm surge levels in the North Sea on 31 January 1953.

A catastrophic storm surge occurred in January 1953, causing the deaths of 300 people in England – and 1,800 in the Netherlands. During the evening of the 31 January, the depression moved southwards into the North Sea and caused devastating floods along the east coast from Hull to Deal in Kent. Hurricane-force winds were recorded at Felixstowe at 8 p.m. The depression reached Canvey Island, in the Thames Estuary, just after midnight, then continued around the North Sea basin to the Netherlands.

Almost 100,000 hectares of eastern England were affected, with major flooding in Norfolk, Suffolk, Essex, the outer Thames Estuary and Kent. Some 24,000 homes were destroyed or damaged, and 40,000 people were evacuated. Damage in monetary terms was estimated at over £5 bn at today's value. In the Netherlands, 50 dykes burst and the sea reclaimed over 200,000 hectares of the polders.

The devastating floods were a 'once in 250 years' event. The storm surge (see Figure 7) resulted in sea levels rising more than 2 metres above normal high water marks (the pressure fell to 966 – 43 millibars lower than the average). Most sea defences along the east coast of England were not designed for such events and many could not hold back the oncoming wave of water. Yet many of the fatalities could have been avoided if an effective flood warning system had been in place and communities had been given sufficient time to evacuate. But at the time, forecasting technology and procedures were relatively primitive – and many phone lines had been brought down by earlier gales.

◀ Figure 8: The height of the storm surge levels in the North Sea on 31 January 1953.

The danger can actually last for hours after the initial wave because a tsunami moves everything in its path and carries it for many metres. The debris makes the wave extremely hazardous. Rivers, streams, and roads provide easy paths for the water and its load to follow, and when the wave retreats, huge mounds of debris – building materials, trees and vehicles – will be deposited in its wake.

Taking it further

To learn more about the Boxing Day Tsunami read 'Tsunami timeline' on your Student CD-ROM.

The first sign of a tsunami is sometimes a small rise in the water level, followed by a deeply receding water level. This can be a remarkable sight – and it may attract people towards the danger. The incoming wave then approaches the shore, rather like an incoming tide but much more rapidly. (A tsunami, in fact, is nothing to do with the tides, so the popular term 'tidal wave' is inappropriate.) The maximum vertical height of the water in relation to sea level is referred to as 'run-up' and the maximum horizontal distance is referred to as 'inundation'.

Case study: The Boxing Day Tsunami

The tsunami on 26 December 2004 that devastated Aceh in Indonesia, parts of Thailand and Sri Lanka, southern India and many islands in the Indian Ocean, killed nearly 300,000 people (two-thirds of whom were women) and left millions homeless. A destructive plate boundary lies 240 km off the coast of Sumatra, marked by a 1,200 km trench called the Andaman–Sumatran subduction zone. Here the Indian/Australian tectonic plate is being forced beneath part of the Eurasian plate. Movement along this junction caused an earthquake, measuring 9.3 on the Richter scale, creating a series of waves measuring up to 20 metres high.

In the aftermath of this disaster, one aspect became obvious: unlike in the Pacific, there was no tsunami warning system operating in the Indian Ocean, and such a system could have saved countless lives.

Case study: Louisiana's wetlands

America's wetland, on the Louisiana coast, is one of the most productive expanses of coastal wetlands in North America, but it is being lost at the rate of at least 60 km^2 a year. In the last 50 years, more than 2,500 km^2 of land has been lost. This area, which covers the Mississippi Delta, is of world ecological significance. The wetland provides rich fishing grounds (95% of all marine life in the Gulf of Mexico spends part of its life cycle here), and it provides winter habitats for more than five million waterfowl and migratory birds.

Offshore oil and gas exploration and development began in the 1940s and the first pipeline canal was dug through the coastal wetlands. Canals now carry more than 24,000 miles of pipeline across Louisiana's shore, anchored on its barrier islands. Those running north–south exacerbate wetland loss because they allow salt water and stronger tides into the marshes, and the east–west canals and levees trap excess salt water on the marshes and swamps.

The wetlands provide protection from hurricanes and storm surges for more than 2 million people living in the coastal zone, including the city of New Orleans. Many goods are transported worldwide via the Gulf Intra-coastal Water Way that was built through the wetlands in the early 1900s. The navigation corridors and port facilities for commerce and national defence are valued at more than $15 bn annually, but erosion of the wetland threatens the transport network and energy installations.

A combination of human and natural causes is contributing to the rapid land loss that makes the marshes more vulnerable to hurricanes and storm surges. Major causes of erosion include subsidence, sea level rise, sediment reduction, the levee system, oil and gas development, salt water intrusion, storms, and barrier island degradation.

Scientists have identified two main reasons for the rapid loss of land:

1. Building canals through the marshes has altered drainage patterns and facilitates the intrusion of salt water into Louisiana's fresh and brackish water marshes. Salt water weakens and kills many of the marsh grasses which bind the sediment. Fresh water withdrawal adds to this problem.
2. Dams and levees built along the Mississippi River – to provide flood protection for its cities and to channel the river for better navigation – have reduced the volume of water and of sediment reaching the coast. The nutrients and sediments that had replenished and rebuilt the wetlands, balancing the natural subsidence of the area, are now funnelled out into the Gulf of Mexico and off the continental shelf.

Case study: Louisiana's wetlands (continued)

This stretch of coastline was badly damaged by Hurricanes Katrina and Rita in 2005. Subsequently the Coastal Protection and Restoration Authority (CPRA) was established as the single state agency to plan and implement the priorities for coastal protection. Residents worry about the survival of Louisiana's only inhabited barrier island, Grand Isle, which sits on the edge of the shrinking marshes facing the waves of the Gulf. The future of this 15 km² island and the nearby wetlands are important for the protection of settlements further inland. Communities built on the marshland may have to be abandoned in the next few decades if no serious restoration efforts are made.

Following Hurricane Katrina, New Orleans city has given support to two particular projects to save the coast:

- The Alligator Bend Project to fill in 160 hectares of open water to rebuild a 10 km stretch of the Orleans land bridge between Lake Pontchartrain and Lake Borgne, and to plant vegetation along the Lake Borgne shoreline
- The Irish Bayou Shoreline Protection and Marsh Creation Project to protect land next to Bayou Sauvage by restoring approximately 120 hectares of marshland.

'Coast 2050' is a strategic plan for restoring the coast sustainably. The main strategies are watershed management, such as river diversions and improved drainage, and watershed structural repair, such as the restoration of barrier islands. Federal and national agencies, local government, and the US Army Corps of Engineers (who carry out major flood defence construction) have worked with scientists, environmentalists, landowners, industry representatives, concerned citizens, and recreational and commercial fishermen to reach consensus on the plan. The restoration of America's wetland will be the largest engineering project ever attempted in the world, but the area is of vital importance to the nation and the world. It will cost billions and will require sustained support.

A separate plan for the Mississippi River would create a series of gates to control the release of silt-laden river water to sustain existing wetlands and rebuild some of those that have been buried by the encroaching Gulf of Mexico. It will mimic the river's natural ebb and flow in some areas, while keeping critical shipping channels open.

▲ **Figure 9:** The Louisiana wetlands, showing the bird's foot delta at the mouth of the Mississippi.

Fieldwork investigation: Studying the nature of waves

Aim:

To investigate the nature and potential impact of wave action on a stretch of shoreline.

Health and safety:

This fieldwork could be dangerous unless you observe the following safety measures:

- You must not stand on groynes or any other structure overlooking the waves unless they are completely solid structures and you can get a completely secure foothold.
- You must not stand on groynes or any other structure overlooking the waves or in the sea unless you are a good swimmer.
- Ideally, you should wear a lifejacket such as that worn by dinghy sailors.
- Never attempt this (or any other) fieldwork alone – there should be *at least two other people* present.
- Do not attempt this fieldwork in stormy or rough weather.

Data collection:

To carry out these measurements of waves, you will need to find a beach with groynes or breakwaters that are safe for you stand upon.

1. Use a ranging pole or a metre rule to measure the maximum wave height by noting the highest and lowest points reached by the waves; you can then work out the maximum wave height by subtracting the height of the trough from the height of the peak. To ensure a reliable result you will need to take an average of at least ten waves and, ideally, do this several times.

2. Measure wave frequency by counting the number of waves passing a fixed point in five minutes and divide by five to get the rate per minute. Repeat this exercise several times and average your results to get a reliable wave frequency rate.

3. Measure the wave period, the time between each wave crest, by dividing the frequency by 60 seconds.

4. Wave length cannot be measured but can be calculated if you know the depth of the water. You should measure the water depth between the crests and troughs of the waves; this can be done standing in the water if it is not too deep or from a safe position on the groyne using a ranging pole. The formula for calculating wave length differs according to depth; the following is the formula for depths of less than 2 metres:

$$\frac{\text{Wave period} \times 3.13 \times \sqrt{\text{water depth in metres}}}{\text{Wave frequency}}$$

5. You can now calculate the wave energy (in joules) using the formula: $740 \times$ wave height squared $\times$ wave length.

6. You can also calculate the phase difference by timing in seconds how long it takes for the swash to reach its highest point up the beach after the wave breaks. Do this at least ten times and work out the average, then divide this by the wave period to get the phase difference.

Data interpretation:

Destructive waves will be higher with shorter wave lengths, they will also be steeper and you can calculate wave steepness by dividing wave height by wave length. They are more frequent so the wave period and wave length will be shorter. Destructive waves have higher phase differences: the most destructive waves are surging breakers with a phase difference of around 0.5 while constructive spilling breakers have a phase difference of more than 1.0; plunging breakers between 0.5 and 1.0 are also more destructive. This fieldwork will be more meaningful if you can compare waves on different stretches of coastline, such as between a bay and a headland, but be aware that the exact conditions will change as the weather changes – if the onshore wind picks up, the wave energy will increase.

Fieldwork investigation: Evaluating coastal property at risk

Aim:
To investigate the potential costs of an eroding coastline.

Data collection:
There are two methods you can use to carry out this investigation: cost-benefit analysis (CBA) and environmental impact analysis (EIA). You could compare two short stretches of coastline, perhaps each one kilometre in length. Ideally they will have different land uses such as residential versus commercial or rural versus urban.

To carry out a CBA you will need to assess the value of the land and property. Secondary data research of property prices can be carried out online or by reference to local estate agents, though this will not provide a complete picture. Business rates (see http://www.voa.gov.uk/business_rates/index.htm) and council tax valuations (see http://www.voa.gov.uk/council_tax/cti_home.htm) can also be obtained. Primary data collection could include a visual assessment of property worth by measuring length of frontage and counting the number of storeys; this could be done alongside a quality assessment of the property (such as state of repair). If property is used for commercial purposes, the nature of the businesses could be categorised in terms of likely revenue or value to the local community (agricultural land could be assessed in terms of the value of its produce. All of these qualitative and quantitative measures should then be weighed against the costs of coastal defences to assess the relative benefits of defence or managed retreat.

To carry out an EIA you will need first to list all of the impacts of coastal erosion in your chosen study location(s). These may be categorised. Ecological impacts may include loss of particular habitats or particular species but consideration may be given to the beneficial or adverse impact further along the coasts (note that coastal defences can cut off vital supplies of sediment elsewhere). Aesthetic impacts may occur where attractive landscape or buildings may be at risk. Commercial impacts will be possible where businesses or valuable property may be lost or personal impacts where private property is in danger. Then you need to assess the scale of the impacts: this can also be categorised according to whether it affects the natural environment (both ecology and geomorphology), the commercial environment, the built environment, or the local community. Construct a matrix of the impacts on one axis versus the scale of the impact on the other impacts. As you carry out your EIA, you will need to enter two scores in each box of your matrix, one for each axis, and these will be multiplied and the totals summed for each column and row in the matrix.

Data presentation and interpretation:
As this will be a comparative exercise, clear comparisons must be shown and evaluated. This can be done using graphs and tables. Annotated photographs should also be used to illustrate the points you are making.

Summary

This chapter has looked at the causes and consequences of coastal erosion and the ways in which the coastal sediment system may be managed. The topics studied include rising sea levels, storm surges and their consequences in the south-east of England, and tsunamis with reference to the 2004 Boxing Day tragedy. Finally the combination of threats to the Louisiana wetlands and their management illustrates the challenge of coastal erosion and its management.

Having studied this chapter, you should now be able to discuss these ideas and concepts and provide located examples of them:

- The increasing risks faced by coastal development on vulnerable coasts, due to rapid coastal erosion and flooding.
- The impact of rising sea levels in areas of dense population and high-value property and important industrial and commercial developments.
  - The particular dangers faced by people living in coastal zones that may be subject to tsunamis and storm surges.

MCQ

To try an exam question using what you have learned in this chapter, turn to page 201.

CHAPTER 22 How is coastal management adapting to new ideas and situations?

Key terms

Hard engineering

Integrated coastal zone management (ICZM)

Managed retreat

Shoreline management plans (SMPs)

Soft engineering

Learning objectives

After studying this chapter, you will be able to discuss these ideas and concepts and provide located examples of them:

- The range of strategies available for coastal management, from hard engineering techniques to the 'do nothing' approach.
- How these strategies have been used and their effectiveness, costs and benefits.
- The development of sustainable and integrated approaches, such as coastal realignment, shoreline management plans (SMPs) and integrated coastal zone management (ICZM).

Coastal management strategies

Marine and sub-aerial processes and mass movement can inflict considerable damage on the coastline, but there are a variety of management strategies available to protect coastal resources – and people. These range from massive civil engineering projects to protect people and property, to 'managed retreat' – accepting the inevitability of coastal erosion. Active coastal defence strategies can be divided into two broad categories: 'hard engineering' and 'soft engineering' (see Figure 2).

▲ **Figure 1:** Before and after: Winterton Dunes in Norfolk. In July 2002, there is some evidence of sand loss as the sea is advancing towards the protective concrete blocks. Two months later, several metres of dune have disappeared, allowing the blocks to fall on to the beach.

Hard engineering methods are used to overcome natural processes. Structures are built to resist wave and tidal energy, and the agents of sub-aerial processes – wind and water – which may cause mass movement. Cliff-foot strategies include sea walls (vertical, curved or stepped), revetments (designed to dissipate energy), groynes (made of various materials), breakwaters, and 'beach pumping', whereby backwash energy is reduced using drainage pipes buried 2 or 3 metres below the beach. Cliff-face strategies include cliff pinning (piles driven through rock to secure it), cliff modification (by stabilising slopes), cliff drainage, and vegetation.

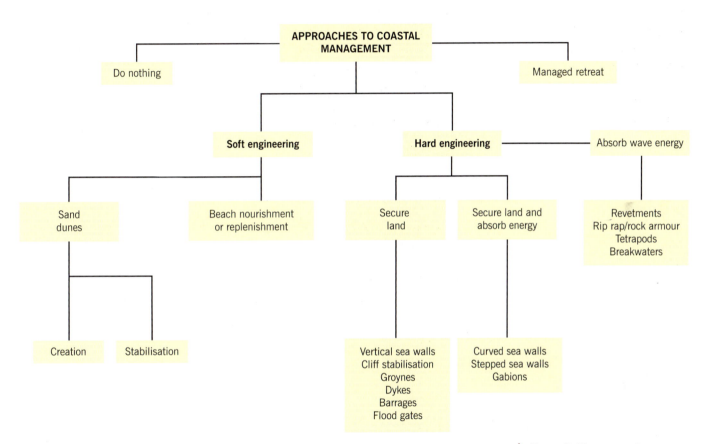

▲ Figure 2: The range of approaches to coastal management.

Soft engineering methods are used to work with, rather than against, the natural processes of marine and sub-aerial erosion. These strategies include beach filling and nourishment, where sand or shingle is brought in from somewhere else to counteract the impact of longshore drift. This is an expensive approach and obviously has to be done regularly. Sand dunes can be stabilised by planting marram grass; this is possible where groynes are also used and dunes are encouraged to develop at the top of the beach to protect the cliff-foot, as at Hengistbury Head in Dorset.

Hard engineering structures, such as sea walls and groynes, have been built to protect, for example, the towns on the Holderness coast (Hornsea, Mappleton and Withernsea) but erosion of farmland in between the towns is not prevented because to do so could have severe knock-on effects further south. Understanding how sediment cells work enables the cost of farmland loss at Holderness to be set against the cost of flooding and loss of habitats in the Humber estuary and on the Lincolnshire coast.

Taking it further

Research exercise: Compare and contrast the different hard engineering structures used to defend eroding coastlines by constructing a table showing the method, a sketch of the structure, its advantages, disadvantages, financial cost and approximate lifespan, and an example of where it is in use.

Taking it further

To learn more about coastal management strategies read 'Research exercise: Evaluating coastal management strategies' on your Student CD-ROM.

There are four coastal planning approaches that can be adopted:
- Hold the line by maintaining or upgrading the level of protection provided by defences.
- Advance the line by building new defences seaward of the existing defence line.
- Managed realignment, allowing retreat of the shoreline, with management to control or limit movement.
- No active intervention, the 'do nothing' option of no provision or maintenance of defences.

The preferred approach will depend on a variety of factors but the most important criteria are technical feasibility, economic viability and environmental impact.

Greater understanding of coastal processes and the impacts of past management schemes on other areas of coastline has led to changes in coastal management. In 1991, the government set up a House of Commons Select Committee to investigate coastal zone planning as a way of encouraging sustainable management (as used in the USA and Australia). Then in 1995, the Ministry of Agriculture, Fisheries and Food (MAFF) encouraged the development of a more integrated approach, using shoreline management plans (SMPs). (MAFF has now been reorganised into Defra – the Department for Environment, Food and Rural Affairs.)

In England and Wales, local authorities and the Environment Agency have developed the SMPs to co-ordinate coastline planning. They are based on the 11 sediment cells, one of which is the east coast of England from Flamborough Head in Yorkshire to Gibralter Point in Lincolnshire. The Holderness coast and the Humber estuary are sub-cells within this larger unit. Viewing this stretch of coastline as a single unit makes sense, because sediments eroded from the Holderness cliffs are transported south to the Humber estuary and to the Lincolnshire coast where mudflats and salt marshes have built up, providing a natural defence against the sea.

Defra has responsibility for policy concerning coastal erosion in England (and the Welsh Assembly has responsibility in Wales) while the Environment Agency implements the policy by building flood and coastal defences. It also carries out research, monitoring and risk assessment. In the Dungeness area, for example, it has been estimated that, each year, about 25,000 residents have a 1% probability of tidal flooding. Regional Coastal Groups, comprising local authorities, the Environment Agency, English Nature and other relevant organisations, have been set up around the country, based on the natural coastal sediment cells. The Groups co-ordinate the preparation of SMPs and coastal defence strategies.

◀ **Figure 3:** Sediment cells around the coast of England, the rectangle shows the location of the Holderness coast.

Case study: The Beachy Head to South Foreland SMP

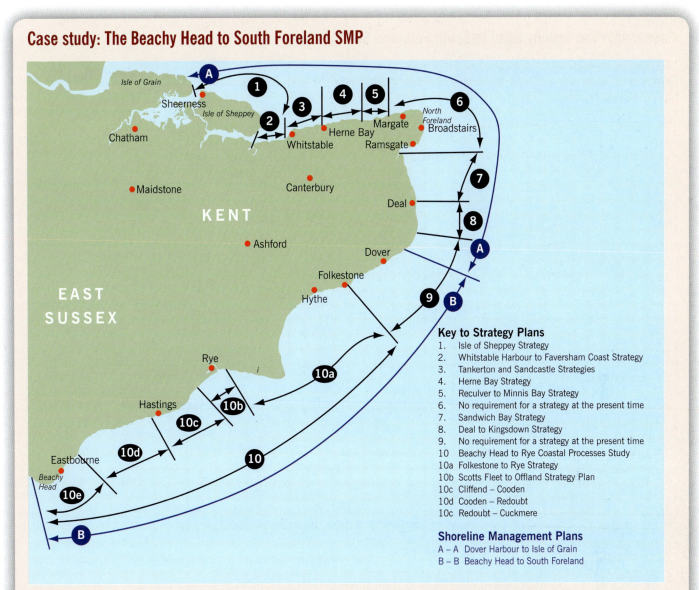

Key to Strategy Plans
1. Isle of Sheppey Strategy
2. Whitstable Harbour to Faversham Coast Strategy
3. Tankerton and Sandcastle Strategies
4. Herne Bay Strategy
5. Reculver to Minnis Bay Strategy
6. No requirement for a strategy at the present time
7. Sandwich Bay Strategy
8. Deal to Kingsdown Strategy
9. No requirement for a strategy at the present time
10 Beachy Head to Rye Coastal Processes Study
10a Folkestone to Rye Strategy
10b Scotts Fleet to Offland Strategy Plan
10c Cliffend – Cooden
10d Cooden – Redoubt
10c Redoubt – Cuckmere

Shoreline Management Plans
A – A Dover Harbour to Isle of Grain
B – B Beachy Head to South Foreland

▲ **Figure 4:** Coastal defence strategies are based upon sub-cells within the larger Beachy Head to South Foreland sediment cell.

The Folkestone to Rye section of coastline (10a in Figure 4) varies from the high clay and sandstone cliffs at Folkestone to the low-lying shingle ridges and farmland of Dungeness and Romney Marsh. The strategy for this section recommends defence options to achieve a 'hold the line' policy for the majority of the coast. A Coastal Habitat Management Plan (CHaMP) has been drawn up as part of the SMP, reviewing the likely environmental results of the four possible management options:

1. Do nothing
2. Hold the present line
3. Allow managed retreat, by removing the terminal groyne at Rye Harbour
4. Allow managed retreat to the AD 1800 coastline only.

Each of these scenarios would result in some loss of habitat, but management has to aim for sustainability while recognising the inevitable consequences of climatic change. Any plan for Dungeness has the obligation to maintain the safety of the nuclear power station. For sustainability, it is generally preferable to allow nature to take its course and to let coastal processes operate unhindered, but here this would require difficult and unpopular short-term management. Doing nothing or allowing retreat would result in large-scale coastal changes but these options would have major social and economic consequences. The SMP for the South East strategic coastline includes the detail listed in Figure 5 on page 196.

Case study: The Beachy Head to South Foreland SMP (continued)

Policy unit	Works for short-term policy	Specific monitoring requirements	Specific study requirements	Responsibility
Hythe Ranges	Maintenance of existing structures	Performance of shingle beach fronting rock/rubble defences	The ongoing strategy will verify the short- and long-term options. The conclusions of this must be reviewed against the SMP and reported.	Environment Agency, Shepway District Council and Ministry of Defence
Dymchurch Redoubt to Romney Sands	Implementation of recently approved Dymchurch scheme, and ongoing maintenance of remaining frontages			Environment Agency and Shepway District Council
Romney Sands to Dungeness Power Station	Dune management at Greatstone		Clarification of Greatstone dune processes to understand past and future development and management approaches	Environment Agency and Shepway District Council
Dungeness Power Station	Ongoing recycling operations to maintain required standard of protection	Annual beach inspections		British Energy and British Nuclear Fuels Limited
Lydd Ranges	Construction of set-back defences to facilitate return to 'natural beach'. Cease current recycling/reprofiling activities	Monitoring to include the response of the shoreline to 'natural' processes along this frontage and changes in habitat	The ongoing strategy will identify the short- and long-term options. The conclusions of this must be reviewed against the SMP and reported.	Environment Agency, Ministry of Defence, English Nature [now Natural England], British Energy and British Nuclear Fuels Limited
Jury's Gap to The Suttons	Construction of new hard defence to improve standard of protection			Environment Agency and Rother District Council
Camber Sands	Continued dune management	Review sand dune movement		Environment Agency and Rother District Council

▲ **Figure 5:** Coastal defence management strategies for Hythe Ranges to Rye.

Within this short stretch of coastline, a range of strategies is being implemented, from the construction of hard defences at Dymchurch to managed retreat at Lydd Ranges. The beach nourishment (transferring shingle from the east side to the west to protect the power station) is essential for safety and will have to continue for many years to come — perhaps questioning the wisdom of building two nuclear installations on such a vulnerable shoreline. There are also sand dunes at Camber requiring soft engineering management.

Hard engineering at Dymchurch and Littlestone

The South Foreland to Beachy Head Shoreline Management Plan analyses the issues and objectives for this stretch of the West Kent and East Sussex coastline. The plan was produced following evaluation of the coastal processes and existing management strategies, and the human, historic and natural environmental features, and consultation with key stakeholders, to determine possible policy scenarios.

◀ **Figure 6:** Shingle extraction at Dungeness. Every year, approximately 30,000 m³ of shingle is taken from here and placed along the southern shore of the Ness, at Broomhill and Jury's Gap.

Case study: The Beachy Head to South Foreland SMP (continued)

This is a low-lying flood risk area where the plan is to protect the villages of Dymchurch, St Mary's Bay and Littlestone-on-Sea, and the road and light railway, by maintaining and improving the current defences. It is expected that the beach will narrow here as the natural supply of sediment from the south west has been reduced following extraction on the Dungeness Foreland. The concrete seawall at Dymchurch is preventing the natural landward movement of the shoreline so the foreshore is being squeezed between rising sea levels and a static backshore line to protect the town.

The sea defences from Dymchurch Village to Dymchurch Redoubt are much older than those adjacent to Littlestone-on-Sea. The original clay embankments have been progressively clad on their seaward face, protected on their crests and had rear return walls added at various dates. Due to falling beach levels, the sloping front aprons, which were originally built of stone, have had to be extended, patched with concrete and, at the easterly end, clad with concrete panelling.

▲ **Figure 7:** A section of the sea wall at Dymchurch. Wooden groynes have been built along this stretch of coastline to trap the eastward movement of sand and shingle.

Soft engineering techniques applied at Camber Sands

Camber Sands is the only sand dune system in East Sussex, just over the border from Kent. It forms a wedge-shape, only 10 metres wide at its eastern end, growing over its 3 km length, to 1 km wide in the west. The tide goes out for almost 1 km at Camber, enabling a full sequence of dunes to have developed – embryonic fore dunes, unstable yellow dunes, running parallel with the coast, and stable grey dunes located on the golf course towards the western end of the system. The dunes have formed over the last 350 years – and are still growing, as 7,500 m^3 of sand are deposited here every year, but now they are restricted by urban development.

A large section of the western end of the dunes is an SSSI, while the rest is designated a Site of Nature Conservation Importance. There are some important animal and plant communities, and many rare species are found here. There are six habitat types – fore dune, shingle, dune scrub, inter-tidal, woodland, and acid dune grassland – and these attract some unusual moths and beetles and provide a valuable site for wintering birds.

▲ **Figure 8:** The sand dunes at Camber Sands are vulnerable to overuse by visitors.

Case study: The Beachy Head to South Foreland SMP (continued)

Camber's large sandy beach became a popular seaside destination early in the twentieth century, and this started to damage the dunes. During the Second World War (1939–45) the dunes were used for military exercises, and concrete tank traps and pillboxes were built because of the threat of invasion. The beach was also used to practise landing manoeuvres prior to D-Day. Post-war restoration included major reseeding of the dunes, but some sand was removed to build Dungeness Power Station. More recently, increasing pressure from tourism, with up to 25,000 people visiting on hot summer days, has resulted in further erosion of the dunes.

Many plants on the dunes are very fragile and easily damaged by trampling, so dune management includes providing paths and encouraging visitors to use them, with guiding posts and fences to protect the most vulnerable areas. Interpretation panels are provided along the paths, telling visitors about the wildlife to encourage them to respect it.

The sand dunes need to be stabilised and not blown further inland, because they are essential in protecting Camber village, behind the dunes, and parts of Romney Marsh, which lie below the high tide level and would otherwise be flooded. The main sea defence strategy is to remove wind-blown sand from the front of the dunes and from public paths going over the dunes. Chestnut fencing is used to trap the sand and to prevent it blowing into the village. Every January, recycled Christmas trees from the local community are 'planted' on their sides in shallow trenches where gaps have been created in the dunes by trampling. The trees trap wind-blown sand, allowing vegetation to grow and stabilise the dunes.

Managed retreat at Lydd Ranges

Lydd Ranges is a largely undeveloped area of shingle ridges, of international nature conservation importance, that is used by the Ministry of Defence as a firing range. Managed realignment of this section of the coastline is proposed to allow the shoreline to retreat naturally, as sediment will be carried eastwards by longshore drift to and beyond the nuclear power station. Coastal retreat is approximately 1 metre per year at the moment, and it is thought that rising sea levels will increase this by only a few centimetres. This low-maintenance policy would involve a progressive loss of the ranges but it would enhance the conservation status of the shoreline by allowing the coastal processes to create a natural shingle beach with its associated habitats. A secondary flood embankment would be needed, however, to prevent flooding of the village of Lydd behind the ranges.

Coastal zone management

Defra funds most of the Environment Agency's flood management activities in England and provides grant aid on a project-by-project basis to the other flood and coastal defence authorities. The coastal zone is a highly complex system with many competing activities, and decisions are taken through a number of different management frameworks. Decision-making on the coast has historically been undertaken on a sectoral basis (from the point of view of ports, or nature conservation, or planning) but today's more integrated approach should help to deliver more sustainable management.

The process of integrated coastal zone management (ICZM) is now believed to be the most effective way of managing the interactions of many of these different activities. A new holistic strategy for managing flood risk is combining all sources of flooding (river, coastal, groundwater, surface run-off and sewer) and coastal erosion under the Water Framework Directive (WFD), effectively following the course of water from its source in the river catchment to the sea. Sustainable development should become more achievable by bringing together the different terrestrial and marine management frameworks.

Within any framework, because the coastal zone is dynamic and constantly changing due to both natural processes and human activities, an ongoing process of policy implementation and evaluation is required if sustainability is to be achieved (Figure 9).

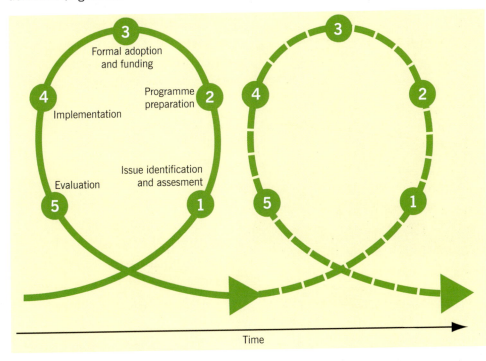

▶ **Figure 9:** Operating the process of integrated coastal zone management.

Source: Olsen et al., 1999

The coastal management strategies in England show what is possible, given sufficient investment. But it is also clear that it is a continuous process and requires constant monitoring and evaluation. Many of the world's largest cities are exposed to coastal flooding and many people around the world are already exposed to coastal flooding from storm surges and damage due to high winds. With continued population growth, urbanisation, the effects of climate change and subsidence, many major port cities need to invest in coastal defences.

Mumbai's Coastal Regulation Zone

In the Mumbai Metropolitan Region (MMR), on India's west coast, 2.8 million people live in an area at risk from cyclone and monsoon flooding, with a one-in-a-hundred annual probability of a storm-surge flood event. By 2070 the number of people at risk to coastal flooding will grow to 11 million. The city is only 10 to 15 metres above sea level and occupies several islands within a large expanse of wetlands. It is a narrow landmass surrounded by sea on three sides, and the reclamation and development of the area between the islands has encroached on to the wetlands. The critical problems in the MMR are this loss of wetlands due to reclamation, plus the contamination from dumping of solid waste, the proliferation of slums, and the destruction of mangroves.

The entire Indian coastline (defined as the land between the low tide line and a line 500 metres inland from the high tide line) has been legally protected since 1991. Within this Coastal Regulation Zone (CRZ), the coast should be kept free of all unnecessary development and protected from environmental degradation – but the policy has been controversial. While every regional government supported the legislation, in reality, the indiscriminate approval of industries, residential buildings, and commercial complexes continues as before; wetlands are reclaimed and mangroves destroyed.

Mumbai's Coastal Regulation Zone (continued)

▲ Figure 10: New developments in Mumbai vulnerable to coastal flooding.

The CRZ should protect natural coastal barriers like reefs, dunes, mangroves, beaches and terrestrial vegetation, and areas likely to be inundated by rising sea levels. Within it, activities that involve mining, polluting or dumping of waste on the waterfront are forbidden. Activities within the CRZ should support the sustainable livelihoods of traditional coastal communities such as fishermen. But the CRZ is viewed as anti-development, and it is often challenged. Much of Mumbai's slum redevelopment project is planned along the shoreline, exposing the most vulnerable section of society to potential tragedy.

Taking it further

To learn more about Mumbai's Coastal Regulation Zone read 'Mumbai's CRZ' on your Student CD-ROM.

The 2004 tsunami damaged parts of India's eastern coast and offshore islands but the disaster was magnified in the stretches of 'naked' coastline, where the coral reefs had been dredged indiscriminately and shrimp farming practised at the expense of mangroves. The MMR has coastal flooding warning systems, evacuation strategies, and detailed plans for coping with the aftermath of a disaster. But the proper implementation of the CRZ, which would reduce the risk of such flooding, seems unlikely because of the pressure for urban development.

Fieldwork exercise

Aim:

To assess the effectiveness of coastal defences.

Data collection:

1. Locate a stretch of coastline with a history of building defences to resist erosion.
2. Map the defences currently in place and take photographs of these defences.
3. Search for maps, photographs and documents showing past coastal defences – there may be useful resources online, or in a local library, that show how this coastline was previously defended.
4. Design a scale to assess the state of repair of the defences – this could work like a bi-polar analysis using antonyms such as new/old, excellent condition/poor condition and sturdy/crumbling.
5. Note the apparent effectiveness of features such as groynes, for example, are they being buried by sand or shingle so much that their effectiveness is diminished?

Data interpretation:

This will be more qualitative than quantitative but it would be useful to find out how much the defences cost to construct and if there are any plans to repair or extend the defences. Attempt to account for the defence strategy adopted with regard to the nature of the onshore zone and the apparent value of the property located onshore. You could also assess their value by finding out the approximate cost and life-span of such resources.

Summary

Human pressures on coastal environments create the need for a variety of coastal management strategies. Such strategies may be short-term or long-term, sustainable or non-sustainable. Successful management requires an understanding of coastal processes and systems, and the demands for coastal management are likely to increase with rising sea levels, more frequent storm activity and continuing coastal development.

After studying this chapter, you should now be able to discuss these ideas and concepts and provide located examples of them:
- The range of strategies available for coastal management, from hard engineering techniques to the 'do nothing' approach.
- How these strategies have been used and their effectiveness, costs and benefits.
  - The development of sustainable and integrated approaches, such as coastal realignment, shoreline management plans (SMPs) and integrated coastal zone management (ICZM).

MCQ

Exam practice

▲ Photographs of Cala d'Or: a recently developed coastal area in Majorca, Spain.

Study the figure.

(a) Explain how conflicts might occur as this 'crowded coast' continues to be developed. (10)

(b) Describe and explain a programme of **fieldwork** and **research** to investigate the **environmental** and **ecological** impacts of coastal development. (15)

(c) Examine a named strategy designed to make the coastal zone more sustainable. (10)

CHAPTER 23 What are unequal spaces and what causes them?

Key terms

Absolute poverty
Counter-urbanisation
Deprivation
Household
Relative poverty
Rurality
Spatial segregation
Super Output Areas
Urbanity

Learning objectives

After studying this chapter, you will be able to discuss these ideas and concepts and provide located examples of them:

• The definitions of inequality and poverty at different scales and in contrasting areas.
• The social and economic causes of inequalities and the processes that lead to uneven levels of environmental quality, social opportunity, wealth and the quality of life.
• The spatial impact of varying opportunity which means that some areas thrive while others struggle and may decline.

▲ **Figure 1:** Looking south towards Canary Wharf from Pudding Mill Lane in Stratford, East London, a distance of less than 2 miles. This area is being redeveloped for the 2012 London Olympics. The three tall buildings to the right are apartment blocks.

Unequal societies

'The richest kids will play video games full of virtual violence while the poorest kids live in shanty-cities full of actual violence.'

James Martin, *The Meaning of the 21st Century*, Eden Project Books, 2006

Schools tend to reflect the area from which they draw their students, so it is likely that most of you in your school or college will come from similar socio-economic backgrounds. But there will also be some differences: some of you will get free school meals; others will be used to foreign holidays. Other schools nearby may seem generally poorer or richer. Some districts in your locality may be more affluent or quite poverty-stricken. You will have an instinctive understanding of relative poverty and affluence.

Elsewhere in the world there will be examples of both absolute poverty and extreme affluence. People are said to be 'affluent' when they have an abundant supply of money, goods or property. Microsoft President, Bill Gates, for example, is said to be wealthier than each of the 70 poorest nations. The wealth of the world is highly concentrated in a few nations and, within them, the real wealth is also often highly concentrated in the hands of a few people. 'Disparity' occurs when there is an inequality or difference in income, status or opportunity. At all scales, such disparity has spatial consequences.

Poverty, as a concept, is defined differently in different societies and definitions change over time. In the UK, if your income is less than 60% of the median wage, after taxes, benefits and adjustment for household size, you are defined by the Government as living 'below the poverty line'. This is a measure of relative poverty, in terms of income or wealth, below which people can be considered to be poor. As income levels rise, so will the poverty line.

Poverty is the most obvious result of inequality. Lack of equal access to sources of wealth in society causes inequality in income and can lead to poverty. If you cannot get a job that pays a living wage, you will not be able to pay essential bills for food, housing, clothing and basic amenities, such as water, gas and electricity.

In a fair society everyone has equal access to sources of wealth, but such equality of opportunity is often hindered. There are several reasons why some people may not have equal opportunities:

- Discrimination may be deliberate where political systems or self-serving interest groups put up barriers to protect the wealth and power of a few people.
- Inequality may be the outcome of natural differences, such as age or poor health.
- Sometimes inequalities are the result of prejudice based upon gender, race or religion.

As geographers, we study the spatial outcomes of social and economic inequalities. Our role is to describe and explain why some areas thrive while others decline.

> 'London has long been characterised by major inequalities between rich and poor, and these have been intensified … in recent years by the growth of very highly paid jobs in financial and business services, the decline of manufacturing industry, and the consequent growth of unemployment and economic inactivity.'
>
> (Chris Hamnett, *Unequal City: London in the Global Arena*, Routledge, 2003)

The causes of inequality

People on lower incomes living in deprived areas often find themselves trapped in a web of deprivation. Poor living conditions are often closely linked with poor health. Poor education leads to fewer skills that can be used in the labour market, while joblessness or poorly paid employment traps people in inadequate housing. The cycle of inequality goes round and round.

Key terms

Relative poverty: poverty is defined in relation to the standards that exist elsewhere in society, so it is a state of relative deprivation. People are in the lowest income groups and so may have inadequate housing, diet, amenities and services.

Key terms

Absolute poverty: a condition characterised by the lack of the most basic human needs, including food, safe drinking water, sanitation facilities, health, shelter, education and information. People are deprived of one or more of these basic human needs.

Examiners' tip

Make sure you understand the difference between the terms 'absolute poverty' and 'relative poverty' and that you can use them confidently when answering examination questions.

Key terms

Deprivation: People are said to be deprived when they lack the resources to enjoy the living conditions and amenities usually experienced by those in the society to which they belong. They may be deprived of adequate housing, sufficient food or access to employment.

Swedish economist Gunnar Myrdal suggested that regions experience a process of 'cumulative causation'. They have an initial advantage, which can trigger development and, via a series of multiplier effects, they develop economically and prosper. This process works in reverse when a region goes into a spiral of decline (see Figure 2). Many industrial towns and cities in the UK suffered a spiral of decline when their local coal mines or steel works closed in the 1980s. Movies such as *The Full Monty*, *Brassed Off* and *Billy Elliot* show how the people caught up in this deindustrialisation struggled to cope with its consequences.

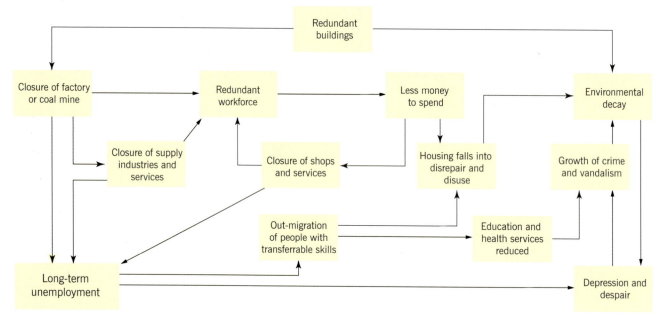

▲ Figure 2: The negative multiplier effect as it might apply in a socio-economically deprived area. Notice that it includes several cycles reinforcing the downward spiral.

Key terms

Spatial segregation: the residential separation of groups within a population or society. A ghetto is an extreme form of spatial segregation.

Key terms

Super Output Area: a geographical area containing a population of around 1,500 (minimum 1,000) used to interpret census and other data to identify areas of deprivation.

People living in areas in decline begin to feel excluded, especially if they see others growing richer. The problem of social exclusion is often the result of a combination of drawbacks, such as unemployment, discrimination, poor skills, low income, poor housing, high crime, ill health and family breakdown. Such problems may combine to create a vicious cycle. Those who experience social exclusion are unable to take part in activities taken for granted by the majority.

Some groups may find themselves socially excluded because they belong to an ethnic minority, or they may be disabled or elderly, refugees or asylum seekers, ex-prisoners, or gays and lesbians. People in a minority group often choose to live in the same neighbourhood, as they feel safer with their own kind. This clustering causes spatial segregation.

While inner city areas have attracted a lot of attention, there are also problems on peripheral estates. Here, local authority housing was originally provided for those displaced after decaying nineteenth-century housing was demolished in the inner city. Some of these estates have fallen into a spiral of decline, especially as male unemployment has risen with deindustrialisation. Not all marginalised or socially excluded groups experience poverty, of course, but where low pay or unemployment are significant factors, there are also environmental consequences.

Poor spaces

Figure 3 shows that commercial property values in 1999 were more than £50 per square foot in the City of London but less than £17.50 in Hackney borough, just a few minutes walk away! According to the 2004 Index of Deprivation, Hackney is ranked the fifth most deprived of the 354 local authorities in England. Of the 137 'Super Output Areas' in Hackney, 66 were in the top 10% most deprived in the country.

Even though Hackney is so close to the City of London, the people who live there are extremely deprived. The quality of housing in Hackney has been quite poor, unemployment levels have been higher than average, and the area has a large non-white ethnic population. These factors combine to reduce opportunities for the local inhabitants, white and non-white, and the area is caught in a cycle of decline.

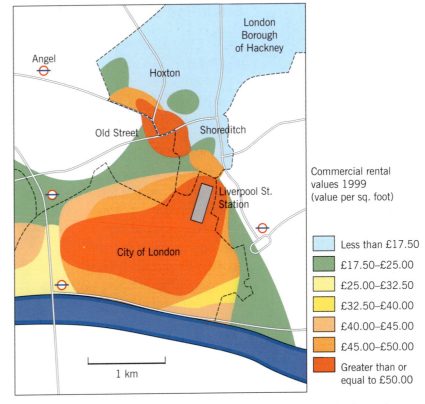

Commercial rental values 1999 (value per sq. foot)

- Less than £17.50
- £17.50–£25.00
- £25.00–£32.50
- £32.50–£40.00
- £40.00–£45.00
- £45.00–£50.00
- Greater than or equal to £50.00

▲ Figure 3: Commercial rental values in the City of London and the Borough of Hackney.

Case study: Hackney, London

Just over 200,000 people live in the London Borough of Hackney, giving it a population density of about 130 people per hectare. The population is young – the mean age is 32, compared to 38 for England and Wales, and about one in four inhabitants is aged under 15. However, there is a considerable cluster of older people living in the southernmost wards, around Hoxton, reflecting the housing policy in the area.

The Borough is ethnically mixed, with 60% of the population being white, compared to 91% for the whole of England and Wales. A quarter of Hackney's residents are black and 12% are Asian or Chinese. While Christians form the largest religious groups, there are also significant numbers of Muslims and Jews. The black and Asian populations are concentrated in wards to the north-west of the Borough.

Hackney has one of the lowest owner-occupier rates in the UK, with only one-third of all householders owning their own home. Twice as many people in Hackney do not have a car, compared with England and Wales. This is not unusual for London, however, which has a better public transport system than elsewhere and, even though Hackney is effectively by-passed by the underground network, it is quite well served by the overground railways (and the East London underground line will be completed in 2011).

Hackney has one of the highest proportions of full-time students in London, and a significantly higher proportion of people with higher education qualifications – some of whom will be postgraduate students. The attraction for students may be the lower-than-London-average property costs.

Hackney also has the highest incidence of schizophrenia and the second-highest incidence of tuberculosis (TB) in inner London.

Breadline Britain

Figure 4 shows estimates of the proportions of households living in poverty in 2001, using a combination of census data and a poverty measure called 'Breadline Britain'. This measure defines a household as 'poor' if the majority of people in Britain would conclude that the resources available to that household constituted living in poverty. This includes factors like owning a television and taking an annual holiday.

As overall living standards rise, poverty can also rise if society becomes more unequal and more people lack what most consider to be necessities. According to the Breadline Britain

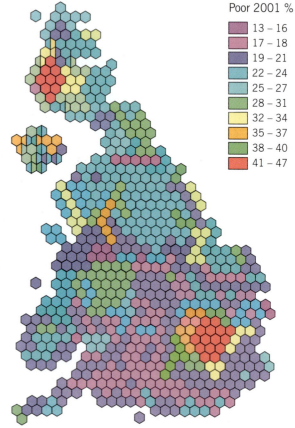

Poor 2001 %

- 13 – 16
- 17 – 18
- 19 – 21
- 22 – 24
- 25 – 27
- 28 – 31
- 32 – 34
- 35 – 37
- 38 – 40
- 41 – 47

▲ **Figure 4:** Households living in poverty in 2001.

measure, 24% of all households in the UK were poor in 2001. And there were concentrations of such poverty in areas such as East London and Glasgow.

How can an area with the richest real estate in the world compare with an area suffering deindustrialisation following the closure of steelworks, shipbuilding yards and manufacturing? It is partly because the size of the areas used on the map is so large, and each of these areas contains many people. Also, poor people, the 'have-nots', often do live quite close to rich people, the 'haves'.

Inequalities can exist at a variety of scales: between neighbouring people and groups, between neighbourhoods, districts or regions, between settlements, and between rural and urban areas. For people to be poor, others have to be rich. To study inequality, you need to study both the poor and the rich.

Wealthy spaces

In a survey of their customers in 2007, Barclays Bank mapped the distribution of people with more than £100,000 available to invest in property or shares. You can see from Figure 5 that, even among the top 20 counties, there is a clear spatial variation from 13% in London to under 2% in Sussex and Devon. The four wealthiest individual postcodes were all in London and the South-East. Cheshire, where Alderley Edge is famously home to some of the UK's top sports stars, was only in eleventh place.

Case study: Billionaire's Row

The Bishops Avenue in East Finchley is probably the richest road in the world. Here you will need at least £3 m to buy a relatively modest five-bedroom house. The most expensive mansion was marketed for £50 m in 2006. This tree-lined km of suburbia is home for some of the world's richest people, including property magnates, Arab princes and Russian oligarchs.

There is always some building work going on, as prospective residents often demolish the house they have bought so that they can build a new one to suit their own tastes. The planning laws are fairly lax and you can more or less build anything on the one-hectare plots. As a result, you will find Texan-style ranches alongside overgrown neo-Georgian houses, and squat marble bunkers that resemble Soviet mausoleums. The road is fully open to traffic, and driving down The Bishops Avenue is an enjoyable outing for ordinary folk who like to poke fun at the vulgarity of the rich and their 'expensive eyesores'.

East Finchley does not have the social prestige of Chelsea and Belgravia, nor the Grade II-listed charm of Hampstead village, but it is more open, green and leafy. It is also very conveniently located for easy access to London's West End or the City, as well as Heathrow airport. But mostly, people probably move to The Bishops Avenue because they want to show off their wealth and status.

Source: 'Down on Billionaire's Row', Coral Walsh, The Observer, April 30 2006

The two maps in Figures 4 and 5 seem to contradict each other: London appears both very rich and very poor. Carefully targeted research is needed to get an accurate picture of what is going on, because maps of the whole country are clearly at too small a scale and cover too large an area. In particular, the data used for Figure 5 is at county level and, while these include urban metropolitan counties such as Greater London and the West Midlands, the 'shires' such as Devon or Yorkshire (actually three administrative counties) include major urban areas such as Plymouth, Leeds and Sheffield, alongside vast swathes of rural land.

Rural and urban spaces

It can be difficult to distinguish clearly between urban and rural settlements. Imagine looking out through the window of a train as it leaves the centre of a city: you will see a gradual decrease in urbanity and an increase in rurality with increasing distance from the city centre. The distinction between rural and urban areas is not clear, because one area slides seamlessly into the other (see Figure 6). This is the rural–urban continuum.

The term rural–urban continuum was originally used by sociologists who were comparing rural and urban societies. Rural communities were seen as close-knit, stable, very structured in terms of social class and composed of people with similar interests and values. Urban society involved far more change and a greater mix of people because they moved around more. Urban inhabitants were more likely to be part of several disconnected groups of friends and colleagues, at work, at home and in recreation.

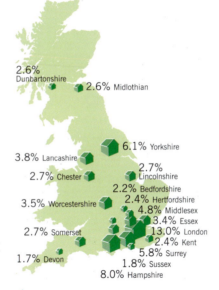

2.6% Dunbartonshire
2.6% Midlothian
6.1% Yorkshire
3.8% Lancashire
2.7% Lincolnshire
2.7% Chester
2.2% Bedfordshire
3.5% Worcestershire
2.4% Hertfordshire
4.8% Middlesex
3.4% Essex
2.7% Somerset
13.0% London
2.4% Kent
5.8% Surrey
1.7% Devon
1.8% Sussex
8.0% Hampshire

▲ Figure 5: The wealthy as a proportion of the total population.

Key terms

Rurality and urbanity: There is no agreed definition of 'rurality', and exact measures vary in different parts of the world, but most measures use demographic, socio-economic, cultural and environmental factors to determine the degree to which a place may be described as rural. 'Urbanity' identifies the other end of the scale to rurality and includes everything that may not be described as rural.

Taking it further

To discover where you stand on the rural-urban continuum read 'Are you an urban or a rural person?' on your Student CD-ROM.

The rural–urban continuum	Little open space High population density **INCREASINGLY URBAN**				**INCREASINGLY RURAL** Low population density Few buildings	
Cloke's Index	*Urban*	*Extreme non-rural*	*Intermediate non-rural*	*Intermediate rural*	*Extreme rural*	
Description	Inner city and city centre	Suburban areas	Rural–urban fringe	Pressured rural areas	Remote areas	
Settlement type	Inner city	Outer city	Edge of city	Villages and small towns	Isolated dwellings	Hamlets
Land use	High rise: business, retailing and residential	Low rise: residential, local services and amenities	Mixed land uses	Counter-urbanised and suburbanised villages and farming	Marginal farming, conservation and recreation	Prosperous farming, recreation
Services and functions	High-order functions and services	Neighbourhood centres with low-order services	Warehouse-scale retail and service functions	Village shop to range of small high street outlets	No services	Post box
Travel time	15 min	30 min	45 min	1 hour	1½ hours	2 hours
Location	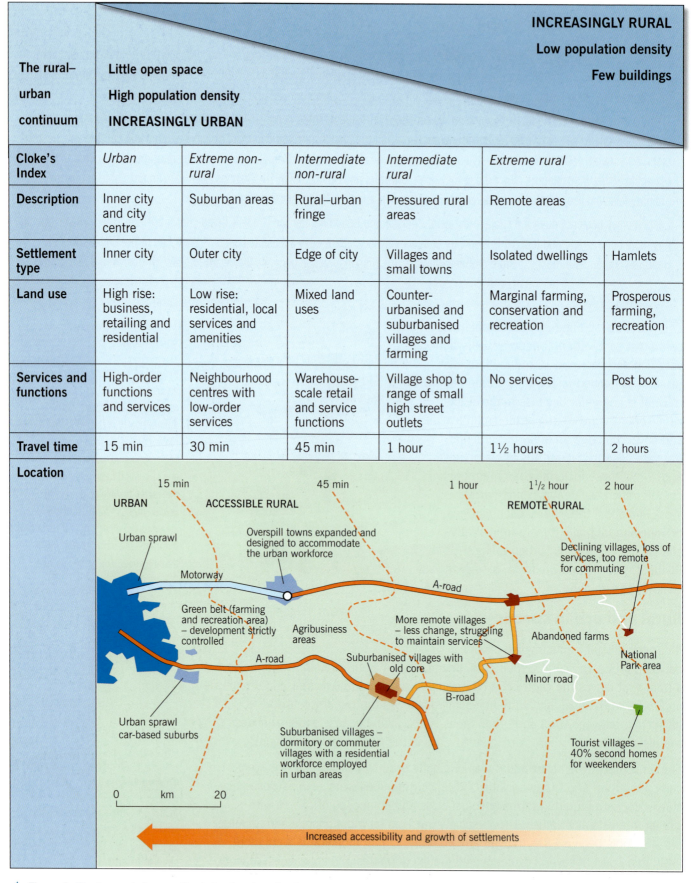					

▲ **Figure 6:** The transect diagram illustrates the changing features along the rural–urban continuum.

Paul Cloke devised an 'Index of Rurality' in 1977 based upon variables taken from the census. Figure 7 lists some of the variables he used and suggests how relevant they may be today. You may consider that in the twenty-first century there are other criteria that could be more useful to measure relative rurality and urbanity: access to services such as a supermarket, bus route or health centre, perhaps, or mobile phone coverage. Car ownership is often taken as a measure of affluence, but as public transport services may be poor or even non-existent in rural areas, a car is essential to people who live there; for them, the size and age of the car might be a better measure.

Cloke's Index variable	Relevance today
Percentage of population who are females aged 15 to 45	Still useful, but 20 to 45 would be better as more teenagers now stay in full-time education.
Occupational structure	Higher proportion of farmers still in rural areas but the number is declining.
Population change between 1961 and 1971	Rural population declined for 200 years until the 1960s, since when it has been growing, except in extreme rural areas.
Commuting pattern	Has increased because of counter-urbanisation and the growth of commuter or dormitory villages.
Distance from urban area of 50,000 or more	Will not have changed much, unless urban areas have seen exceptional growth. New towns will affect this variable.
Percentage of people aged over 65	Rural areas still have more elderly people, but for different reasons. Young people continue to move away and older people now move to the countryside after retirement.
Household amenities	Not a useful indicator now as the quality of housing everywhere has improved – very few homes lack bathrooms, inside WCs or running hot water now.
Population density	Still lower, though intermediate areas may have medium densities.
Recent inward migration	There has been significant counter-urbanisation since the late twentieth century.

Figure 7: Cloke's 'Index of Rurality' – the variables used and their relevance now.

Unequal rural spaces

People living in the countryside have plenty of access to open space and fresh air but they may have to travel some distance to a cinema or to get a takeaway meal. More importantly, vital services such as the post office or a doctor's surgery may also be miles away. In this respect, rural people may suffer deprivation.

Urban dwellers may also find it hard to get to see a doctor in some poorer inner-city areas. A low concentration of GPs and high levels of deprivation often coincide in cities, and there has been concern that nearly twice as many doctors apply for rural positions as those applying for positions in urban deprived areas.

Clearly, straight comparisons between rural and urban areas are not possible because both contain extremes of rich and poor – and many people on middle incomes. There are also degrees of urbanity and rurality. While poverty is well documented in inner cities, it may be just as bad, if not worse, in some of the most rural areas of England and Wales, as shown in Figure 8.

Examiners' tip

You should take care never to make sweeping statements about differences between people or places.

Key terms

Counter-urbanisation: the process of decentralisation as people move out of major urban centres to rural villages and small towns.

Examiners' tip

Make sure you fully understand the distinction between the terms 'counter-urbanisation', 'suburbanisation', 'urbanisation', and 're-urbanisation'. Easy marks are often lost in examinations when candidates get these terms mixed up.

Generally, the most deprived rural areas are those that are most distant from the urban areas (Figure 8). Most of Cornwall and large swathes of Devon, Norfolk, Lincolnshire and Cambridgeshire are classed as most deprived. People living in rural areas close to urban centres tend to have higher incomes than those in more remote rural areas. This is, however, because of counter-urbanisation, which results in an abundance of high earners living in rural commuter areas.

The pattern in Wales is slightly different because the most significant areas of highest deprivation are in the former industrial areas of the south. There are also small areas of deprivation in the more rural areas where declining farm incomes have had a significant impact.

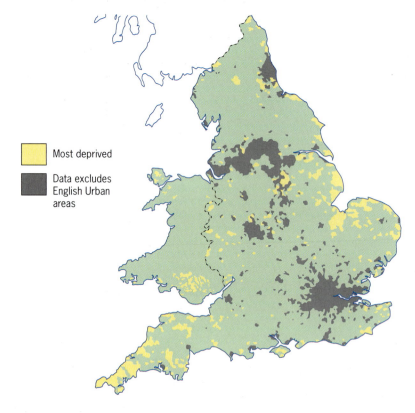

Most deprived

Data excludes English Urban areas

▶ Figure 8: The 20% of the rural population considered the most disadvantaged in England and Wales.

Case study: The Penwith District of Cornwall

The county of Cornwall is defined as predominantly rural by the OECD (Organisation for Economic Co-operation and Development). Penwith is the most westerly district of Cornwall and includes the tourism hot spot of Land's End. The district has an ageing population, a low-wage economy, and a significant shortage of affordable housing, partly due to second-home ownership.

In 2001, Penwith had a resident population of 63,058, with over one-third of the population living in villages, hamlets or isolated settlements. There are three small towns: Penzance (population: 12,000), St Ives (10,000) and Hayle (8,000), but over the summer months there are nearly 800,000 staying visitors and over 1 million day trippers, many visiting the popular tourist destination of Land's End.

Penwith's average wage was one-third less than the national average in 2004. Not surprisingly, therefore, there are comparatively high levels of child and adult poverty here. There are some areas with high levels of deprivation although these tend to be within the urban wards of Penzance and Hayle.

Unequal living spaces

Housing costs vary hugely in different parts of the UK so there will be spatial differences in the occurrence of poverty because housing is the main expense for any household. Figure 9 shows the average price of houses sold in different regions in early 2005 and average disposable household incomes at that time. Apart from the huge variation in house prices throughout the UK, it can be seen that housing is more affordable in some regions than in others.

Averages hide a great deal, of course. Greater London house prices, for example, are exaggerated by the number of very expensive houses in places like Chelsea and Hampstead. Such averaged statistics also say nothing about the type or quality of housing.

	Average house price Jan–Mar 2005	Average disposable household income 2005*	Ratio of house price to income
Greater London	288,500	15,900	18
South East	221,000	14,900	15
South West	196,800	13,300	15
East Midlands	149,500	12,500	14
West Midlands	151,500	12,100	13
East Anglia	172,000	14,200	12
Wales	133,600	11,900	11
Yorks and Humber	130,300	12,200	11
Northern Ireland	122,700	11,600	11
North West	127,800	12,200	10
North	119,600	11,400	10
Scotland	117,600	12,600	9

*Disposable household income represents the amount of money available to households less taxes, National Insurance and pension contributions, and interest paid.

Sources: www.pattinson.co.uk; http://news.ulster.ac.uk; www.scotland.gov.uk; National Statistics, March 2007

The property market is rather like a game of Monopoly. Some real estate is much more expensive because of its location. Locations differ so much because housing closely reflects income, class, culture and aspirations. As such, housing will be characteristic of an area's economy and social mix.

Rows of terraced houses were built in the nineteenth and early twentieth century to house working-class people, many of whom worked in factories. As the factories closed in the late twentieth century, these houses took on new lives, according to their location. In inner London boroughs, due to the shortage of properties, 'workers' cottages' were gentrified by young professionals and may now sell for as much as £500,000. In inner city Salford, on the other hand, you could buy a whole street for less than that, and many such properties are being demolished.

Examiners' tip

Beware of statistics! Always check the source of the figures – is it reliable? Does the author have a hidden agenda? Have the numbers been manipulated to prove a point? The more careful you are when you use statistics, the more reliable will be your interpretation of them.

◀ **Figure 9:** House price and household income ratios by UK region in 2005.

Taking it further

Compare property prices in different parts of the country by checking property for sale websites. Choose a particular house style and age (perhaps one like your own home) and note how the asking price for such a home can vary, depending on location. Alternatively, log on to the website of a national builder, such as Barratt Homes, George Wimpey or Bryant Homes, and see how their prices differ for similar-sized properties in different parts of the country. There are also websites where you can look up how much properties have sold for – you could look up your own street and compare them with others.

▲ **Figure 10:** Private residential property protected by an electronically controlled gate.

Local need and demand are crucial. The housing market may depend on the health of the local economy – as demonstrated by Myrdal's multiplier effect. Accessibility is also crucial. In London and the South East, there is a close correlation between house price and distance from the nearest tube or railway station. Proximity to motorway junctions is also often a valuable asset for both commercial and domestic property.

The location of good schools has a dramatic impact on property prices. More affluent parents will compete to move into an area to ensure that their children get the best education, boosting the local housing market. Increasingly, too, as a response to their perception of crime, richer people are choosing to live in gated communities, where an electronically controlled gate restricts access to a group of properties.

Home ownership is strongly related to a household's demographic and socio-economic characteristics. Older people are more likely to own their own home, while lone parents with dependent children are far more likely to rent their property. Ownership also varies by ethnic group: in 2001, 80% of Indians and 70% of White British people and Pakistanis were owner-occupiers, compared with only 25% of people of Black African origin.

Investigating environmental quality

House-builders sell an image to buyers. Notice the language they use – 'luxury apartments' or 'executive development'. Often the name of the development projects an image. Rural images are associated with names like 'meadows' or 'fields', even though such spaces are covered in bricks and tarmac. Urban developments that are targeted at young professionals will include words like 'wharf' or 'harbour'.

▲ **Figure 11:** A new housing development.

Environmental quality will be a reflection of an area's wealth, but will also influence people's perception of the area. A prospective house-buyer will research the districts in which they wish to live and they will pick the nicest area they can afford.

People's view of their environment will differ. Some will love the noise and bustle of the city centre; others will prefer the quiet and solitude of the countryside. The services and amenities that you might require will differ significantly, say, from those preferred by your grandparents. These differences provide great opportunities for geographical investigations.

Fieldwork: A survey of housing quality using photographic evidence

Aim
To investigate housing quality as an indicator of inequality.

Method
Create a photo-log of houses in various states of care and repair.

Equipment
If your mobile phone includes a camera you have all the equipment you need. A digital camera is useful but not essential – you could buy a single-use camera though you will have to be more careful to capture the right images straight away.

Risk assessment
Not everyone is going to thank you for taking photographs of their homes. Some neighbourhoods may be less safe, especially those where people may be suffering deprivation. You may be at risk of personal injury.

Health and safety
- Work in a group of two or three and stay with your friends at all times.
- Tell your parents or your teacher where you are going and when.
- Don't venture into unfamiliar neighbourhoods.
- Don't carry out this work after dark (also the flash photography would not work well).
- If possible, ask permission to take a photograph but don't pester the entire street.
- Be understanding and tactful!

Data collection
Collate your photographs in a hard-copy log-book or computer file with dates and locations attached (keep a back-up copy).

Data interpretation:
Annotate each photograph with observations about the evidence for inequalities. These observations could be positive or negative: new double glazing may be just as informative as a broken window about an area.

Summary

There are several social and economic causes of spatial disparities and these often work in combination, leading to uneven levels of environmental quality, social opportunity, wealth and quality of life. The spatial impact of different and changing opportunities means that some areas can thrive while others struggle and may decline.

Having studied this chapter, you should now be able to discuss these ideas and concepts and to provide located examples of them:

- The definitions of inequality and poverty at different scales and in contrasting areas.
- The social and economic causes of inequalities and the processes that lead to uneven levels of environmental quality, social opportunity, wealth and the quality of life.
- The spatial impact of varying opportunity that means some areas thrive while others struggle and may decline.

MCQ

To try an exam question using what you have learned in this chapter, turn to page 245.

CHAPTER 24 What impact do unequal spaces have on people?

Key terms

Assimilation
Food poverty
Community
GIS
Marginalisation
Multiple deprivation
Polarisation
Gentrification

Learning objectives

After studying this chapter, you will be able to discuss these ideas and concepts and provide located examples of them:
• Inequality creates marginalised groups in a variety of ways in rural and urban areas.
• Inequality can lead to social and economic exclusion and polarisation by denying opportunities and access to services.
• Marginalisation and segregation may be caused by inequalities based upon gender, age, race and religion, employment, education, income, or health and disability.

Access to wealth is not equal. The processes that initiate inequality are many and varied but may include employment, social class, education, health, age, gender and ethnicity. So some people may become marginalised, left out of the mainstream and unable to capitalise upon their abilities or to fulfil their ambitions. Such people become socially and economically excluded.

While poverty may lead to social exclusion, they are not synonymous – affluent people may be socially excluded if they are physically disabled. Have you ever wondered how easy it is for disabled people to get to the shops in a pedestrianised street or a shopping mall, for example?

Key

Factors you are born with
Factors you will acquire
Factors you may control

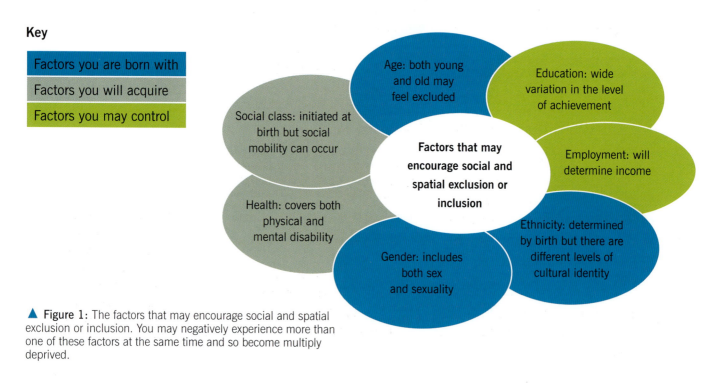

▲ **Figure 1:** The factors that may encourage social and spatial exclusion or inclusion. You may negatively experience more than one of these factors at the same time and so become multiply deprived.

Defining unequal spaces

Geographers like to distinguish between 'space' and 'place'. We talk about 'place' as somewhere that has meaning for a person or group of people. Your places will include your classroom, your home and the places where you hang out with your friends.

As a geography student you can go out and measure all sorts of things, from the gradient of slopes to the relative locations of shops, but how do people relate to those spaces? That's where place comes in. Interviews, open questionnaires, mental maps and attitude surveys are ways in which we can assess people's sense of place within the spaces they inhabit.

You may live in or near the centre of a large city and feel quite comfortable with the noise, the congestion and the crowds of people from many different cultures. You may be 'street-wise' when it comes to life in the city. Or you may have grown up in the country and enjoy the quiet and the wildlife around you. Many of you probably live in the suburbs, the vast residential settlement that has been wrapped around every urban centre in the last century or so.

How do you feel when you venture away from your home territory? Are there any places where you feel socially excluded? Are there places where you are socially included but others may feel (or actually be) excluded? We are all discriminated against somehow at sometime, and the ways in which we are set apart will change as we grow older.

It is more positive to talk about social inclusion because we are all members of communities. In fact, you are a member of several different communities simultaneously depending on where you live and what you do.

The idea of communities is very important in understanding spatial inequalities. People who are socially excluded are excluded from mainstream communities and their access to the benefits of such communities is limited or barred. Changes in the make-up of the population of an area can disrupt community spirit.

- The mass clearance of nineteenth-century inner-city housing and relocation of people to new local authority housing estates that took place in the 1950s and 1960s often led to the break-up of established communities. This was especially acute where terraced houses were replaced with high rise blocks of flats – as at Hulme in Manchester – because many people were isolated in their apartments.
- Rural communities in more pressured areas have been disrupted by the number of incomers, many of whom commute to the city for work and other amenities, or by second-home owners who are absent for much of the time. Villages around Cambridge have experienced considerable in-migration by city workers; and the indigenous population in some, such as St Ives, have found themselves priced out of the housing market.
- Gentrification of urban working-class districts displaces and replaces poorer residents and changes the character of the community. Islington in London is a classic example: the Barnsbury area was taken over by affluent young professionals in the 1960s and the ethnically mixed, working-class community was pushed out.

▲ Figure 2: Some people consider 'hoodies' to be threatening.

Key terms

Community: a spatially or socially delimited group of people having common interests.

Key terms

Gentrification: neighbourhood renewal by more affluent, usually young professional people who move in and renovate older properties. Less affluent residents are displaced and the character of the area alters as new shops and services open to serve the new residents.

Taking it further

Have a look at www.poverty.org.uk for UK statistics on poverty and social exclusion.

Social exclusion

In 1997, the UK Government set up the Social Exclusion Unit to tackle the problems of inequality and deprivation. Their remit was to help improve government action to reduce social exclusion by producing 'joined-up solutions to joined-up problems'. After consulting with local authorities, businesses, the voluntary sector and other agencies, the Unit worked on specific projects, to create jobs and encourage enterprise in deprived areas and to renew neighbourhoods.

The Unit's work has also focused on specific factors of social exclusion, such as mental health, debt, children in care, lack of access to transport, re-offending by ex-prisoners, teenage pregnancy, rough sleeping, truancy and school exclusion. One product of their work is Connexions, the youth advice and support service for 13 to 19 year olds in England.

Some social exclusion is not geographical, as it cuts across spatial boundaries. As geographers, we are interested in the spatial impacts of exclusion and the ways in which minority groups can be included. First, we need to establish the spatial patterns, that is, how dispersed or clustered a group may be. Some patterns of distribution are illustrated below.

Figure 3 shows some hypothetical distributions for an ethnic minority group of the same size within an urban area which has been divided into four wards. Clearly some distributions are more dispersed and more random than others. Also, analysis of data at the ward level would not necessarily pick up the actual geographical distribution. It is important to consider this when interpreting secondary data.

There are pros and cons to spatial segregation.

Negative features of spatial segregation
- It is a divisive feature of society
- It reduces social interaction between groups and individuals
- It leads to misunderstanding and mistrust
- It may be caused by some seeking to exclude others
- It can prevent social and economic advancement.

Positive features of spatial segregation
- It is a way of accommodating difference
- It allows a group to maintain its social cohesion
- It reinforces cultural values
- It provides protection from attack
- It enables provision of specific amenities and services to a group.

Lists adapted from 'Chapter 5: Race and Ethnicity' in Michael Barke and Duncan Fuller, *Introducing Social Geographies*, Arnold (2001), p.106.

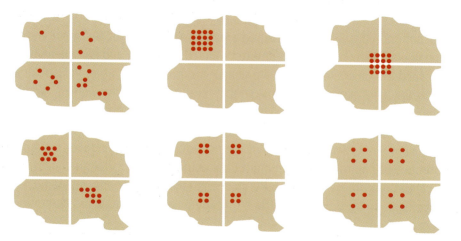

▶ **Figure 3:** Hypothetical patterns of segregation.
Adapted from 'Chapter 5: Race and Ethnicity' in Michael Barke and Duncan Fuller, Introducing Social Geographies, Arnold (2001), p.100.

Ethnic places

Ethnic clusters may be formed by choice or by force. Under the apartheid regime in South Africa, black and mixed race people were legally obliged to live in townships, such as Soweto, separately from white people. Prior to the success of the civil rights movement in the USA, black people had to sit at the back of buses and use different schools and even different public toilets from whites. These examples illustrate forced spatial exclusion.

The first spatially separate ethnic group is thought to be the Jewish ghetto in Venice. In 1516 the city's ruling council confined all the Jews into a *'getti'*. The gates were locked at night and Jewish people were only allowed to run pawn shops and lend money, trade in textiles and practise medicine.

▲ **Figure 4:** A sari shop in Brick Lane, East London.

Exclusion may be more subtle than legally enforced segregation. Market forces may be used deliberately or unintentionally to 'spatially sort' an ethnically mixed population. Often ethnic groups cluster by choice: in Greater London, for example, certain districts are favoured by particular ethnic groups:

- Irish in Kilburn
- Australians in Earls Court
- Jews in Golders Green
- South Koreans in New Malden
- Pakistanis in Waltham Forest
- Bangladeshis in Tower Hamlets
- Indians in Hounslow and Southall
- Chinese in Soho
- Greek and Turkish Cypriots in Haringey
- West Indians in Notting Hill and Brixton.

> **Key terms**
>
> Assimilation: the process by which communities and the minorities within them intermix and become more similar.

The advantages of such voluntary clustering are the social networks available for in-migrants, others speaking their own language, the proximity of specialist shops selling, for example, saris or halal meat, and places to worship, such as mosques and synagogues. In such areas people are able to retain their cultural identity.

There is a long history of spatial segregation of ethnic minorities but, over time, they become more dispersed or desegregated in a process of assimilation. Successive generations are exposed to and adopt the host culture, and they inter-marry with other ethnicities. In most London districts now there is a multicultural mix of people, and nowhere is there an area where one group is so dominant as to totally exclude others.

Case study: Spatial segregation in Chicago

White exclusionary tactics in Chicago included agreements among white people not to sell their property to black people, and any black people entering white areas were physically attacked. Estate agents increased business turnover by moving blacks into selected areas to encourage whites to move out, and the properties were then subdivided for resale. By 1950 over half the black inhabitants of Chicago lived in exclusively black districts.

Case study: Spatial segregation in London

Ethnic minorities are less concentrated in the UK than in the USA. The most concentrated group are the Bangladeshi community who live in Spitalfields in London, nicknamed 'Banglatown'. Its centre, Brick Lane, was originally an area of brick and tile manufacture, and has become famous following the book and film about the life of immigrants there. People from Bangladesh largely chose to live there, following a long tradition.

The first immigrants to Brick Lane were Huguenots (French Protestants). They were followed by Irish migrants and then Jewish people before the Bangladeshis arrived. With the first wave of in-migration, the area became a centre for weaving and the clothing industry and remains so today, with the addition of some of the best Bangladeshi curry houses.

Taking it further

Research: Using census data, look up the proportions of ethnic minorities in your area at ward level and map their distribution. Are there noticeable clusters of people? Does your area have a history of in-migration from particular groups? Follow this up with fieldwork on local businesses. Where are there shops that cater for particular ethnic groups? Map them to see if you can identify any patterns.

Gendered places

In Britain, you are living in a society where men and women are, or should be, treated equally. Key legislation – such as the 1975 Sex Discrimination Act, the 1976 Race Relations Act and the 1970 Equal Pay Act – outlawed inequalities on the basis of gender and ethnicity. In 2007 the Equality and Human Rights Commission, whose role is to work against inequality, was set up, combining three existing organisations:

- Commission for Racial Equality (CRE)
- Disability Rights Commission (DRC)
- Equal Opportunities Commission (EOC).

One strand of the Women's Lib movement in the 1970s sought to 'reclaim the streets'. The phrase has since been adopted by people campaigning against globalisation but, originally, the purpose was to make it safe for women to use the streets after dark. Women were protesting against sexual harassment and assault, and for their right to use public space alone, or with female friends, especially at night.

Even now, many women know that they should take care in certain places and situations, although issues of personal safety are not exclusively female. Young men experience a far higher incidence of personal assault and mugging, perhaps because they take more risks. There are quite clearly places that are essentially more feminine or more masculine, such as football grounds and beauty parlours – not that either sex is excluded – and this is by choice.

Elsewhere in the world, such freedoms as those enjoyed in the UK are not available. In Saudi Arabia, for example, women are not allowed to drive. Access to education for girls is not equal to that for boys in many less economically developed places. Similarly, access to work is restricted.

All limitations have spatial outcomes. Young males in working-class areas have experienced alienation following deindustrialisation and this is often associated with outbreaks of rioting, and anti-social crime including gang culture. Gangs of youths are very territorial, and while this is frequently associated with protecting markets for drug-dealing, membership of gangs is also about identity and belonging.

Support for football clubs is usually quite territorial. A top club like Manchester United may enjoy a global distribution of fans, but most teams draw much more local support and there are often very clear boundaries in cities with two or more professional teams, such as Sheffield or Liverpool.

Gay communities are more clearly geographically defined in the USA (San Francisco) and Australia (Bondi Beach) than in Europe, but there are places where gays and lesbians choose to live because they feel safer and more comfortable. There are higher-than-average numbers of gay people in Brighton and Hebden Bridge, for example. City centres have clusters of gay leisure spaces, pubs and clubs, such as Canal Street in Manchester. Such locations represent gay exclusion by choice. They are not exclusively gay, of course, but just have a higher proportion than in other places.

Elsewhere such freedoms are not available. In Zimbabwe, for example, homosexuality is illegal: the government has made it a criminal offence for two people of the same sex to hold hands, hug or kiss. In such countries there are no safe places for homosexuals and they are socially and politically excluded.

▲ **Figure 5:** Enjoying life in Canal Street, Manchester.

Young and old places

Age is a great divider. You, or your older brothers and sisters, will probably feel quite at ease in the city centre at midnight – most of the late-night businesses there, the pubs and clubs, are targeted at young people. But how would your grandparents feel?

In a couple of years' time many of you will be at university, enjoying the student life. A student at Nottingham Trent University has written about the 'booze culture' in the city centre. He noted that Nottingham is reputed to have the most bars per 1,000 people of any UK city, with over 350 bars within the city centre. On an average Friday or Saturday night there can be up to 70,000 people out drinking.

This inevitably leads to some violent incidents. Statistics regularly show that 60 to 80% of violent crime is alcohol-related, and alcohol is believed to be a contributing factor in 70% of weekend night admissions to hospital casualty units. Also, every year up to 11,000 people are admitted to the Queen's Medical Centre in Nottingham with alcohol-related diseases.

For many older people, behaviour that may be fun to the young revellers is extremely unpleasant and really quite scary. Many UK town centres become 'no-go zones' in the late evening for those who do not enjoy the booze culture. It is a form of social exclusion with a spatial outcome.

Many older people, and especially older women, feel excluded from urban centres at night, particularly at the weekend. Nearly half of all 16 to 34 year olds go 'out on the town' at least one evening a week, while only 15% of the over-55 year olds do. In fact, over 70% of over-55s generally do not go out at all in a town centre in the evening. Thus access to urban centres changes for different age groups at different times of the day.

In our society, older people and youths are sometimes seen as problem groups. The gang culture provides youths with a sense of community and they identify their own space or territory. They group together for defence, fearing attack from other groups, but also they engender a fear of crime in others, especially older people.

Older folk do not like 'hoodies'. When the Bluewater shopping centre in Kent banned youths wearing hooded tops and baseball caps, it experienced a sharp rise in visitor numbers – which made the headlines. Less publicity was given to the simultaneous ban on anti-social and intimidating behaviour, swearing and smoking (then legal) at the complex. The managers claimed its code of conduct was not targeting youths, but others said it infringed young people's rights.

It is suggested that older people present a problem as the old-age dependency ratio is rising as people live longer. In the UK, the increase in numbers of old people has been contained for over 30 years because the 'baby boom generation' have been in work and able to support them. But now the baby boomers are reaching retirement age themselves and their needs will have spatial consequences.

The provision of housing for older people includes not just retirement homes but also sheltered apartments and bungalows. Ideally these should be integrated, to avoid exclusion, rather than separated from other housing. Figure 6 shows a development of about 30 warden-assisted bungalows which have been conveniently built next to the local shops as part of a much larger development of family houses and apartments.

Within the same housing estate a small playground has been provided for younger children (Figure 7). Lack of provision for teenagers, however, makes this a popular, though less suitable, place for informal games of football – despite a sign forbidding ball games. Teenagers sometimes congregate here at night, too. Thus it has been suggested that young people create their own spaces within constraints set by adults.

▲ **Figure 6:** Sheltered homes for older people. These bungalows in Long Eaton, Derbyshire, are warden-assisted.

▲ **Figure 7:** This small playground is used more by older children and teenagers and only occasionally by pre-school children accompanied by parents or grandparents. One of the swings was stolen just days after it was installed.

Unhealthy places

Health is another indicator of inequality. Every local authority area in England has a Community Health profile. This uses key health indicators and enables comparison locally, regionally and nationally, as well as over time. The profiles are designed to help local councils and health trusts to decide where, in their local area, resources are needed to tackle health inequalities.

On the national scale, a north–south health divide has been identified. People in the north are more likely to smoke and drink more than those in the south, and this is linked to poorer mental health and a shorter life expectancy. Clearly, there are complex issues involving the inter-relationship of factors already examined in this section.

Health researchers are using GIS to analyse data from a range of sources to identify the people who need targeted health care. They are finding that it is necessary to work at sub-ward level, using Super Output Areas, in order to pinpoint where preventative health care should be offered – and often it involves just one or two streets.

Disabled places

Most of you reading this will be fit and healthy, and will take your fitness for granted. How accessible is your local town centre to people with walking difficulties? Many shopping streets have been pedestrianised – which is great if you can walk, but imagine if you could not.

Shopmobility is a charity set up to facilitate public access. Disabled people register with their local Shopmobility scheme, which lends manual wheelchairs, powered wheelchairs and powered scooters to members of the public with limited mobility so that they can shop and visit leisure and other facilities within their town, city or shopping centre.

There have been several Acts of Parliament designed to combat discrimination against the disabled and to improve access in public places. Your school or college is now legally bound to ensure that physically impaired students and teachers can access its facilities, in order to be socially inclusive, but sometimes this is quite difficult in older buildings.

Education

There is a strong link between social class and educational achievement, and this has a geographical outcome. At every level of education, upper- and middle-class children tend to do better than working-class children. Areas and schools with higher proportions of working-class inhabitants have lower levels of educational achievement, which can be measured with average SATs or GCSE scores. The table in Figure 9 shows this very clearly.

Measures such as the numbers of pupils receiving free school meals and the numbers speaking English as a second language are also used to differentiate schools. Underachievement at school is linked with poverty, overcrowding and family instability. Success at school can be affected by ethnicity, family structure, gender, health, housing and social class as well as parents' education, employment and income. Correlations between these factors and education are based upon averages and you can probably name some exceptions, but politicians and planners study the trends and act upon them.

Parents also act upon perceived differences between schools and levels of achievement, and this reinforces spatial patterns of relative success. It can also have an impact on the housing market as more affluent people move closer to better schools to live within their catchment areas and the competition pushes up houses prices.

Taking it further

If you live in England you can check out the health profile for your local area – look them up on www.communityhealthprofiles.info.

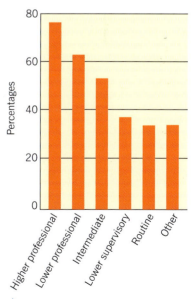

▲ Figure 8: A pedestrianised street in Sheffield city centre

▲ Figure 9: Percentage of pupils in England and Wales achieving five or more GCSE grades A* to C in 2002, according to the social class of their parents.

Source: www.statistics.gov.uk

Participation in further or higher education is strongly influenced by people's social and economic background. There is also a clear relationship between higher qualifications and greater earnings, and the likelihood of being employed is greater for those with higher qualifications. The situation becomes self-perpetuating – rather like Myrdal's multiplier effect.

Researchers have found that disadvantaged areas often have been so for decades. In London, Hackney and Islington have the lowest levels of achievement, despite the gentrification that has taken place. Richer parents here simply transport their children to better, often fee-paying, schools elsewhere (with an extra impact on road congestion).

Working places

Throughout this section on unequal spaces, reference has been made to levels of affluence and relative poverty. Underlying all the analysis is an understanding about how much people earn and how much they can purchase with this money (which differs between places at both national and international levels).

Clearly levels of income are related to types of employment, and educational achievement partly determines employment and income.

Throughout the second half of the twentieth century, employment in manufacturing declined and the service sector increased. Deindustrialisation particularly affected semi-skilled and unskilled manual workers – the traditional working class. Distinctions between working- and middle-class separate manual from non-manual workers (like the North American blue-collar and white-collar workers).

Such change had a spatial impact because industry is not evenly distributed. So unemployment hit northern and Midlands industrial towns and cities far harder than southern settlements. The south was not immune – there were significant industrial losses there too (in London, for example) but manufacturing formed a smaller proportion of the economy.

The growth in new jobs has also been spatially uneven. The economy of the City of London has boomed with the growth of the financial sector but this has benefited those in managerial and professional occupations rather than redundant manual workers.

Comparing the urban London Borough of Hackney with the rural Cornish District of Penwith, you will see from Figure 11 that Penwith has far fewer people in professional and intermediate occupations but noticeably more 'small employers and own account workers'. Many of these will be farmers or small businesses catering for the tourist trade. Hackney has more than twice the national average long-term unemployed; contained within this figure are students and people who have never worked (many of whom would be housewives).

These rather broad statistics hint at important differences in access to wealth and you should compare them with the information about the two places given in other chapters for more detailed explanation.

Taking it further

If you log on to www.dcsf.gov.uk/performancetables, you can look up the latest performance tables for all the schools in your local authority. You can then map these scores and see how they correlate with other data, such as those on social class, unemployment and ethnicity. Use Spearman rank correlation to analyse these data.

▲ Figure 10: Many jobs have been lost in textile manufacturing in the UK as production has been transferred abroad. This factory in Derbyshire was one of many ancillary industries, formerly supplying goods and services to textile manufacturers, that have been forced to close.

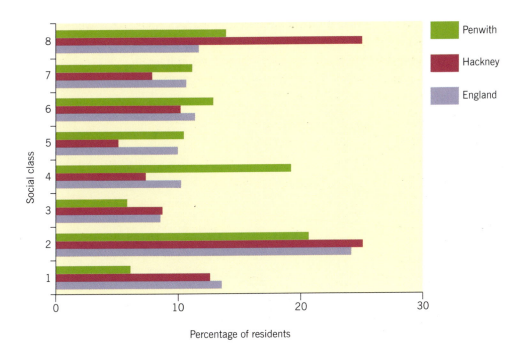

Key to social classes

1	Higher managerial and professional occupations
2	Lower managerial and professional occupations
3	Intermediate occupations
4	Small employers and own account workers
5	Lower supervisory and technical occupations
6	Semi-routine occupations
7	Routine occupations
8	Long-term unemployed

▲ **Figure 11:** Social class of residents of Hackney Borough and Penwith District in Cornwall, compared with England overall.

Food poverty

Many of us take it for granted that we can shop regularly for food at a supermarket near home, and it may also supply clothes and household goods, and provide ATM services, a café, a chemist and a filling station. Supermarkets now provide for about 80% of food shopping in the UK, compared with 50% 25 years ago. If you have a good supermarket nearby, or have easy access by car, you have the opportunity to buy a wide and healthy range of food.

Major retailers employ geographical skills when deciding where to locate new branches. Of course, they will take note of the locations of competing retailers but essentially they will be looking for the optimum place to find the most customers, to make the most money. Obviously the richer the customers, the more profit the retailers can make, so poor areas do not attract retailers.

When such market forces combine with a spiral of decline, neighbourhoods may lose shops in their vicinity. Further, people who remain in such areas, perhaps unable to afford to move, and with poor access to transport as they cannot afford a car, are effectively cut off from good food stores.

This has led to what is called 'food poverty'. Some of the poorest parts of the country have become 'food deserts' – areas where it is almost impossible to buy healthy food at reasonable prices. There are food deserts in urban and in rural areas. Sometimes there are food shops nearby but they sell little or no fresh food.

Food poverty occurs when people lack shops in their area or have trouble reaching them, and these factors are often combined with insufficient knowledge about what constitutes a healthy diet (see Figure 12). Old people and those on low incomes are the worst affected. It is estimated that some 4 million people in the UK are affected by food poverty.

Key terms

Food poverty: the inability to obtain healthy, affordable food.

Taking it further

Investigate food poverty on www.sustainweb.org and www.fareshare.org.uk/whatdo/food_poverty.html.

A study of Sandwell in West Bromwich found that 90% of households were within 500 metres of a shop that sold junk food and fizzy drinks but less than 20% were within 500 metres of a shop selling fresh fruit and vegetables.

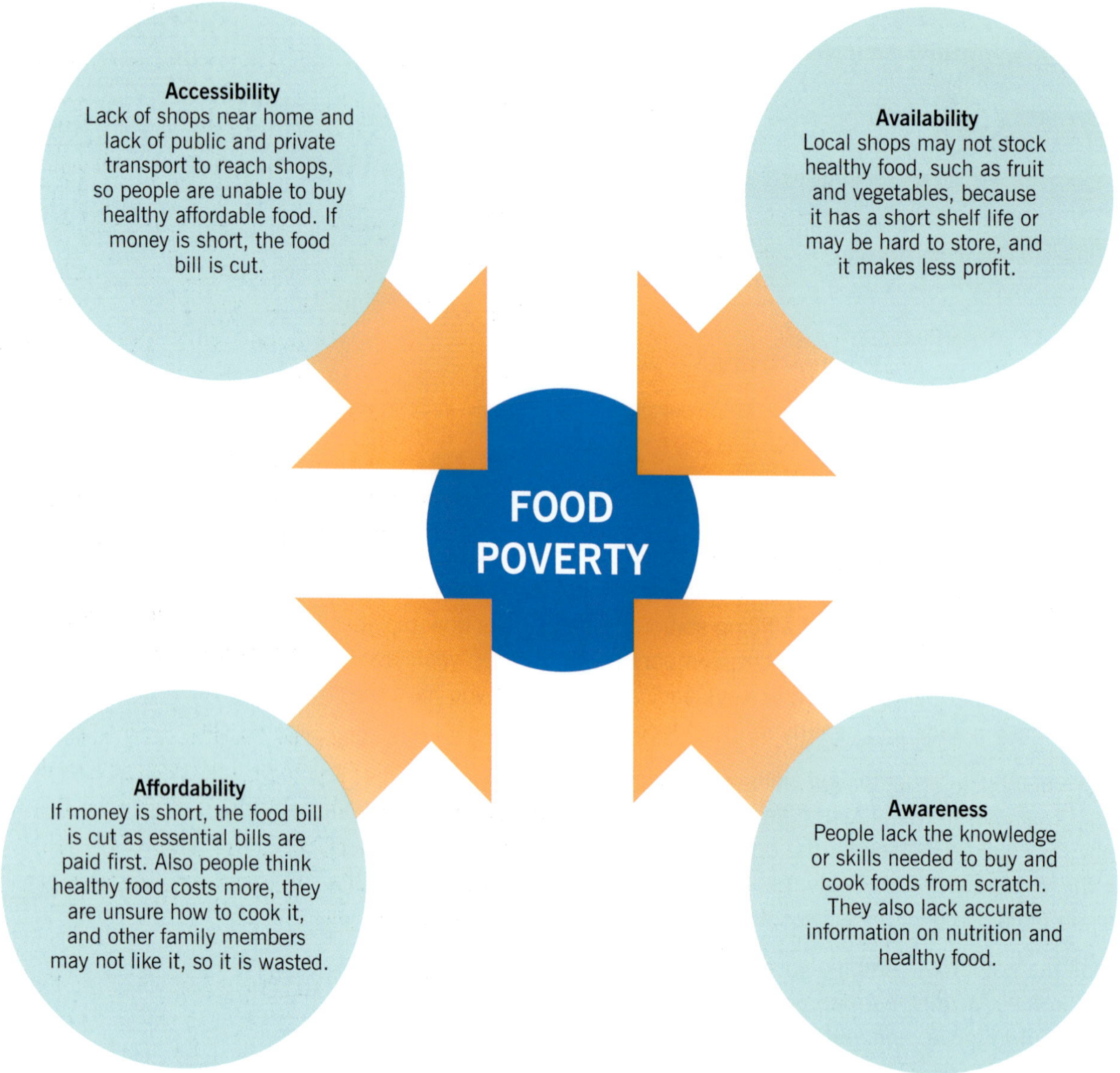
Accessibility
Lack of shops near home and lack of public and private transport to reach shops, so people are unable to buy healthy affordable food. If money is short, the food bill is cut.
Availability
Local shops may not stock healthy food, such as fruit and vegetables, because it has a short shelf life or may be hard to store, and it makes less profit.
FOOD POVERTY
Affordability
If money is short, the food bill is cut as essential bills are paid first. Also people think healthy food costs more, they are unsure how to cook it, and other family members may not like it, so it is wasted.
Awareness
People lack the knowledge or skills needed to buy and cook foods from scratch. They also lack accurate information on nutrition and healthy food.

▲ Figure 12: The factors that combine and lead to food poverty. (The four words beginning with A should help you to remember them.)
Source: Adapted from the Food Access Network at www.sustainweb.org

Food poverty can result in a poor diet, which is linked to diet-related ill health and its associated social and economic costs. Consequently, poor people who lack access to healthy food and have the lowest intakes of fruit and vegetables are far more likely to suffer from diet-related diseases such as cancer, obesity, diabetes, or cardio-vascular disease. About 10% of deaths in the UK are due to diet-related ill health.

Fieldwork: Mapping support for local sports teams

Aim

To identify the sphere of influence of a local football team.

Data collection

Ask regular football supporters in your area where they live – just their postcode will do – and which team they support. If you support a local team, it should be easy to talk to other fans. If not, question your fellow students. Some people may support the team where they used to live. Additionally, you could ask how often they attend home matches, enabling you to relate distance from the ground to frequency of attendance.

Health and safety

Do not approach football fans you don't know when they are marching towards the ground and demand to know where they live. Crowds of football fans are not always as friendly and helpful as you may hope.

Data presentation

You can map the support of teams by looking up the postcodes online on the Post Office postcode finder (although they restrict the search to a dozen postcodes a day). Other websites such as UpMyStreet and Multimap will provide the same function but will also have limits (this is for commercial reasons) – it's frustrating, but persevere! By mapping where local team supporters live, you can identify the sphere of influence of the team. Either draw desire lines from where each supporter lives to the football ground, or draw one line joining all the points furthest away from the ground.

Data analysis

Organise your data according to how far from the ground

supporters live and how often they attend home matches. Either list them, draw a scattergraph and carry out a Spearman rank correlation, or put the data into a table like the one below.

	Within 5 miles	5.1–10.0 miles	10.1–15.0 miles	15.1–20.0 miles	More than 20 miles
Up to 5 matches per season					
6–10 matches					
11–15 matches					
16–20 matches					
More than 20 matches					

Having drawn up this table, you could test the hypothesis that the further away people live, the less likely they are to attend matches. Carry out a Chi-squared test.

Data interpretation

Look for patterns on the map to explain the shape of the sphere of influence. There may be 'intervening opportunities' such as other teams located nearby that influence the pattern.

Conclusion

This should summarise what you have found out by referring to your investigation aims, questions and hypotheses.

Evaluation

One way to extend this exercise would be to map the support for a nearby rival team. For example, you could compare Sheffield United with Sheffield Wednesday or Bristol City with Bristol Rovers. This exercise is likely to work better for teams in lower divisions – Premiership support can be nationally or even internationally distributed.

Summary

This chapter has examined how different groups of people are affected by inequality. The focus has been on marginalised groups, those who are spatially segregated or socially marginalised, and how inequality impacts upon their quality of life, opportunities and life experiences.

Having studied this chapter, you should be able to discuss these ideas and concepts and to provide located examples of them:
- Inequality creates marginalised groups in a variety of ways in rural and urban areas.
  - Inequality can lead to social and economic exclusion and polarisation by denying opportunities and access to services.
  - Marginalisation and segregation may be caused by inequalities based upon gender, age, race and religion, employment, education, income, or health and disability.

MCQ

To try an exam question using what you have learned in this chapter, turn to page 245.

CHAPTER 25 How can we manage rural inequality and improve the lives of the rural poor? How successful have particular schemes been?

Key terms

Extreme poverty
Human Development Index
Regeneration
Renewal
Rural idyll
Sustainable development
Water poverty

Learning objectives

After studying this chapter, you will be able to discuss these ideas and concepts and provide located examples of them:

- There are social, economic and environmental problems and barriers that create rural inequality and need to be overcome.
- These problems and barriers to equality include lack of access to affordable housing, local employment and basic services, and may be difficult to overcome.
- The strategies to reduce rural inequalities include community involvement and empowerment, improved access to transport and services, development of local employment opportunities, and the use of appropriate technology and other sustainable solutions.

Living with rural inequality

'The village and its hinterland is one of the poorest places on the planet. A few wells and boreholes are the only source of water and most of those are contaminated. Most people rise early to tend their own small plots of vegetables before trying to earn the typical daily wage of just 50p. But they offer warmth, friendliness, and hospitality.'

Sarah Boseley, *Guardian*, 20 October 2007

If you live in a rural area, you will have to travel further than your friends in the city to get to the cinema or to get a takeaway pizza. You may have a long journey every day to and from school or college. Unless you are a devoted fan of the countryside and its recreational opportunities, you may frequently moan that 'there is nothing to do' there!

◀ **Figure 1:** The Tuesday market in Katine, Uganda.

People in their 20s may be more concerned about finding somewhere to live in the countryside. Rural wages are generally lower than those in urban areas and rural housing costs have been rising. Affluent city dwellers have moved to the countryside but continue to commute to the city to work, or they have bought second homes, pushing up the price of property in rural areas.

Both age groups may be identifying some of the barriers experienced by those who live in rural areas in the UK. These are not as acute as those experienced by rural dwellers in poorer countries, of course. People living in places like Cornwall may experience relative poverty but those in rural Uganda, such as the villagers of Katine, experience absolute poverty. According to the UN, you are living in 'absolute poverty' if you have less than $2 a day; and those on less than $1 a day are in 'extreme poverty'.

Case study: Katine village, Uganda

Katine is one of the most deprived villages in the world. Its inhabitants have too little to eat and their water comes from contaminated wells. Most of the villagers live in extreme poverty as their daily income is no more than the equivalent of $1. Where money is so scarce, recycling is an important source of work. Plastic washing-up bowls, flip-flops and old radios are repaired and sold; clothes come second-hand from the UK and USA.

Most children eat only once a day, when they get home around 5 p.m. Their education is partial, interrupted by family chores such as fetching water, child-minding, and working in the fields, or simply limited through hunger or the lack of an exercise book and a pen.

Young children pump water from boreholes into yellow plastic jerry cans holding five or ten litres of water, then walk several kilometres home. Eight wells, springs and boreholes are Katine's only source of water, and most are polluted. Contaminated water causes disease and death in many children.

Katine does have a health centre with a fully equipped operating theatre, but it has never been used because it has neither running water nor electricity. Malaria is responsible for nearly a quarter of deaths in Katine. It most often affects babies and pregnant women but few people possess a good mosquito net and there are not enough drugs to treat the disease. They are even short of disinfectant.

Adapted from 'It starts with a village...' www.guardian.co.uk/katine/2007/oct/20/welcome

International measures of inequality

In the UK, we do not expect to see people experiencing absolute poverty because the welfare state is designed to help those who have fallen below the poverty line. The UK ranks near the top of the Human Development Index (HDI) in sixteenth place, whereas Uganda comes 154th out of 177 countries. Uganda, in fact, is one of 27 African countries in the bottom 30.

The HDI is now widely used to measure well-being and it is useful for distinguishing between countries at different levels of development. It combines statistics on life expectancy, literacy, education, and standards of living. Measures such as this are dramatically illustrated by programs such as Worldmapper (Figure 2).

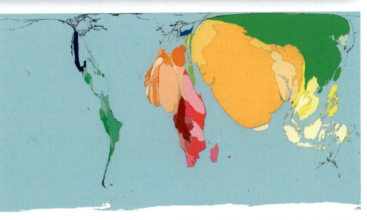

▲ Figure 2: People living in absolute poverty: the size of the territory shows the proportion of people living on less than or equal to $2 in purchasing-power parity a day.

Barriers to rural equality

In Katine and many other parts of the world, extreme poverty is the principal barrier to equality. If you cannot afford a pen to write with in school, you are not likely to learn the skills you need to progress in the world. Many poorer people live in places that present environmental barriers to social and economic development. These include climate, topography, remoteness and inaccessibility.

Even with useful mineral and fuel resources and a good climate for tropical agriculture, land-locked Uganda remains one of the world's least developed countries. Sometimes barriers to equality may be political, and several African countries have been handicapped by wars (civil and international) and by corruption at the highest level.

There are also social barriers to equality, including inertia, ignorance, and lack of educational opportunity, and economic barriers include lack of access to higher-paid employment. The rural poor in Cornwall may seem rich to the average Ugandan, but making ends meet in a low-wage economy, such as Cornwall's, presents daily challenges.

In the nineteenth century, Cornwall was an industrial county, its wealth founded upon the primary industries of tin and china clay. Today the remnants of these mining and quarrying activities have become museums, although the rising price of metals in international markets – needed to supply the rapid industrialisation in China and India – is making tin mining a profitable enterprise again.

Now Cornwall is noted for its tourism, a highly seasonal and poorly paid source of employment. It is also a popular destination for retirement migration, while young people tend to leave the county for better-paid work elsewhere. Notice how these factors affect the county's population structure in Figure 3.

Rural West Cornwall illustrates well the problems experienced by those who live in rural areas and who lack access to affordable housing and basic services. For example, post office closures have upset people everywhere, but those living in more rural areas may now have to travel much further to their nearest post office. In many places, the local sub-post office, village shop, church, chapel and school have been converted into private dwellings.

For those people who are 'counter-urbanising', rural areas hold an attraction sometimes based upon the idea of a cleaner, quieter, safer life. This 'rural idyll' reflects happy family life, the work ethic and good health. But the rural idyll often conceals levels of deprivation quietly tolerated by isolated individuals scattered throughout the countryside.

According to the Countryside Agency, a greater proportion of people on low incomes in remote rural England suffer from poorer health than other rural and urban areas. Rural deprivation tends to be invisible for several reasons:

Taking it further

Human Poverty Index (HPI): rather than measure poverty by income, the HPI uses indicators of the most basic dimensions of deprivation – a short life, lack of basic education and lack of access to public and private resources. The HPI concentrates on the deprivation in the three essential elements of human life already reflected in the HDI – longevity, knowledge and a decent standard of living. Look it up via http://hdrstats.undp.org/indicators/1.html

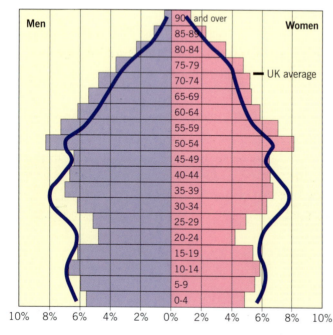

▲ Figure 3: The population structure of Cornwall, based upon the 2001 Census. The blue lines represent the shape of the national pyramid for comparison.

Source: www.statistics.gov.uk

- Rural communities are remote.
- Many deprived households, mixed with affluent in-migrants, keep their poverty secret.
- The poor tolerate their material deprivation because of the perceived benefits of the rural idyll.
- Newcomers do not see the poverty because it does not fit the rural idyll they are seeking.

So the idea of the rural idyll can act as an obstacle for people in the take-up of benefit entitlements because they fear loss of self-esteem. Overcoming this resistance is a fundamental task for those seeking to tackle social exclusion in rural areas.

Case study: Penwith, Cornwall

A report on poverty and deprivation in West Cornwall in the 1990s found that:
- In 1994 Cornwall had the greatest proportion of low-paid workers in England.
- Average weekly earnings in Cornwall in 1991 were £213 per week, compared with £225 nationally.
- All the available information showed that Cornwall was one of the lowest-waged counties in England.
- Despite the seasonal pattern of employment, even at the height of the summer the rate of unemployment in Cornwall is higher than in the rest of the South West.
- Cornwall's lone parents are likely to be suffering greater poverty than their counterparts in urban areas.
- Wards with higher levels of poverty, unemployment and poor housing conditions also tended to have higher levels of morbidity, and higher mortality rates.

There was a clear pattern in which the lowest levels of provision of services and amenities coincided with the most sparsely populated areas:
- 49% of settlements lacked any permanent food shop and 23% had only one.
- Only 18 settlements had a banking facility.
- Less than half of the settlements (245 out of 556) had a post office facility, with a loss of five post offices in West Cornwall since 1991.
- 30% of parishes had no daily milk delivery.
- 32% of settlements had no meeting place.
- 77% of settlements had no group for elderly people.

A combination of factors, including length of travel time, difficulty of journeys, and uncertainty about bus services (many people are confused by the timetables since some buses run only during school terms) deterred elderly people from using GP and other health care services. Also the weakening of rural community networks, the result of migration, made informal support and care (from family, friends and neighbours) less available, at a time when formal care is subject to cuts due to constraints on local government spending.

Reducing rural inequality

The strategies that may be applied to reduce rural inequalities will depend on the nature of the inequality in relation to the location. Clearly, the solutions needed in Penwith and in Katine will be different. The strategies to alleviate inequalities are generally divided into top-down approaches, where governments and non-governmental organisations such as charities provide aid and assistance, and bottom-up initiatives, where disadvantaged groups organise to improve their situation.

Taking it further

Research idea: using online resources, survey the availability of transport services in a rural sub-region. Such information can easily be mapped to show the extent of the services.

▲ **Figure 4:** The Trawscambria bus service from Aberystwyth to Cardigan.

There is a range of solutions to the problems caused by rural equalities, including:

- Involving and empowering the local community through self-help groups, support for women and older people, co-operatives and community forums.
- Encouraging the growth of local employment opportunities by extending broadband access, farm diversification or adding value to produce.
- Improving the provision of, and access to, transport and services, using dial-a-bus, mobile services and deliveries, or post offices in pubs.
- Developing the use of appropriate technology, such as farming for environmental protection, diversification, developing reliable and clean water supplies, alternative energy schemes.

Whichever solution, or package of solutions, is best applied in any location, they must be sustainable.

Finding the right solution starts with understanding what disadvantaged people see as acceptable ways to deal with their inequality. A recent review of social inclusion in rural areas suggested the need to work directly with those who are socially excluded rather than through community representatives. The people who were identified as needing to be engaged in discussion were:

- Low-waged farm and seasonal workers
- Lone parents
- Households in which no one is employed
- Older people, especially those who live alone
- Manual workers and the self-employed approaching retirement age
- Rural young people who may migrate to urban areas.

Those most in need of help are often the hardest to communicate with. In Devon, where rural social exclusion is very similar to that experienced in Cornwall, an organisation called 'Open Hearts, Open Minds' links local government with community and voluntary organisations to provide tools and resources to tackle social exclusion. One such tool is the 'sociogram', which can be used to establish what support is accessible for individual people so that, through discussion, they can determine what support is needed.

This kind of outreach initiative can be instigated by the public sector and local strategic partnerships can work as key players in determining the success of social inclusion strategies. The voluntary and community enterprise sectors are also important in helping to work out flexible and innovative initiatives.

Many community regeneration and renewal strategies work by providing funding and advice for local initiatives. Small groups, businesses and individuals propose ways to help their community and are offered advice and expert assistance on obtaining funding and implementing schemes. When combined, small-scale initiatives promote community regeneration. There is a complex network of organisations and initiatives, including Community Regeneration Programmes, through which the district councils provide front line support, advice and guidance for voluntary and community groups and businesses in the area.

Regeneration teams aim to help community or voluntary groups and local people:
- to obtain support, funding, practical help and advice from other agencies
- with project development and funding applications
- by sharing experience and knowledge of project development and programme management
- to promote their work to the community and other agencies more effectively.

Case study: Strategies to reduce inequalities in Penwith, Cornwall

Objective 1 funding

West Cornwall qualifies for European Union 'Objective 1' support because it is one of the EU's most deprived regions, which affects its educational achievement, housing standards, access to services, incomes, health and life-span. Objective 1 programmes focus on providing and attracting funds to develop infrastructure (notably transport), education and training, and employment and enterprise assistance in the most deprived regions. Support for environmental protection is also provided.

Local strategic partnership

West Cornwall Together is the 'local strategic partnership' for Penwith and Kerrier Districts. It is a partnership of public, private, voluntary and community sectors, with a mission to improve the quality of life and standard of living of local people. Rural deprivation is a key issue, so West Cornwall Together has commissioned research from the University of Bristol in order to understand this more fully. The aims identified for West Cornwall are:
- Job opportunities for all in a prosperous area
- Housing of sufficient quality for all community needs, including the homeless
- Safe and strong communities, eliminating discrimination and celebrating diversity
- A healthy and active life for all residents
- Learning opportunities that promote excellence, education and training for all
- Environmental protection, valuing the distinctive landscape and making the best use of resources
- Culture and heritage that is protected, enhanced, celebrated and internationally recognised.

Community regeneration

The Community Regeneration team for Penwith District Council supports the development of projects such as community and play facilities. They also manage the Village Halls Grant Scheme locally and the Penwith Small Grants Scheme for voluntary and community groups.

Village halls and other community buildings are focal points for rural communities. They provide a venue for social occasions such as parties, wedding receptions, guide and scout groups as well as other activities such as local health clubs, farmers' markets, clubs for older people, and ICT facilities. 'Community Halls for Rural People' works with 'Action with Communities in Rural England' (ACRE) to raise awareness of available funding and advice for village halls and to provide useful contacts.

Heritage development and job creation

West Cornwall has a rich heritage, with significant places such as the Iron Age village at Chysauster, the open air Minack Theatre, the Barbara Hepworth Museum, and the Porthcurno Telegraph Museum, as well as its industrial history, as preserved, for example, by the National Trust at the Levant Mine. The development of such cultural resources provides employment and generates income from tourism.

The re-use of old industrial sites and surrounding land enables the management of the landscape for biodiversity and amenity. Micro-generation and the harnessing of natural energy resources at such sites is encouraged and enhances their educational benefit as well as increasing their sustainability.

Encouraging local enterprise by providing support to local entrepreneurs, and fostering business growth and inward investment through new workspace development, generates employment and income. Improving broadband access across the whole of the UK is one of the Government's top priorities and enables businesses to locate in rural areas.

Improving transport services

West Cornwall Community Wheels is a not-for-profit community transport organisation providing services in Penwith and Kerrier. It operates two dial-a-ride services that link with local bus and rail services to enable people to travel to work, visit doctors' surgeries, and shop in local towns. A car scheme also operates, with volunteers using their own cars to give lifts to passengers, including schoolchildren, social services' clients and patients. There is also a minibus hire facility.

When you research rural inequalities and their management, you may find a huge amount of information to show how bad things are and a bewildering network of organisations set up to make things better. It is much harder to find the success stories. They are there – you may spot them on field trips or on holiday – but they are often quite small-scale and, individually, may seem insignificant. Yet a weekly bus to a nearby shopping centre, a kids playground, a refurbished village hall, or a carefully restored beam engine in its own little museum can make a major difference for local inhabitants.

These amenities would seem like amazing luxuries for the people of Katine in Uganda, however, where just a running tap with clean water would improve the quality of so many lives. In parts of the world where large numbers of people experience absolute and extreme poverty, reducing rural spatial inequalities starts with the most basic of human needs: potable water supplies, efficient sanitation, a nutritious diet, and health. There are many charities set up to combat such poverty, some of them quite specific in their aims. Others focus on small areas.

▲ Figure 5: 'Wheels to Work' in West Cornwall provide a suitable 'set of wheels' to rural residents whose transport needs cannot be met in other ways. All riders receive protective clothing and safety training.

Taking it further

In the UK, the following regions were recognised as in need of Objective 1 funding in 2006: Cornwall and the Isles of Scilly, South Yorkshire, West Wales and the Valleys, and Merseyside. See a map of EU Objective 1 regions at http://ec.europa.eu/regional_policy/objective1/map_en.htm

Taking it further

See www.westcornwalltogether.org.uk/regeneration.htm for more information.

Case study: Strategies to reduce rural inequalities in Katine

In 2007, the African Medical and Research Foundation (AMREF) set up a 3-year project, in partnership with the Guardian and Observer newspapers and Barclays Bank, with the aim of transforming the lives of the 25,000 people living in Katine village and the wider sub-county.

The project aims to reduce poverty, to improve community health, to increase access to safe water, sanitation and hygiene, to extend access to primary education, to increase incomes, and to provide a role for the community in decision making.

The objectives were chosen in response to the needs of the community in Katine. AMREF and the project implementation partners, FARM-Africa and Barclays, spent time talking to community members, assessing the services and facilities available, and used their experiences of working in Uganda to develop achievable objectives.

The project targets those who will benefit most. In health care, this means people living with HIV/AIDS, children under five, women and young people. In education, it means ensuring that all girls attend school alongside the boys and that education is accessible to those with disabilities.

By working with farmers' groups, village health teams, parent–teachers' associations, and by establishing community committees, local people can be at the centre of their own development and the work can be responsive to their needs. To ensure that the good work continues once the three-year project is completed, work will also focus on developing the skills of both formal workers (teachers, health workers, government employees) and the community volunteers who are delivering essential services to the community – the village health teams, for example.

Sustainable solutions

In September 2000, a UN Declaration was accepted by the General Assembly which established eight Millennium Development Goals (MDGs) to be achieved by 2015. They were agreed by all countries and all the leading development institutions, and they have encouraged unprecedented efforts to meet the needs of the world's poorest people. It is hard to disagree with these goals and progress is slowly being made towards them. For example, the number of people living in extreme poverty fell nearly 19% between 1990 and 2004.

Taking it further

See www.un.org/millenniumgoals/ for more information.

The Millennium Development Goals
1. Eradicate extreme poverty and hunger
2. Achieve universal primary education
3. Promote gender equality and empower women
4. Reduce child mortality
5. Improve maternal health
6. Combat HIV/AIDS, malaria and other diseases
7. Ensure environmental sustainability
8. Develop a global partnership for development.

Some organisations, like AMREF, believe that, in order for development to succeed, the gap between communities and government needs to be closed. A partnership approach, such as that adopted in West Cornwall, is increasingly seen as the way to combine the best features of action from above and below, and may prove more sustainable in the longer term.

'Sustainability' covers a wide range of concepts. Originally it was closely linked with development that did not have an adverse impact upon the environment. The use of appropriate technology to achieve sustainable solutions applies in all countries. Increasingly, we use this term to identify development that is also socially and economically sustainable.

In Uganda, the charity WaterAid works with local communities to improve their water supply. Diseases from unsafe water and poor sanitation are responsible for half of the deaths in children under five in Uganda. The charity involves the local community, training local people to work as pump mechanics or health and hygiene promoters. They also set up committees of local people to promote the use of and manage the water supply.

In all WaterAid projects the community is involved in planning, building, maintaining and managing the schemes. This is an essential step in development; it ensures that communities feel a sense of ownership and responsibility for their project, and this makes them more sustainable, providing lasting improvements to people's lives.

Over 1 billion people lack access to a clean water supply, and 2.5 billion people lack access to basic sanitation. This is described as 'water poverty', and charities like WaterAid are pledged to tackle this poverty by developing sustainable resources, targeting services at the most marginalised groups, such as older people, the poor, disabled people and women, and by holding key decision-makers to account through transparent and open planning processes.

Fieldwork: Investigation 1

Aim:

To carry out a survey of present and past services and functions (shops) in a small village.

Data collection

1. Walk through the village, listing all the shops and services you can find and locating them on a sketch map or base plan.
2. Take photographs of significant services (post office, surgery, village store).
3. Use old maps, photographs, guides and directories, which you may find in a local reference library, to establish services in the village in previous years.

Risk assessment

This is a low-risk exercise, but you should always take care and be respectful when approaching local residents – they may not be too happy to have their neighbourhood scrutinised and photographed.

Also, it is not advisable to wander down quiet country lanes without keeping an eye and ear out for traffic!

Health and safety

Always tell someone in a position of responsibility (parent or teacher) when and where you are going to do your fieldwork.

Never go alone.

Data presentation

Draw comparative maps – possibly using overlays, depending on how you draw the maps, to indicate change. Very large maps (greater than A3 size) are not advisable.

List 'before' and 'after' services, and categorise them according to their type (such as convenience and comparison goods).

Conclusion

It is probable that you will find a reduction in the number of services and functions in the village, unless it has experienced significant growth as a result of counter-urbanisation.

Evaluation

Consider how you might extend your investigation, perhaps by carrying out a questionnaire survey of residents on their use of local services and functions. Or possibly by locating further information on the past history of the village.

Fieldwork: Investigation 2

Aim:

To compare the provision of services and functions in a group of rural settlements.

Data collection

1. Select a small survey area of between 5 and 10 km², depending on the density of settlements – ensure that you have no more than five villages.
2. First use an OS 1:25 000 map to identify services for local residents (not visitors and tourists) such as pubs, post offices, churches and schools. Note that these may not necessarily be located in the villages.
3. Visit all the villages and hamlets within your study area and record all the services and functions you can find.

Data presentation

On a map of your study area, use proportional symbols to identify the number of different services and functions and their location.

◀ **Figure 6:** This village store in Peak Forest in Derbyshire sells everything from bread to wellies, as well as providing post office and off-licence services to the local people.

Fieldwork: Investigation 3

Aim:

To carry out a questionnaire survey of rural residents.

Data collection

1. Select a small survey area of between 5 and 10 km², depending on the density of settlements – ensure that you have no more than five villages.
2. Design a short questionnaire to find out where local people shop for convenience goods and where they access key services, such as their GP.

Data presentation and interpretation

If you have designed your questionnaire effectively, you should be able to both list your data in a summary table and to carry out 'cross-tabular analysis' whereby you can see, for example, that the people who work in the village shop less frequently in the nearest large town than those who work elsewhere. This will enable you to carry out much more meaningful statistical analysis, such as scattergraphs and Spearman rank correlation.

Summary

This chapter has looked at the impact of inequality in the UK and in Uganda, and at the strategies being implemented to improve the quality of life and standard of living of people in Penwith and Katine. It has focused on the situation of rural people whose relative isolation can compound their social and economic exclusion with real spatial exclusion.

Having studied this chapter, you should be able to discuss these ideas and concepts and provide located examples of them:

- The wide range of social, economic and environmental problems and barriers that create rural spatial inequalities, including lack of access to affordable housing, local employment, and basic services.
- The strategies to reduce rural inequalities that involve top-down or bottom-up approaches to improve access to transport and services or develop local employment opportunities.
  - The partnership approach that encourages community involvement and empowerment.

MCQ

To try an exam question using what you have learned in this chapter, turn to page 245.

CHAPTER 26 What strategies can be used to combat inequality in urban areas? How successful have particular schemes been?

Key terms

Index of deprivation
Redevelopment
Regeneration
Renewal

Learning objectives

After studying this chapter, you will be able to discuss these ideas and concepts and provide located examples of them:

- There are social, economic and environmental problems associated with urban inequalities.
- Key players involved in delivering solutions include international agencies, charities, governments, local and regional authorities, independent groups and individuals.
- Solutions to urban inequalities include self-help schemes, traffic and public transport schemes and other town planning initiatives, business initiatives and measures to reduce crime.

'The sense of decline and neglect in many of these areas is palpable: the built environment . . . has now taken on all the classic, ominous characteristics (boarded-up windows, barbed wire surrounds) of the enclaves of high crime and violence associated with Los Angeles and its ghettos in the months leading up to the 1992 riots. Public space is often colonised by young men in baseball caps and cheap khaki.'

(I. Taylor (1997) 'Running on empty', quoted in the Observer, 14 May 2006)

▲ Figure 1: The graffiti painted on this concrete-clad block of council flats sums up the feeling of despair.

Barriers to urban equality in the UK

The quotation describes one of a number of 'problem' estates in Britain, where joy-riding and other uncivil behaviour is common. These problems can be seen as a response to the lack of employment for young men. Although there has been new job creation in many such areas, it has mostly been in the services sector, but these are often jobs 'usually done by women'. This is called the 'feminisation' of the workforce and has not helped the young men's situation.

Newspapers often sensationalise the problems of social exclusion by exaggerating the idea of 'no-go' estates, and a Church of England bishop has caused controversy by suggesting that Islamic extremism has turned some communities into no-go areas for people of a different faith or race. The common theme is that within urban areas there are groups of people – the socially excluded – who are spatially segregated and marginal to the social and economic life of the city.

The reasons for their sense of exclusion, and the negative response of others who are not excluded, have been examined in detail in earlier chapters. The barriers to inclusion include, first, lack of access to properly paid employment, which may be due to an inadequate education – or there may be a language barrier. Age and health are, of course, insurmountable barriers for some. Other barriers exist because of prejudice, such as those based upon gender and ethnicity. Whatever their causes, differences in income lead to spatial segregation, which can also have an environmental impact in terms of the quality of housing, levels of pollution and access to recreational space.

Taking it further

Defining ethnicity and race: race is based on biological distinctions or physical criteria whereas ethnicity relates to culture and lifestyle of a group linked by birth.

Case study: Hackney, inner London

Hackney was named the 'Worst place to live in the UK' on a Channel 4 programme in 2006. Here are ten facts about Hackney that may explain why:

- It has a higher proportion of lone-parent households than London as a whole or England and Wales.
- 28% of its households (housing 35% of the population) are described as 'overcrowded' – the third highest in England and Wales.
- The number of schoolchildren receiving free school meals is three times the national average.
- 40% of the residents are from non-white ethnic backgrounds, compared to 8% of the UK population.
- Its employment rate is some 14% lower than the wider London rate and 19% lower than the national average (2006).
- The area had the highest unemployment rate in England and Wales in 2001.
- Higher than average numbers of the residents have a long-term illness or are permanently sick or disabled.
- The number of people infected with HIV in the borough was five-and-a-half times the average for England in 2001.
- The crime rate was 42 per 1,000 population in 2005–06 compared to a national figure of 26 per 1,000.
- Education results are poor; only 51% of students achieved five or more A* to C grade GCSEs in 2006, although this had improved from 31% 4 years earlier.

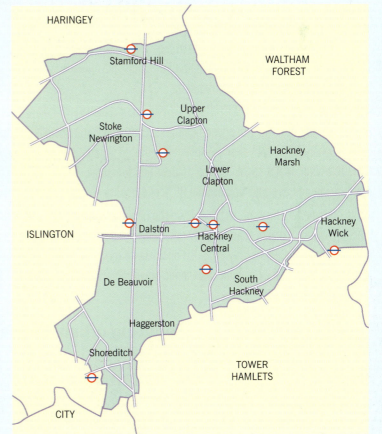

▲ **Figure 2:** The location of, and main districts and railway stations in, the London Borough of Hackney.

Case study: Hackney, inner London *(continued)*

Hackney is a relatively deprived area partly because of the quality of its housing. In the mid-twentieth century many crumbling Victorian terraces were replaced with poorly designed council-owned tower blocks, which soon fell into disrepair. More than half the borough's inhabitants lived in such properties by 1981, though this proportion has since declined as the worst blocks have been demolished and others have been renovated.

High rates of unemployment and long-term sickness are common in areas with higher proportions of people who formerly worked in manufacturing. London, like many other cities, experienced deindustrialisation in the 1970s and 1980s. The new jobs created in business and finance, however, required different skills and attracted a different labour force.

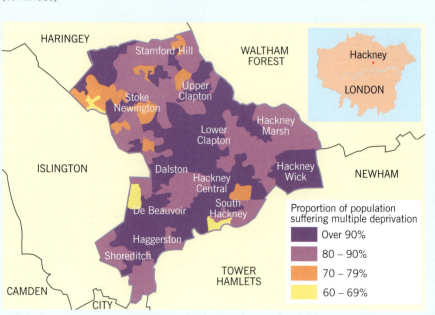

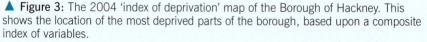

▲ **Figure 3:** The 2004 'index of deprivation' map of the Borough of Hackney. This shows the location of the most deprived parts of the borough, based upon a composite index of variables.

Source: http://www.go-london.gov.uk/boroughinfo/profiles/id/hackney.doc

Hackney is the fifth most deprived borough economically and socially in England. The 'index of deprivation' (see Figure 3) is used to identify where this deprivation is most concentrated. Almost half of Hackney's school pupils are eligible for free school meals and more than half do not speak English as their first language. The borough has a larger proportion of people of minority ethnic origin than the London average, and around 90% of students enrolled at the local sixth-form college are from minority ethnic groups.

While average incomes are slightly above the national average, the cost of living in inner London, and in particular the cost of housing, is much higher than in many other parts of the country. Many Hackney residents find that, despite their best efforts, they are socially and economically excluded because so many factors have combined to concentrate long-term social deprivation in their local areas, where they now lack economic power and marketable skills.

Taking it further

Data from the Index of Deprivation can be mapped and used to identify and interpret patterns as in Figure 3. Planners in Hackney use these data to identify which neighbourhoods need specific help such as housing improvements; they can prioritise and target areas for regeneration funding. Such maps can be related to those showing other information such as housing tenure, crime, health or educational achievement.

Reducing urban inequality in the UK

Over many decades, successive British governments have applied policies to alleviate poverty and improve the living conditions and opportunities for disadvantaged people. Since 1945, the welfare state has provided free health care, pensions and benefits. Education across all levels has been extended, and successive schemes have been introduced to generate new jobs, especially in response to deindustrialisation. Millions of houses have been demolished and many more homes have been constructed.

Examples of urban policy initiatives in the UK since 1945

When	What	How	Where (examples)
1946–1967	Reconstruction (physical action)	New Towns and Expanded Towns Comprehensive Development Areas	Basildon, Swindon Glasgow
1967–1979	Renewal (social action)	General Improvement Areas Housing Action Areas	Nottingham Manchester
1979–1991	Redevelopment (economic action)	Enterprise Zones Urban Development Corporations City Action Teams and Task Forces	Swansea London Docklands Toxteth in Liverpool
1991–2000	Regeneration (integrated action)	Single Regeneration Budget City Challenge	Northampton Hulme in Manchester
2000–	Renaissance (sustainable action)	Sustainable Communities Plan Estate Regeneration Scheme	Thames Gateway Longbridge in Birmingham

Local authorities built many thousands of council houses until the 1980s, when the right-to-buy policy was introduced. Slum housing (mostly Victorian) was cleared in many cities and replaced by large apartment blocks, such as Hulme Crescents in Manchester (Figure 4). Some of these buildings turned out to be inappropriate housing for poor families and pensioners, and they have since been demolished and replaced with lower density housing.

Top-down, government-led initiatives do not always achieve the required outcome – Hulme Crescents, for example, were built with the finest of motives – but they produce substantial changes. Bottom-up action can also bring significant change. Individual housing improvement has gentrified whole areas in some cities, but less affluent people have not always benefited from this. Despite many urban initiatives, a few of which are listed in the table above, spatial inequalities and their consequences for social and economically excluded people still remain, with only piecemeal improvements.

A spectrum of players is involved in any urban renewal strategy. In the 1990s, the idea of partnership was increasingly promoted – especially between the public sector and private investors. More recently it has been recognised that local people need to be involved in the partnerships too – effectively joining up the top-down and bottom-up approaches.

Large-scale change – involving town planning initiatives, traffic and public transport improvements, business initiatives, and crime prevention – must involve local, regional and national government. But small organisations, such as local charities, residents' associations and community action groups, can also make a difference, if only to raise the awareness of politicians and business people.

Taking it further

You do not need to know all the details of urban policy since the Second World War for your AS examination, but what happened in the past sometimes helps to explain the urban structures and problems that have been inherited today. It is an interesting historical story of attempts, not always successful, by many well-meaning people to improve the lives of those less fortunate than themselves.

▲ Figure 4: Hulme Crescents in Manchester. These deck-access flats were poorly built and soon started to fall into disrepair. They have now been replaced with two- and three-storey houses.

Source: http://image.guardian.co.uk/sys-images/Shopping/Pix/pictures/2002/08/02/hulme384.jpg

Case study: Regenerating Hackney

Hackney has received much government money to deal with its urban problems. For example, between 1993 and 1998, under the City Challenge initiative, £37.5 m of government money, plus £113 m from the Council, charities and non-profit-making organisations, and £160 m from the private sector, was spent revitalising the area. The range of projects included large-scale commercial developments, refurbished buildings and housing schemes, community-based education, training and employment initiatives and crime-prevention activities.

Almost 3,000 dwellings were completed or improved, 9,900 jobs created or safeguarded, 107,000 m^2 of business space created or improved, and 570 new businesses started. The worst estates in the borough were improved by demolishing a number of tower blocks and replacing them with more traditional homes – particularly on the Nightingale, Clapton Park, Trowbridge, Holly Street and New Kingshold estates. A deliberate attempt was made to employ local labour.

Hackney has also received funding under the Comprehensive Estates Initiative, the Single Regeneration Budget and the Estate Regeneration Scheme. The regeneration of Hackney has been criticised, however, for leaving the borough with fewer affordable homes after demolition, and fewer former tenants after completion. It is suggested that gentrification is pushing working people out of inner London through a combination of government and local authority housing polices and market forces.

The regeneration of Holly Street, for example, involved the demolition of 3,000 council homes. Around 2,000 homes were built as replacements – 800 of these were housing association homes, while the rest were open market sales. Only one in ten of the original tenants returned to the area after redevelopment and the economic profile of the new residents in Holly Street is more affluent than the displaced community. It is now claimed that the social problems of poverty and deprivation in Holly Street have been solved here, but in truth, they have just been dispersed elsewhere.

There are many schemes, involving a wide range of people and agencies, working to improve the lives of disadvantaged people in Hackney. The list below identifies just a few of the initiatives currently ongoing or planned:

- The City Fringe Partnership covers parts of four London boroughs – Tower Hamlets, Hackney, Islington and Camden – and is implementing programmes to promote business and individual enterprise.
- The Thames Gateway London Partnership extends east from the City to the outer boroughs of Havering and Bexley. An Urban Development Corporation will manage the provision of new housing, appropriate public services, transport and environmental infrastructure, together with developing training and employment opportunities.
- The East London Business Alliance uses the skills, influence and resources of the private sector support social and economic regeneration by focusing on volunteering, employment and mentoring.
- The Hackney PowerMaths Project trains teachers across Hackney to use innovative IT software to teach mathematics and raise achievement.
- The underground's East London Line Extension into Hackney, Islington and Southwark will also stimulate growth and investment in these areas.
- BSix – Brooke House Sixth Form College – was built in 2002 to serve the young people of Hackney and East London. The college has raised aspirations and increased opportunities for local young people.

Despite criticisms of its housing policies, the Hackney Borough council has succeeded in attracting new business start-ups and bringing jobs into the area, and their education and skills programmes have successfully equipped and provided basic skills and training for local residents. Now they are benefiting from the northward expansion of the City and Docklands, and the London Olympics and Paralympics Games.

Urban inequality in the developing world

In less developed parts of the world, unemployment is not an option for the poor – they must work to live. Even those who would normally be members of the dependent population (children and the elderly) are forced by poverty into low-paid employment. They are thus either exploited or work in the informal sector. Many of the urban poor are the rural poor who have migrated into urban areas, but there is a crucial difference for them: everything that is consumed has to be paid for, because there is no subsistence sector in the city – no space to cultivate food, no wild produce, no common grazing, no source of free fuel and little free water.

India, for example, calculates its poverty line on the basis of the ability to provide 2,100 calories per day for an adult in an urban area – a luxury for many. Images of affluence are displayed daily to those who have no hope of achieving wealth legally. Migrants pushed into the city by abject rural poverty have no legal access to housing-sites or rights to set up in business, and without these legal rights they cannot get water or electricity. Many are unavoidably caught up in criminal activity and in a vicious cycle of degraded living conditions. The residents of affluent and middle-class areas are becoming increasingly afraid of the proximity of the urban poor and are sealing themselves off in gated communities, with high levels of surveillance and guarding.

Taking it further

If you look up Mumbai's population statistics, you will find a wide range of numbers. Counting populations always produces inaccurate results; some people just do not want to be counted but, of course, enumerating slum dwellers in an area experiencing high migration rates is not likely to be precise. Also, it depends on the administrative area for which figures are given. So remember that statistics can be unreliable.

Case study: Mumbai, India

Mumbai is the world's fifth most populated metropolitan area, with a population of 19 million and an average density of 22,000 people per km², but the most densely populated areas house four times this number. The quality of life for Mumbai's inhabitants is closely related to the availability of physical space. The slums never underwent any planning, infrastructure construction or implementation of basic amenities such as water supply and drainage.

The Mumbai slums have always existed but they have grown significantly since India's independence in 1947. They were originally found around the textile mills in Byculla and housed the mill workers in one-room tenements, called chawls. Since then they have spread into neighbouring areas such Dharavi – Asia's largest slum, despite the slum clearance implemented by the Municipal Corporation.

Slum dwellers make up 60% of Mumbai's population, estimated to be between 10 and 12 million people. They live in the heart of the city, on the streets, along railway tracks, near water pipelines and on the boundaries of the airport (hindering expansion plans that include a new terminal and taxiways). The conditions in the slums are terrible, with inhabitants constantly having to deal with issues such as lack of water, no sewerage system, lack of public transport, pollution and housing shortages. Infant mortality is as high as it is in rural India and the death rates 50% higher.

▲ Figure 5: Mumbai Metropolitan Area.

Case study: Mumbai, India (continued)

Population growth is caused by both natural increase and in-migration but, as is typically the pattern of urban growth, the contribution of migration to population change in Mumbai has declined consistently alongside rising natural increase (see Figure 6).

Many migrants to Mumbai are employed in industries requiring semi-skilled and unskilled workers with minimal educational qualifications, but the growth of employment in services such as telecommunications, construction and real estate has not matched the loss of manufacturing jobs. Former factory workers have been absorbed by the informal sector, resulting in its share of total employment increasing over time. So the benefits of economic change have been unevenly distributed, and Mumbai's rich and poor co-exist with very different access to basic services.

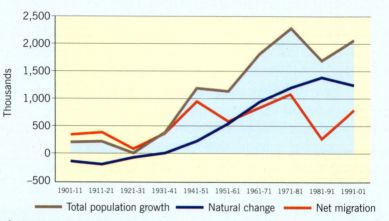

▲ **Figure 6:** Population growth in Mumbai, 1901–2001. Growth from natural change overtook growth from migration in the 1950s. The drop in in-migration in the 1970s coincided with extensive slum clearance and policies designed to encourage people to stay in rural areas.

The more poor people move from rural to urban areas, the more poverty is becoming urbanised. Globally, about 1 billion people – 18% of the world's population – live in the crowded slums of inner cities and in the vast, mostly illegal squatter settlements and shantytowns. There are many different methods of addressing the plight of the slum dwellers:

- a common approach is for governments to sanction slum clearance and then build low-cost housing paid for by state;
- the UN is financing small loans for slum dwellers to improve quality of their own shacks and, after natural disasters, to build new homes;
- in site and situation schemes governments provide land for new development and install services such as water and electricity, local people obtain a plot for a low rent and build their own houses;
- through cross-subsidisation, low-cost housing is built as part of larger commercial redevelopment schemes.

Case study: Rebuilding Mumbai

Housing in Mumbai is scarce and expensive. The authorities are encouraging private investors to redevelop the city slums and have implemented a variety of policies to improve housing for the poor. Slum policies have evolved from clearance in the 1950s and 1960s to protection and provision of civic amenities in the 1970s, when central government provided grants for basic amenities including water, sanitation and power.

In the 1980s, under the Bombay Urban Development Project (BUDP), 'cross-subsidisation' was introduced in which developers were required to allocate at least 20% of all housing projects to affordable housing. In 1995, the newly established Slum Rehabilitation Authority (SRA) took this further and making more land available for building. Builders demolish entire slum neighbourhoods and pay nothing for the land, using part of it for tenements to house the original residents and part to build lucrative tower blocks.

Case study: Rebuilding Mumbai (continued)

In this way, low-cost housing is cross-subsidised by revenue from the sale of luxury apartments and slum dwellers are given free apartments, 21 m² in area – the size of a typical shanty.

The SRA programme is the only way for Mumbai's urban poor to get access to otherwise unaffordable land and subsidies from the market. But there have been problems; many living there say they wanted their slums back, they liken the new flats to being caged in a poultry farm. To free up land for new building, a major demolition drive, between November 2004 and March 2005, destroyed an estimated 92,000 homes leaving about 300,000 people homeless. Many of the slum communities only find out about the demolition when the bulldozers move in. But some do welcome the resettlement because it gives them new dignity and it is peaceful.

Critics of the rehabilitation scheme who point out that:

- The horizontal slums may become vertical ones, without the vibrant street life and sense of community.
- Building skyward will strain public services and disrupt the livelihoods of the street sellers and shopkeepers.
- The poor may not be able to afford the upkeep of capital-intensive buildings.
- The tenements may become ghettos.
- The slum dwellers lose their self-sufficiency. In a slum, a broken pipe is fixed by a local handyman, but in a tower block, professional help is needed.

Residential patterns in Mumbai are being altered fundamentally. In the past, the slums coexisted with better-off residential complexes. The accelerated slum-clearance programme has forced many to relocate to the peripheral areas of the suburbs. But planned development of suburbs has not succeeded so far, because of lack of supporting infrastructure such as transport networks.

Healthy and sustainable cities

Poorer people are less healthy than richer people, as shown by the figures for life expectancy and the incidence of diseases, such as tuberculosis, chronic heart disease, some forms of cancer, HIV-Aids, malaria, and diarrhoeal diseases. The differences are linked to the quality of housing and to the wider urban environment, the working conditions and lifestyle. There are clear differences at the international scale, as shown in the table.

Causes of death in developing and developed countries

The World Health Organisation (WHO) is the UN body responsible for global health matters. Their 'Healthy Cities' programme encourages local governments to focus on health inequalities and urban poverty, and to include health considerations in economic, regeneration and urban development planning. It is a global initiative and, in the European region alone, over 1,200 cities and towns from more than 30 countries are involved. These cities are working on healthy urban planning and on encouraging healthy physical activity.

Developing countries	Developed countries
HIV-Aids	Ischaemic heart disease
Lower respiratory infections	Stroke
Ischaemic heart disease	Chronic obstructive pulmonary disease
Diarrhoea	Lower respiratory infections
Cerebro-vascular disease	Lung cancer
Childhood diseases	Car accident
Malaria	Stomach cancer
Tuberculosis	High blood pressure
Chronic obstructive pulmonary disease	Tuberculosis
Measles	Suicide

▶ Figure 7: The top ten causes of death in developing and developed countries.

243

The concept of a 'healthy city' includes personal safety and the perception of risk in relation to crime. Thus planning healthy communities involves consideration of the design and planning of neighbourhoods for crime prevention and community safety in order to reduce anti-social behaviour and the fear of crime. The use of CCTV and neighbourhood policing contribute to this. Healthy and sustainable city planning also includes extending traffic-free zones, cycle routes, park-and-ride schemes, congestion charging, and the development of bus and tram services, plus the provision of open spaces and sport and leisure facilities to encourage a healthy lifestyle. Such initiatives extend beyond the inner city to suburban and fringe zones through innovative neighbourhood design.

Fieldwork investigation: Evaluating the success of a local regeneration scheme

Aim:
To assess the effectiveness of a local regeneration project.

Introduction:
Some regeneration schemes will be further advanced than others; it would be useful to compare before and after situations but not essential. There may be some scope for looking at the impact for local inhabitants of a development in progress as a large construction project will create temporary work directly on site plus ancillary (indirect) benefits for local suppliers. On the other hand, there may be considerable disruption as roads are obstructed, causing traffic congestion, and noise and dust levels may rise with building works in progress. Select from the data collection methods below, you will not need to use all of them, just those most appropriate for your project.

Data collection:
1. You need to find out about initiatives in your local area. Typing 'regeneration' and the name of your local town into your search engine should lead you to the information you need about your local council's aims and plans.
2. Visit the area (access on a building site will not be permitted for health and safety reasons) and take photographs.
3. Depending on the nature of the project, you can carry out an environmental impact assessment or smaller bi-polar analyses to determine the environmental consequences of the scheme.
4. A questionnaire of local residents may be appropriate – investigate their opinions of the value of the project in terms of both personal and wider benefits or losses.
5. Download census data for the area, focusing on indicators such as occupation, ethnicity, age structure and household composition, that is, indicators of social inequality or exclusion.
6. Also online you should be able to obtain local employment data for the area.
7. If the scheme is under construction or has been completed, find photographs of the area before it commenced – these will be available either online or at your local reference library.
8. If the area is primarily used for retailing, find Goad Plans in your local library; these are maps that record the name of the retailer and the type of goods being sold, they are updated every two years and are very useful for seeing how the patterns of retailing change.

Data analysis:
A good technique is SWOT analysis whereby you should identify the Strengths, Weaknesses, Opportunities and Threats of the regeneration scheme. This is sufficiently flexible to be used whatever information you collect and regardless of the how far your local regeneration project has progressed. Alternatively, a detailed environmental impact assessment may enable more quantitative analysis to be carried out.

Data interpretation:
This is most likely to be a qualified judgement; realistically there will be advantages and disadvantages to every regeneration scheme and different groups of people may experience different outcomes. However you assess the impacts, ensure that you strive for objectivity and always support any assertion you make with valid evidence.

Summary

This chapter has examined the management of inequalities in urban areas through two case studies, Hackney and Mumbai. Clearly these urban areas face significantly different challenges, but in both their local authorities have experienced mixed success in their efforts to improve the standards of living and quality of life of the residents. The gap between rich and poor may seem impossible to narrow. But, at the very least, the living conditions of the poor should be tolerable, so much work remains to be done in some parts of the world.

After studying this chapter, you should be able to discuss these ideas and concepts and provide located examples of them:

- There are social, economic and environmental problems associated with urban inequalities.
- Key players involved in delivering solutions include international agencies, charities, governments, local and regional authorities, independent groups and individuals.
- Solutions to urban inequalities include self-help schemes, traffic and public transport schemes and other town planning initiatives, business initiatives, and measures to reduce crime.

Exam practice

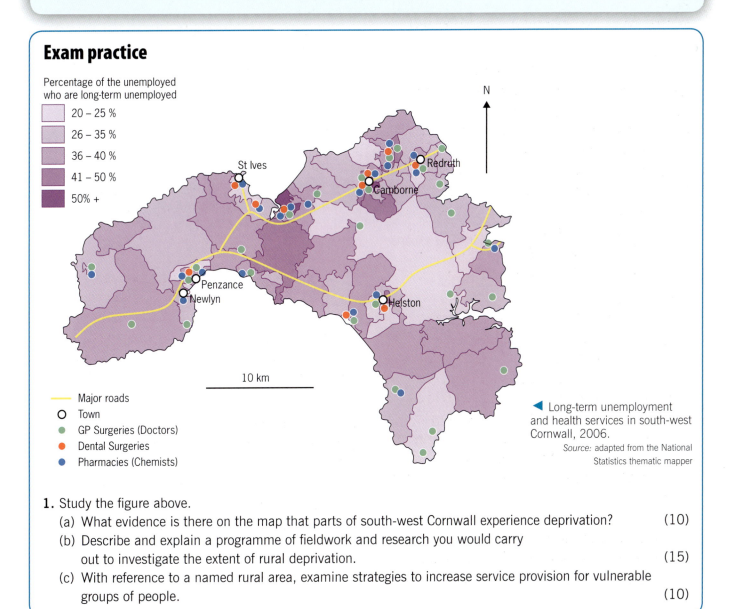

Long-term unemployment and health services in south-west Cornwall, 2006.

Source: adapted from the National Statistics thematic mapper

1. Study the figure above.
   (a) What evidence is there on the map that parts of south-west Cornwall experience deprivation?   (10)
   (b) Describe and explain a programme of fieldwork and research you would carry out to investigate the extent of rural deprivation.   (15)
   (c) With reference to a named rural area, examine strategies to increase service provision for vulnerable groups of people.   (10)

CHAPTER 27 What is rebranding and why is it needed in some places?

Learning objectives

After studying this chapter, you will be able to discuss these ideas and concepts and provide located examples of them:

- The wide variety of regeneration and rebranding methods used.
- The range of rebranding ideas used in both rural and urban environments.
- The reasons why rebranding is needed in some places more than it is in others.
- Some examples of why urban decline is hard to stop once it starts, and why some rural regions face similar decline.

What is rebranding?

Rebranding is a term that originated in the world of corporate capitalism. In that world it often involves a major 'makeover' of a company's logo, its sales 'pitch' and sometimes, although not always, its products or services. Recent examples include both McDonald's and Microsoft. In the UK, a less successful corporate makeover was the rebranding of the Post Office as 'Consignia' – which was very rapidly abandoned. Cities have employed marketing experts to rebrand them, choosing slogans felt to be helpful in their re-imaging process. Only one slogan, 'The Big Apple', is a term that grew out of popular culture rather than an invention of marketing experts.

◀ Figure 1: The sun sets for the last time on Hudson's Department Store in 1998. Hudson's had been the 'Harrods' of Detroit, but as the motor industry left the city and the population fell, many shops closed and, eventually, this big store was demolished. Many attempts at regenerating Detroit have since taken place.

All types of places, from extreme rural to extreme urban, are likely to face problems that require attention by the public authorities and private businesses that have an interest in them. In a world that is changing more rapidly than at any other time in history and in which national economies have become more and more exposed to the powerful forces of globalisation, local populations have had to think on their feet in order to stay competitive. This has frequently involved attempts at replacing 'traditional' but decaying structures of employment with new and, potentially, sustainable alternatives. This process consists of two main elements:

1. Regeneration projects, whereby inward investment is brought into an area or region. This has multiple forms, including new places of employment, sports arenas, cultural centres, heritage sites and leisure facilities.
2. Re-imaging, whereby the area or region is effectively 'sold' using new packaging, with new content, much like corporations changing their logos. This is to give any regeneration projects the impetus that they might need to attract people to them.

Ultimately both of these elements are more likely to be associated with places in decline or, at least, places with well-known problems. Place marketing is already a multi-billion dollar industry in the USA and has grown rapidly in Europe. The principle of place marketing is to build on an existing place image, if largely positive, or create an entirely new one if the existing one is negative.

Detroit used to be known as 'Motown' (Mo(tor) town) because of the dominance of the car industry, but when that industry declined, the city became known to many as 'Detroit – Murder capital of America'. Not surprisingly, the city has now been rebranded as: 'Detroit – Cars, Culture, Gaming, Music, Sports'.

Once the new image has been created, it has to be communicated to potential customers – individuals, governments and private businesses.

In order to know the existing image of different places, market research has been conducted, using focus groups, to understand how they are popularly viewed. The table below shows the results when people were asked for words that they associated with various European countries. (This was how it was in 1995 for adults. No doubt times and images have changed since then.)

Recent city rebranding slogans

Stockholm
Inspired in Stockholm
Singapore
Live it up in Singapore
Hanover
The City of International Fairs
Berlin
Capital of the New Europe
Chicago
Business Capital of America
Hong Kong
City of Life
Amsterdam
City of Inspiration
New York
The Big Apple

▲ **Figure 2:** Two images of Glasgow: rebranded as 'Scotland with style' or as seen by a resident of Tongland – 'U R ENTERIN TONGLAND!'

Key terms

Rebranding is a change of image through the development of a marketing strategy. Regeneration is the practical changes that take place on the ground.

◄ **Figure 3:** Images of European countries by word association.
Source: http://lib.tkk.fi/Diss/2003/ isbn9512266849/isbn9512266849.pdf

Country	First five images, in order of popularity
Belgium	Brussels, chocolate, Tintin, beer, capital of Europe
Denmark	Vikings, Hans Christian Anderson, Copenhagen, Lego, football
Germany	Beer, Berlin, motorways, Goethe, serious
Spain	Barcelona, bullfighting, paella, art, Juan Carlos
France	Paris, wine, Gerard Depardieu, food, fashion
Ireland	Green, the Irish Pub, James Joyce, Celtic design, U2
Italy	Rome, pasta, art, shoes, Pavarotti
Portugal	Port wine, Lisbon, explorers, Algarve, football
United Kingdom	Shakespeare, London, BBC, Royal family, Beatles

The multiplier effect is another way of saying that money is spent more than once, so if a new industry arrives and new jobs are created, then more jobs are also created in shops, restaurants, and so forth. Similarly, it works the other way around when industries pull out of a city or region – the negative multiplier.

This is a very competitive world, and selling places is a very competitive business. There are over 500 regions in Europe and about 100,000 urban communities. Worldwide, there are about 300 city-regions with populations larger than 1 million. Almost all of these places are trying to attract the limited (if very large) amount of money from all sorts of groups, from transnational corporations down to individual tourists. An urban regeneration programme that fundamentally changes the character of an urban area typically involves the rebranding of the area concerned. This may be very controversial because the redevelopment might result in the in-migration of well-off residents, business infrastructures, and cultural and leisure facilities that are more suited to better-off people than to the poorer original inhabitants (who might even be driven out by rising property prices and rents).

Meanwhile many rural regions, even in poor LDCs, suffering from declining income from agriculture and out-migration of the young, are faced with a battle to attract alternative sources of income, frequently from leisure and tourism.

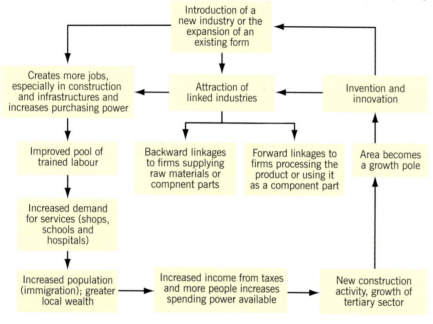

▲ **Figure 4:** The cumulative causation model.

One of the key principles here is the 'multiplier effect' and, for places in a spiral of decline, the 'negative multiplier'. The idea owes much to Gunnar Myrdal's explanation of why rich regions tend to stay rich and poor regions get relatively poorer, shown in Figure 4.

How to rebrand

Rebranding a place has to involve a little more than just changing its name. Renaming a place generally happens for political reasons. Thus St Petersburg became Petrograd, then Leningrad, only to become St Petersburg again. Bombay has become Mumbai, and Saigon was renamed Ho Chi Minh City.

Cumulative causation is the economist's way of saying that one thing leads to another. Once a strategy (including rebranding) has successfully attracted a new business or enterprise then its arrival will stimulate further enterprises to locate in the district and an upward spiral begins (see Figure 4).

There have been many different routes adopted in rebranding. They fall into a number of distinct categories.

Sport: Engineering change around a major sporting venue has been a popular route to rebranding a city and attracting investment into some of its poorer areas. The Olympic Games in Barcelona in 1992 were used to help regenerate poorer areas of the city, whilst building the City of Manchester stadium for the Commonwealth Games was the keystone in the redevelopment of this old industrial area.

Cultural facilities: The development of art galleries, museums and cultural 'events' has been central to the regeneration of many inner city areas in the UK, including Liverpool, Glasgow, and Bristol.

Technology and science: A specific 'hub' of scientific activity is sometimes created to act as a catalyst, speeding up the arrival of new hi-tech industries. These can be combined with leisure activities, as in the Cité de l'Espace in Toulouse.

Retail developments: The term 'food deserts' was coined a few years ago to describe urban areas that lacked adequate shopping facilities. After years of out-of-town shopping developments, planners have frequently used in-town retail developments as key elements in urban regeneration schemes. The development of a major Tesco store in the Seacroft district of Leeds is an example. By creating 500 jobs, the Tesco store also attracts customers from neighbouring districts, stimulating trade for other retailers, thus creating more employment opportunity and generating additional wealth for one of the poorest areas in northern England.

Education: Closely related to the development of hi-tech industries is the development of university departments or wholly new university campuses in areas that are targeted for regeneration. These new academic institutions will in turn attract new industries, built on mutual dependency. The blueprint here is 'Silicon Valley' an iconic 'brand' in California and its relationship with Stanford University.

Leisure and entertainment: In 2007 Manchester won a nationwide competition to be granted a licence for Britain's first super-casino. This was to be built in East Manchester, close to the City of Manchester stadium. The super-casino would have had a minimum customer area of 5,000 m² and up to 1,250 unlimited-jackpot slot machines. The government also expected the super-casino to have hotels, conference facilities, restaurants, bars and areas for live entertainment. Doubts about the value of super-casinos have since led to these plans being abandoned.

Why do urban areas need to rebrand?

In the last 50 years, urban areas have faced significant problems that are frequently the result of forces outside of their direct control. That is to say, national and global changes have impacted on cities, sometimes quite dramatically. This has been most obvious in the industrial cities – which grew from the nineteenth century onwards, basing their wealth on primary or secondary industry. These have been affected greatly by the disappearance of primary industries, especially coal-mining, and by the decline of secondary industries, especially the heavy industries, such as iron and steel and the related 'metal-bashing' industries like shipbuilding.

In many cities, decline is visible not only in the centre but also on the margins, where urban landscapes merge into rural landscapes. These marginal areas have been neglected by planners in the past and were labelled 'drosscapes' by the American landscape architect Alan Berger.

The reasons for this decline are not always simple. It is also important to recognise that, as industries mechanise, the process may involve loss of employment but not necessarily loss of output. This is true of the car-industry, for example. The UK is still a major manufacturer of motor vehicles although almost entirely by foreign-based TNCs operating outside major cities in 'new' areas (Honda at Swindon).

In summary, there are four basic reasons why some cities rebrand:

1. Places are increasingly at risk as a result of changes in the global economic, political and technological environment.
2. Places are increasingly at risk from the inevitable process of urban decay.
3. Places are facing a growing number of competitors for limited resources.
4. Places have to increasingly rely on their own resources to face competition.

Taking it further

Backwash effects involve the negative impact that rich regions have on poor regions. They drain their labour and stunt their industrial development because the products from the rich regions are almost always higher quality and sometimes cheaper than those from the 'poor' regions.

Examiners' tip

It is important to note that most urban regeneration programmes use more than one of these routes.

Key terms

'Drosscapes' are large areas of abused and damaged land on the margins of cities where urban sprawl meets urban dereliction – landscapes of wasted land. They are a world of contaminated former industrial sites, mineral workings, rubbish dumps, container stores, polluted river banks, sewerage works and large expanses of tarmac used for airport car parks.

Case study: The rise and fall of Detroit

The city of Detroit was founded in 1601 by a French adventurer and explorer, who called himself 'Antoine Laumet de La Mothe, sieur de Cadillac'. After years of precarious existence as a trading post, changing hands between the French, the British, the Americans and the Canadians, Detroit ultimately became an American city and one of the most important manufacturing cities in the young USA. Profiting from its situation on the important trading routes and within reach of the natural resources of the Great Lakes region, Detroit grew rapidly as a centre of transportation. And later, in the early twentieth century, it developed as the centre of the new motor vehicle industry – hence its nickname 'Motown'.

The majority the early US car pioneers, such as Henry Ford, William Durant (founder of General Motors), the Dodge brothers and Walter Chrysler, established factories in Detroit. 'Fordism' and the production line were born here in the 1910s, as the rapidly growing city sucked in labour from Europe and from the deep south of the USA. But in the 1960s the US car industry began to decline and relocate, some of it into the surrounding suburbs of Wayne County. This marked the beginning of a very difficult period for the once prosperous and successful city of Detroit. And this difficult period has yet to end for much of what is now termed America's 'rustbelt' region.

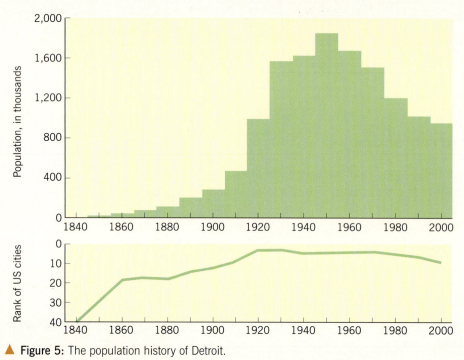

▲ **Figure 5:** The population history of Detroit.

Detroit's need for rebranding is obvious both to the casual observer but also to anyone looking at the recent history of the city and some of its unusual characteristics:

- Detroit is 'hollowing out' as well as shrinking, as industry and people leave the city centre.
- It displays the very rare phenomenon of 'reverse commuting' – with more people driving out than into the central city in the morning.
- It has one of the largest debts of any US city, and has been close to bankruptcy on many occasions.

- It experienced serious urban riots in 1967. The '12th Street Riots' accelerated the rate of 'white flight' to new suburbs beyond the city limits.
- It is the most racially segregated city in the USA. 85% of the city's population is black, whilst the surrounding areas of Wayne County are predominantly white.
- It has rates of unemployment of up to 45% in the largely black inner city suburbs.
- 47% of the population are functionally illiterate.
- 72% of children are born to single mothers.
- It is home to Eminem and the White Stripes.
- It was known as the 'City of Champions' in the 1930s with a string of successful black athletes and the Detroit Tigers winning the World Series in 1935.
- Detroit is the 'crime capital' of the USA, coming top of the table for murder and violent crime. The map (see Figure 6, page 251) shows the 'yellow' low income area of the city of Detroit as it stands out as an island of poverty in the richer 'sea' of surrounding Wayne County.

Case study: The rise and fall of Detroit (continued)

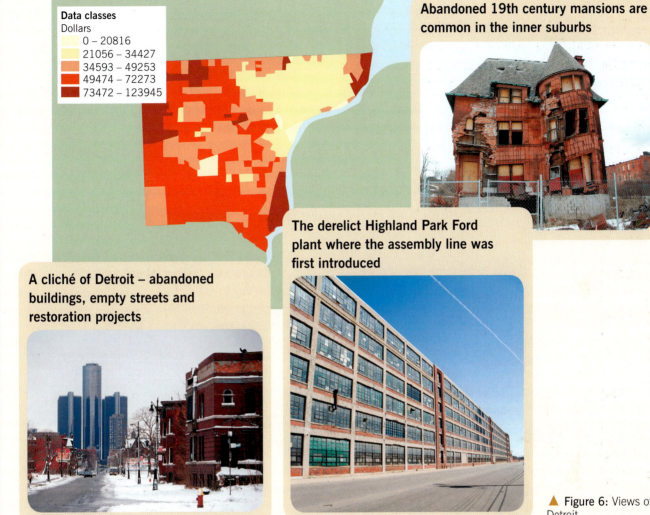

Data classes
Dollars
- 0 – 20816
- 21056 – 34427
- 34593 – 49253
- 49474 – 72273
- 73472 – 123945

Abandoned 19th century mansions are common in the inner suburbs

A cliché of Detroit – abandoned buildings, empty streets and restoration projects

The derelict Highland Park Ford plant where the assembly line was first introduced

▲ **Figure 6:** Views of Detroit.

The need for rural rebranding

Most people who live in rural areas experience a high quality of life, when compared to those who live in urban areas. They live longer than their urban neighbours, they suffer lower crime rates and they do better in school.

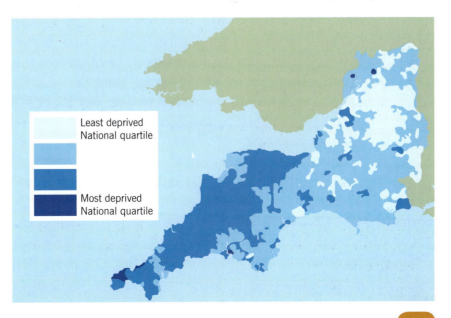

- Least deprived National quartile

- Most deprived National quartile

▶ **Figure 7:** South west England, showing the poverty in Cornwall.
Source: www.swo.org.uk/imd2004/map_book/imd.pdf

Key terms

Super Output Areas (SOAs) are the smallest areas from which UK data can be gathered. They are all about the same size to make comparison easier. There are 35,000 SOAs in the UK. SOAs vary between 1,000 and 1,500 residents, making comparison easier.

However, the pattern on the ground is complex. In the UK there are significant pockets of deprivation that are often disguised at a regional level – and many of these are in rural areas. The Super Output Area (SOA) database shows these areas clearly. Rural deprivation on a more general scale is often related to distance from the core growth regions of an economy. In the case of the UK, London and the South East are growing rapidly by almost every economic and demographic criterion. London is a global city, a management hub of the world economy, with a large number employed in financial services (over 45% in some areas of London). Figure 7 shows Cornwall to have a large number of SOAs in the third and fourth quartiles – in the bottom half – of the national league table.

Remote rural regions do not benefit greatly from the economic growth of the core regions. In fact they may be damaged by it through the impact of migration or the backwash effects that rich regions have on poorer regions.

There are three recognisable and interrelated types of poverty that are associated with these less successful rural regions: financial poverty, access poverty and network poverty. So the need for rural rebranding is shown in a poor performance in a number of areas: economic, demographic and social and cultural.

Case study: Cornwall

Cornwall is a rural county in a peripheral location, with an estimated resident population of 501,000 (ONS, 2002).

- Its peninsular location has ensured that Cornwall has remained, until quite recently, one of the most remote and isolated parts of Great Britain, although this has allowed it to maintain much of its own cultural identity.
- Cornwall's landscape masks the levels of deprivation within the county. The 'Indices of Multiple Deprivation, 2004' ranks Cornwall as being the second most deprived county (after Durham) and the most deprived of all shire (non-metropolitan) counties. 33% of households in Cornwall live in areas ranked within the 25% most deprived nationally.

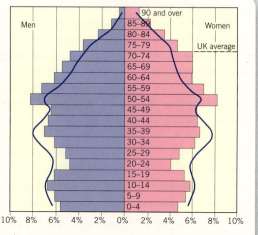
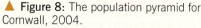

▲ **Figure 8:** The population pyramid for Cornwall, 2004.

- The remoteness of Cornwall has led to a weakened local economy that has been unable to link effectively to national and international trade.
- Cornwall attracts large numbers of migrants who are either late in their job careers or actually retired, impacting on house prices.
- In many of the former industrial and mining (both for tin and china clay) communities there is real poverty and deprivation. Cornwall today has the lowest earnings levels in England and is poorer than many inner city areas.
- Population projections herald a drop in 25 to 44 year olds, the heart of the labour force, and a steady growth in those over 65.
- The county contains widely scattered villages and small towns. Only 31% of the population live in towns of over 10,000 inhabitants, compared to 80% in the England and Wales as a whole.
- The large number of smaller communities makes it particularly difficult to provide an adequate and economic range of services to cater for the needs of relatively small numbers of people in individual settlements.
- Over time, many parts of the county have experienced rural depopulation and townships significant socio-economic hardship.
- In April 2005, average earnings for full-time male employees in Cornwall were 25% below the average for Great Britain.
- The decline of traditional industries has left a legacy of scarred landscapes, abandoned buildings and run-down town centres.
- In 2005, Cornwall's GDP was 75% of the UK average. Meanwhile, Wiltshire had a GDP of 115% of the UK average.
- In Cornwall, a typical small home (terraced) cost nearly eight times the average Cornish annual income — compared to just five times the average income across England and Wales in 2004 due to the desirability of Cornwall as a holiday area.

Fieldwork

Aim:

To evaluate the need for rebranding by investigating two contrasting areas (either rural or urban, or one of each).

1. Choose two local areas of contrasting characteristics; for example one could be on the margins of a city in a 'drosscape', one in a more remote rural area.

2. Use photographs, Google Earth (on the internet) and SOA databases to compare these areas in terms of their deprivation.

3. Construct an Environmental Quality Survey to assess the areas.

4. Construct a questionnaire for local people to identify the 'image' that the location has. This questionnaire should be stratified to distinguish between three groups:
   (a) Long-term residents (lived in the area for 3 years or longer)
   (b) Short-term residents (lived in the area for less than 3 years)
   (c) Visitors – people who are not resident in the area but visiting on business or for personal reasons.

5. You could add your own impressions by brainstorming a 'word association' view of the place. Do this by taking photographs or video material of both places and show them to the whole group. Ask them to write down the first three words that they think of when they have seen the images. For some groups it might be best to give them a list of possible words to choose from. Gather up all the responses and put them into a table; then take the three most common responses.

6. Conduct a document search to explore issues and problems faced in these areas, including access issues.

7. Use a placecheck form (www.placecheck.info/placecheck_form.htm) to identify special issues and problems.

Risk assessment

This is a low-risk exercise, but you need to take special care when conducting environmental surveys, and taking photographs. People may not take kindly to too much discussion about 'deprivation', so keep to the point of the exercise.

Health and safety

Make sure that all fieldwork is conducted with at least one other person, and make sure that a responsible adult knows where you are at all times. Take care when crossing roads.

Data presentation

It would be sensible to gather your primary data about the areas before exploring the secondary databases. This will allow you to present your data in tables and map form before examining the secondary sources. Comparisons can then be made between your data and the secondary data for the two areas.

Conclusion

Try to offer a view about which area is more in need of rebranding, giving reasons that don't just state the obvious ('it has more problems and is more deprived'). Try to identify the nature of that deprivation, using both your own evidence and that of the secondary sources.

Evaluation

Think about how you could extend this investigation or refine it in order to explore different issues. This might include looking at areas that have already experienced some regeneration or rebranding policies.

Summary

Having read this chapter you are aware of what rebranding means and the range of ideas that have been developed to help places regenerate. Through the case studies of Detroit and Cornwall you now appreciate why some places are in more need of rebranding than others and why that task is quite difficult in some areas. You will be able to discuss these ideas and concepts and provide located examples of them:

• The wide variety of regeneration and rebranding methods used.
• The range of rebranding ideas used in both rural and urban environments.
• The reasons why rebranding is needed in some places more than it is in others.
   • Some examples of why urban decline is hard to stop once it starts, and why some rural regions face similar decline.

MCQ

To try an exam question using what you have learned in this chapter, turn to page 280.

CHAPTER 28 Who are the 'rebranding players' and what strategies exist for places to improve themselves?

Rebranding strategies

The aim of rebranding a place is to 'sell' it to potential 'customers', who will belong to one or more of the groups listed below. The nature of the rebranding may very well need to vary, according to the target group that is being pursued.

1. Visitors
   - Business visitors who may be attending a conference or on a sales trip.
   - Non-business visitors who may be tourists or simply travelling to visit relatives and friends.

2. Residents and employees
   - Professionals (doctors, university teachers, etc.)
   - Skilled employees
   - Local wealthy people
   - Local celebrities
   - Investors and entrepreneurs
   - Semi-skilled and unskilled workers.

3. Business and industry
   - Older heavy industries
   - New hi-tech industries
   - Quaternary sector employers.

4. Exporters
   - International businesses
   - International travel companies.

▼ **Figure 1:** The urban regeneration plan for Swansea in South Wales. As with many industrial cities in the UK, the plans focus on old industrial areas – especially those with a waterfront – and attempt a 'holistic' approach that tackles a wide range of urban problems with a wide range of solutions.

The process of rebranding is generally started by local or regional government forming a planning group, involving as many people in the local community as they think might be useful – the local players. The planning group then has three key tasks to perform:

1. Diagnosis – identifying the problem or issues confronting the area.
2. Vision – developing a set of goals that address the problems identified by the diagnosis.
3. Action – developing a set a practical policies that will help achieve the vision.

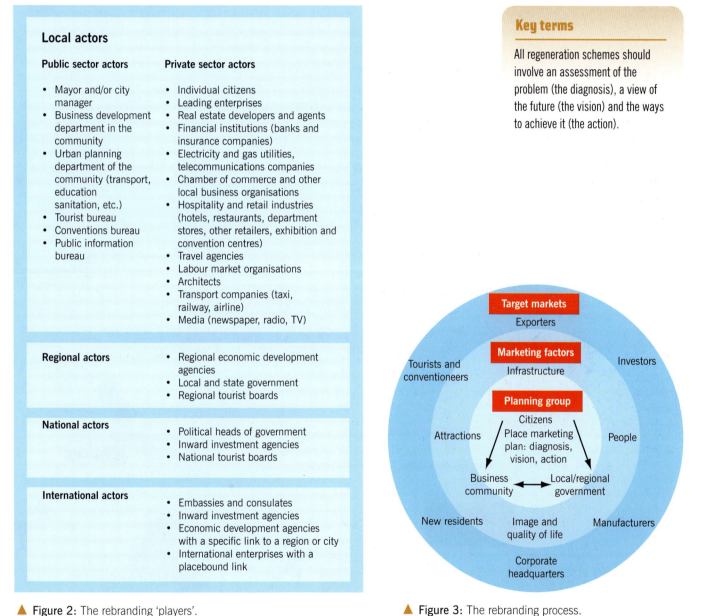

Local actors

Public sector actors	Private sector actors
• Mayor and/or city manager • Business development department in the community • Urban planning department of the community (transport, education sanitation, etc.) • Tourist bureau • Conventions bureau • Public information bureau	• Individual citizens • Leading enterprises • Real estate developers and agents • Financial institutions (banks and insurance companies) • Electricity and gas utilities, telecommunications companies • Chamber of commerce and other local business organisations • Hospitality and retail industries (hotels, restaurants, department stores, other retailers, exhibition and convention centres) • Travel agencies • Labour market organisations • Architects • Transport companies (taxi, railway, airline) • Media (newspaper, radio, TV)
Regional actors	• Regional economic development agencies • Local and state government • Regional tourist boards
National actors	• Political heads of government • Inward investment agencies • National tourist boards
International actors	• Embassies and consulates • Inward investment agencies • Economic development agencies with a specific link to a region or city • International enterprises with a placebound link

▲ **Figure 2:** The rebranding 'players'.

Source: Kotler et al., 1999.

▲ **Figure 3:** The rebranding process.

Source: Kotler et al., 1999

Key terms

All regeneration schemes should involve an assessment of the problem (the diagnosis), a view of the future (the vision) and the ways to achieve it (the action).

Investigating the rebranding of rural areas

The task is to investigate a range of strategies that have been used in the rebranding of rural areas. It is important to note that not all of these schemes and projects will be identified by the key players as 'rebranding' exercises. So a number of alternative titles should be used when conducting research, especially secondary research – for example, 'regeneration', 'renaissance', 'renewal' or 'revival'.

Defining the areas: The distinction between rural and urban areas is not categorical, and before embarking on fieldwork it would help to understand that the distinction is no longer as clear as once it was. Until now, in the case of rural areas, there have been two main types of definition in use: one based upon land use and the other based upon social and economic factors. Since measures of social and employment structure no longer clearly distinguish between urban and rural areas (largely because of declining employment in agriculture in rural areas), the best way forward to identify rural settlement patterns – small rural towns, villages, hamlets and scattered dwellings.

Rural and urban areas, therefore, are now defined by their population – their size and location relative to other places, rather than by their function (what they do), which may be much the same for most 'rural' settlements and most 'urban' places.

So two groups of rural settlements have been identified:

- Those settlements more than 30 km from urban areas, in 'sparse' regions – the more remote parts of the country.
- Villages in 'less sparse' regions that are much more urban in general character. These settlements are likely to be different, simply because of the proximity of urban centres, but they remain 'villages' because of their size.

'Primary' evidence of rebranding strategies can be gathered in a number of ways, including questionnaires, photographs and land-use surveys. (Primary data is gathered by you or other members of the group.)

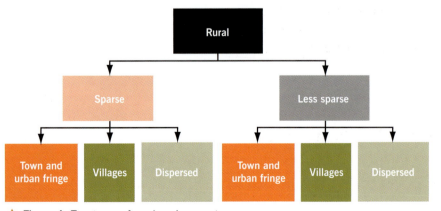

▲ **Figure 4:** Two types of rural environment.

▲ **Figure 5:** The sparse rural regions of England and Wales.

'Secondary' material will be gathered in a number of ways, including newspapers, maps, census information, internet and published research. (Secondary data is previously gathered information, found in published form or on the internet.)

There are several rural rebranding strategies that can be explored. Three aspects are considered here.

The image: Figure 6 shows the image of the Lake District that is now used on all its promotional literature. It conveys a view of the landscape that is tranquil, deeply rural and suggestive of a wide variety of activities based on water and land only lightly used for farming. And, unusually, there are very few clouds in the sky and not a single human being in view.

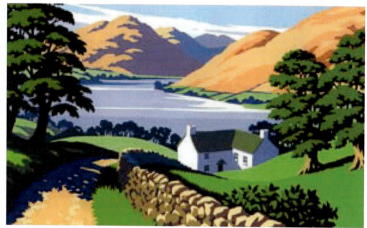

▲ **Figure 6:** The new 'view' of the Lake District.

The target customers: In 2007, Cumbria Tourism appointed an advertising agency, Cheethambell JWT, in a £2m contract, to change the Lake District's 'Love the Lakes' strapline and rebrand the area as an ideal destination for wealthy urbanites to spend their weekends, visiting the bars and cafés. Cumbria Tourism claims that the rebranding will build on the region's reputation for natural beauty but will also position it as a 'vibrant, world-class, twenty-first-century destination'.

> Jane Clancy, managing director of Cheethambell, said: 'The Lake District is not only a beautiful landscape famous for its amelioration qualities which soothe the soul but also it is a high-ground destination with chic boutiques, restaurants, accommodation and spas – as well as funky bars, beer cafés and bistros . . . there's some terrific local food and shops. It's a very powerful combination – a bit like Harrods with Harvey Nicks thrown in.'

(www.guardian.co.uk/print/0,,329839677-103500,00.html)

The 'heritage' business: The idea of heritage relates to a celebration of the past. That isn't always a 'real' past and it can often be sold through fictional characters.

Since the 1970s, 'heritage' has become big business. Museums have multiplied, 'Heritage Centres' are commonplace in historic towns, and groups of enthusiasts rescue old machinery, from tanks to trains. Large numbers of people visit abbeys and stately homes, or re-creations of the recent industrial past at places such as Dudley, Beamish and Ironbridge. The term 'heritage' has achieved official recognition: the Historic Buildings and Monuments Commission for England now trades under the name 'English Heritage'.

Many other communities have used their association with the past to their advantage. In some cases, the association is with fictional characters, as with 'Herriot Country' in North Yorkshire, an area popularised by a TV series *All Creatures Great and Small*, based on a series of books by 'James Herriot', recounting the adventures of a local vet. The TV series ran between 1978 and 1990 but nearly 20 years on, 'Herriot Country' is still used.

Taking it further

How does English Heritage's mission statement support this view?

Taking it further

To learn more about rebranding rural towns read 'Stroud – a food town' on your Student CD-ROM.

▲ **Figure 7:** The centre of Birmingham today.

Urban rebranding through promoting a new identity

Many urban planners would suggest that Detroit has more problems to solve than almost any other city in the developed world. Its current rebranding strategy is to emphasise its youth culture, its music and its cultural diversity:

The brand positioning and its graphic representation: 'Detroit – Cars, Culture, Gaming, Music, Sports', was introduced at a meeting attended by nearly 400 tourism, hospitality, and civic leaders.

According to Larry Alexander, president of the Bureau, the new identity was developed after more than a year of extensive research to positively shape tourist perceptions of the region over time.

> 'The brand identity resulted from surveys of more than 1,300 visitors and focus groups in five cities that identified Detroit as 'the American city where cool comes from', said Alexander. 'This identity focuses on five strengths that best set us apart from other cities – our auto heritage, our music heritage, our distinctive cultural product, Vegas-style gaming, and sports. Together, these strengths, delivered the way Detroit delivers them, give us a rare opportunity to own a very powerful and compelling idea – and that's the first order of business in building a world-class tourism brand identity.'

> 'The research found that among 11 regional cities (including Chicago, Toronto, Cleveland, Pittsburgh and Indianapolis) Detroit was the only city perceived to offer a travel experience appealing primarily to young adults.'

(http://www.hiphoppress.com/2007/01/detroit_metro_c.html)

This strategy is new for a city that has a once proud but now sadly declining history as an industrial town. Rebranding an industrial city into a post-industrial cultural centre poses its own challenges. That problem has been addressed by the city authorities:

- Research suggested that when asked to describe an ideal 3 days in Detroit, the tendency was to include attractions and destinations throughout the metro area and not just in the centre.
- Visitors noted that many of Detroit's tourism offerings were not always easy to identify nor well-promoted. As a result, the city established five 'Tourism Destination Districts' to provide a ready way for visitors to understand Detroit's dispersed tourism locations.
- The districts invite visitors – through marketing, advertising and hotel/attraction packages – to experience Detroit in concentrated, smaller destinations: Downtown, Dearborn/Wayne, Macomb, South Oakland and North Oakland.
- Schematic maps will provide an easy way for visitors to understand each district and the links between them, so that they can navigate to attractions throughout the city.
- In each district a committee of local business and economic development leaders guide the creation of specific marketing strategies for the area.
- The marketing materials will include several non-traditional campaign elements designed to reach younger people, including podcasting, blogging and advertising on prime time television shows aimed at 21 to 34 year olds.

(http://www.ci.detroit.mi.us/plandevl/advplanning/masterplan.html)

▲ **Figure 8:** The Renaissance Center in Detroit.

Urban rebranding using sport

It remains unclear whether large sporting projects offer long-term benefits to cities or not. This issue will be explored in Chapter 30. Whatever the doubts may be, there is seldom any shortage of candidate cities for large sporting occasions, such as the football World Cup or the Olympic Games.

The suggested benefits of the project for London are outlined as follows on the promoters' website:

The London 2012 Olympic and Paralympic Games will be the catalyst for the regeneration of the Lower Lea Valley in East London.

The area in and around the Olympic Park is a site of huge potential. It has a young, diverse community, but is also home to significant areas that would benefit from redevelopment.

Much of the site itself is contaminated, derelict and abandoned. The waterways in the area have suffered from years of neglect.

The 2012 Games will help to revitalise this part of London and open the east of the capital to development opportunities. The new shopping area at Stratford City will be an important part of this growth.

The creation of one of the largest new urban parks in Europe in 150 years will bring new homes for Londoners, vastly improved transport links and world-class sports facilities available for the local community.

The development of the Olympic Park will deliver numerous benefits:
- Significant employment and business opportunities, with jobs being created in the construction and operation of the Olympic Park and development after the Games.
- Over 4,000 new homes will be built for the Olympic Village; these will be converted, post-Games, to form newly created neighbourhoods.
- The parklands will restore and enhance the recreational and ecological role of this important river valley.
- The Park will also host a mix of world-class sports venues and training facilities. It will also be a place for recreational cycling, walking, bird watching, fishing, wetland and outdoor classrooms.
- New roads, bridges, footpaths and cycleways will help bring together the communities around the Park.

(http://www.london-2012.co.uk/Urban-regeneration/)

Much is made of the sustainability of this project and, indeed, almost all urban rebranding exercises now make much of their 'sustainability'. In the case of the London Olympics this definition is offered:

Being 'sustainable' means providing for people's current and long-term needs, improving quality of life while ensuring a healthy and thriving natural environment. The Games give us the chance to show how changes to the way we build, live, work, do business and travel could help us to live happy and healthy lives, within our planet's resources.

But no mention is made of broader sustainability issues, such as the costs of getting the athletes, their coaches, families, supporters and much of the world's sports media to the event.

▲ **Figure 9:** East London in the post-Olympic period, as it seen by the planners.

Rebranding coastal resorts

Britain's coastal resorts developed in the nineteenth century, as sea bathing became associated with good health. Blackpool is probably the best known but its recent history has been troubled as holiday makers have pursued foreign sunshine rather than windswept British shorelines. Its Victorian growth was built upon being the preferred destination for the working class of the north-west cities of Manchester and Liverpool. The industrial decline has added to its woes, and made it harder for it to rebrand.

Much of Blackpool's attraction was its entertainment because, even in its heyday, the beach was often a rather bleak place. The first amusement park – 'Blackpool Pleasure Beach' – was founded in 1896, with the following mission statement:

> We wanted an American-style Amusement Park, the fundamental principle of which is to make adults feel like children again and to inspire gaiety of a primarily innocent character.
>
> (W.G. Bean, founder of Blackpool Pleasure Beach)

A rebranding exercise in recent years has turned the Blackpool Pleasure Beach into the 'Pleasure Beach', which attracts about 6 million visitors a year. In the 2006 figures for theme parks, Pleasure Beach was joint 11th in the world by attendance (joint with Universal Studios in Florida). It was the only UK amusement park to make it on to the 'Top 25 Parks in the World' list.

The three proposals below are part of Blackpool's rebranding, which concentrates almost exclusively on the tourist and leisure industry.

Proposal 1: The council and national business interests were keen to turn Blackpool into a casino resort making it the centre point of gambling in the UK. Researchers said the super-casino would be good for the Blackpool economy, where the number of tourists visiting is dropping by up to 2% each year. Critics pointed out that the main beneficiaries of super-casinos are the shareholders and managers of the companies who seldom live very close to these places. This has now led to a halt to the super-casino development.

Proposal 2: A second project is the £500 m scheme to build 'Storm City', a proposed multi-themed indoor entertainment complex on a 12 hectare site. Storm City would house:

- A 12,000 seat arena
- Four world-class hotels
- Retail areas
- Five themed entertainment areas
- Rooftop gardens
- Blackpool's own version of the London Eye.

In March 2007 Blackpool Council signed a 3-month deal to work exclusively with the developers of Storm City.

Proposal 3: A third scheme, Talbot Gateway, is primarily aimed at the local population, but will also benefit those holidaymakers travelling to the town by rail. The project will transform what is at present a rundown area around Blackpool North railway station into what Blackpool Council hope will be a world-class gateway, with new office and retail space, and a public plaza. Incoming rail passengers will exit into the new plaza, with views down to the seafront, making their arrival at Blackpool a much more pleasant experience that at present. This is one of 12 key projects organised by the regeneration company ReBlackpool, which is behind much of the town's current and future development.

Fieldwork

Aim:

To explore the range of strategies used in one rural area and one urban area to regenerate and/or rebrand that area.

(Note: It would be sensible to plan and carry out this piece of work at the same time as the work conducted for the other chapters of this Unit.)

Rural research

1. Conduct a survey of a rural area, including at least one village, to record evidence of rebranding. All shops and services in a settlement should be listed and a scoring system devised to assess whether or not these showed evidence of rebranding.
2. A document search should be conducted to explore evidence of rebranding in the local area, the key players and the source of funds.
3. The local authority and other 'players' should be approached to gather data about recent rural changes.
4. Interviews with local residents should be conducted to establish perceived recent changes in the local community.

Urban research

1. A retail survey of the town can be conducted to establish land use. This can be done for the whole centre or selected streets, according to the size of the centre.
2. Conduct interviews with residents to establish perceived recent changes in the town/city.
3. Use old 'Goad maps' to establish changes in the nature of the retail centre.
4. The local authority and other 'players' should be approached to gather data about recent urban changes and future plans.
5. A document search should be conducted to explore evidence of rebranding in the local area, the key players and the source of funds.

6. Qualitative surveys such as mind maps and oral histories can be used to develop a profile of the urban area, both before and after the regeneration projects.

Risk assessment

This is a low-risk exercise, but you need to take special care when conducting interviews and taking photographs. Residents may not take kindly to too much discussion about 'deprivation' or the success or failure of regeneration projects, so keep to the point of the exercise.

Health and safety

Make sure that all fieldwork is conducted with at least one other person, and make sure that a responsible adult knows where you are at all times. Take care when crossing roads.

Data presentation

A table should be produced showing a list of strategies, and their aims in terms of income, employment and environmental change. These should be tabulated against the key 'players' and the funding sources. They can be mapped to identify clear target areas, and any 'flagship' projects.

Conclusion

For both areas the conclusion should try to assess whether there is:

(1) An overall regeneration plan for the area – is there a diagnosis, a vision and an action plan?
(2) An identifiable group of key players driving the process.

Evaluation

Ideas for extending this work should be addressed. One route would be to explore any differences in how these rebranding exercises are viewed by the local communities. This will link usefully to later topics.

Summary

Having studied this chapter you are now in a position to answer questions about the processes and principals involved in urban and rural rebranding. You will be able to recognise how these strategies differ in scale and in purpose, and you will be able to discuss these ideas and concepts and provide located examples of them:

• The strategies and people involved in the rebranding process.
• The variety of ways by which rural areas have been rebranded and how to research these ideas.
  • The variety of ways by which urban areas have been rebranded and how to research these ideas.

MCQ

To try an exam question using what you have learned in this chapter, turn to page 280.

CHAPTER 29 How successful has rebranding been in the countryside?

Key terms

Critical mass
Diversification
Sustainable development
SWOT analysis

Learning objectives

After studying this chapter, you will be able to discuss these ideas and concepts and provide located examples of them:
- The variable success of rural rebranding schemes.
- The various methods used to achieve that success.
- How to evaluate the success of rural regeneration schemes.

In order to measure the success of rural rebranding it is necessary to return to the problems and issues that rebranding and rural regeneration schemes should be trying to address. These are the economic, demographic, and social and cultural problems, and each can be analysed even further.

The economic challenges in rural areas include a limited range and number of job opportunities, the relatively low comparative incomes in rural areas, and a lack of inward investment, especially in new technology industries. Demographic challenges are felt as a result of the changing population structure through out-migration of the young, and also through in-migration. The social and cultural issues are varied. There is a lack of affordable housing, a lack of access to health services, a loss of schools, low educational attainment and a changing sense of local identity.

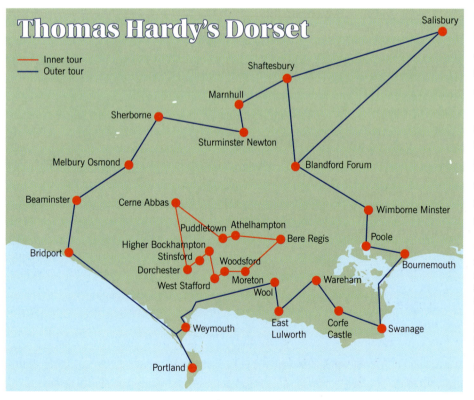

◀ Figure 1: Rural rebranding on a regional scale in the UK often involves associating an area with either a real or fictional history, hopefully cashing in on nostalgia and a longing for the past that will attract people to a region. Thus Dorset and adjacent counties exploit the reputation of the Victorian novelist Thomas Hardy and his well-known novels which describe the local landscape.
Source: www.britainexpress.com/images/jpaul/hardy-tour2.gif

Evaluation

Before embarking on a rebranding exercise it is important that the concerned 'players' in rural areas take a hard look at their region so that they can discover the best way forward. They might, for example, do a SWOT analysis, an important preliminary technique in which the Strengths, Weaknesses, Opportunities and Threats faced by an area can be assessed. The following is one such assessment of rural tourism taken from South East England Development Agency.

Strengths: The South East region has great strengths: an attractive and varied countryside and coast, distinctive small towns and villages, a superb heritage, excellent footpath network, proximity to London and 'gateway' entry points, an extensive network of cultural events and excellent sporting venues.

Weaknesses: The region has an image of overcrowding and lacking dramatic physical features. Some of its accommodation is of variable quality and relatively high cost. It lacks branded 'products' and its marketing is fragmented. It has poor west–east transport links. The tourism industry has recruitment difficulties and skills gaps, particularly in catering.

Opportunities: There are growth markets to be tapped (the over 55s, short breaks, near continentals, activity and special interest holidays, etc.) and an opportunity to develop a properly branded farm-based accommodation 'product'. There are two prospective National Parks, under-used assets such as the River Thames and Thames footpath, a growing interest in healthy lifestyles and green issues, and opportunities to encourage a wide range of countryside activities (walking, cycling, etc.) and to promote local produce.

Threats: Inappropriate development could lead to loss of distinctiveness, degradation of the environment and loss of tranquility. It can be difficult to access good advice for those wishing to diversify into tourism and leisure. There is too much fragmentation of effort. Tourism tends to be seasonal, and there is increasing competition from overseas and other UK markets. Moreover, the continuing impact of September 11th makes it harder to attract long-haul overseas visitors, with implications particularly for the better known heritage attractions in the South East.

www.seeda.co.uk/Publications/docs/RuralTourism.pdf

Rural tourism

The role of rural tourism as a potential economic tool is well recognised. It is estimated that tourism in rural areas makes up 10 to 20% of all tourism activities. A EuroBarometer (1998) survey shows that 23% of European holidaymakers choose the countryside as a destination every year. The majority of small- and medium-sized enterprises (SMEs) in the EU are in tourism and employ less than five people each. Many are comprised of two family members.

Rural areas provide a special appeal to tourists because of the mystery associated with the rural environment, its distinct culture, history and geographic characteristics. Rural tourism is a growing sector of the world's fastest growing industry. It offers many benefits to the rural community, and it can be developed locally in partnership with other small businesses, local government and other agencies. Its development is not usually dependent on outside firms or companies and their decisions on whether they want to be in the area or not. When considered against other economic development, such as manufacturing, rural tourism is less costly and easier to establish. It works well with existing rural enterprise and can generate important secondary income on farms. While airlines and railways, with their national and international linkages, may provide the best public transport, and global hotel groups give the highest standards of branded accommodation, it is very often the rural area and its attractions that delivers the bulk of the visitors' experience and defines their view of the destination.

Key terms

The critical mass (in this context) is the minimum number of tourists needed in a rural region to lead to significant multiplier effects.

The 5 As of rural tourism
Accommodation: B&B, self-catering, small hotel, hostels, campsites, caravan sites.
Access: airport, rail service, bus, booking system, web links, links with travel industry.
Available services: bank, taxis, car hire, boat hire, restaurants, shops, arts and entertainment.
Amenities: countryside, lakes, mountains, forests, rivers.
Activities: attractions, pubs, walks, fishing, golf, farm visits, heritage sites.

On the other hand, there are several factors reducing the effectiveness of rural tourism as a rural development instrument, including:

- Limited number of entrepreneurs in rural areas
- The conservative nature of some investors
- Short supply of spare capital in rural areas
- Small scale and dispersed nature of the industry, involving 'micro enterprises'
- The need for co-ordination, co-operation and partnership with government agencies to develop a 'destination' – as distinct from a 'stop-off point'
- Fragmentation in product provision and marketing efforts
- Lack of policy for the management development and marketing of rural tourism.

A 'critical mass' to provide the holiday experience

Successful tourism involves getting people to stay longer in the area. A rural area must aim to be a 'destination' rather than a place to 'stop-off'. A failure to achieve a critical mass, that is, a sufficient concentration of facilities, accommodation and attractions, means that a rural area lacks the ability to draw visitors to it for anything more than an hour or so a day. It is in the interest of local providers to work together to create a critical mass of tourism products in the area if they are to achieve economic benefits from longer stays. Communities that have been successful at developing tourism have developed high-quality tourism products and put together professional structures to liaise with the market and achieve results. A resource audit of an area, based on the '5 As', will help to establish if the area has the 'critical mass' to provide the holiday experience.

Developing rural technology

Absence of technology is a major issue in many rural areas. An increasing dependence upon technology both in business and for private individuals as a means of communication means that its absence is a disincentive for inward investment and a further cause of outward migration. In recent years the growth of broadband provision in the UK has been patchy, with urban areas far cheaper and thus more profitable for providers than the more remote and dispersed rural regions. There have been a large number of local schemes that have sought to address this problem.

In Scotland 'Connected Communities' has been extending broadband provision in the Western Isles. It is a government and locally funded enterprise which is using the internet to overcome one of the key problems for rural regenerators – access. Its mission statement explains:

> Connected Communities is a next generation broadband wireless network, connecting businesses, communities and services across the populated islands of the Outer Hebrides of Scotland.

> High-level broadband communications is a prerequisite for future development and underpins our aspirations to grow the economy and break down geographical barriers. Our aim is to develop the concept of a Connected Hebrides, a place which combines quality of life offered by rural living with global connectivity, opportunities for employment and inward investment, business creation, skills and learning.

(http://www.connectedcommunities.co.uk/)

Case study: Dipsticks Research in Northumberland

Dipsticks Research is an example of a successful enterprise that has overcome the supposed disadvantages of being in a rural location. It is a rapidly growing knowledge-intensive business, which relies on ICT technologies to conduct market research. Its headquarters were established in 1997 in a former farmhouse and buildings in Keenley, Allendale, in rural Northumberland in the north of England, one of England's most remote and sparsely populated rural areas. The District of Tynedale, where Allendale is located, has a population density of just 26 persons per km. Keenley is about an hour's drive from the city of Newcastle.

Dipsticks Research was founded by a husband-and-wife team with backgrounds in advertising and marketing. The company now has five directors and around 30 full-time employees, with a further 20 staff at its Computer-Assisted Telephone Interviewing (CATI) centre, 48 part-time fieldwork supervisors, and over 600 part-time fieldwork interviewers. Dipsticks is now a major local employer, not only in a remote rural part of Northumberland, but also in the nearby market town. The success of Dipsticks Research is founded on providing rapid and reliable research at reasonable rates. The company's location allows it to offer better value than urban-based agencies, and its team of research professionals ensures excellent levels of customer service. Dipsticks' clients include national government departments such as 'One NorthEast', the London Development Agency and Northumbria Police.

The firm processes around 4,500 individual cases per month, with the flexibility to expand that capacity quickly to meet individual client briefs. All functions are operated in-house, ensuring Dipsticks does not need to sub-contract any critical functions, and always retains control of the research project. The growth of Dipsticks illustrates the potential for rural localities to host cutting-edge, technologically innovative and growth-oriented businesses in what were previously agricultural settings. Indeed, the attractive rural surroundings (produced and still managed by farmers) were an important part of the appeal for the entrepreneurs in locating their new enterprise.

▲ **Figure 2:** The current HQ of Dipsticks in Allendale, Northumberland (for more information see www.dipsticksresearch.com).

Dipsticks got its moment of fame when it featured in a Newsnight presentation with Jeremy Paxman about change in rural England. Its success has led to a relocation to the local market town of Hexham, still pretty rural if not quite so lost in the mists of Northumberland as Allendale!

Farm diversification

Diversification is the broadening of an enterprise beyond its core function. In a rural context, it includes the many farmers who seek to supplement their income by developing other enterprises.

There are various schemes available for farmers to diversify – and thus protect or increase their income. Although farming is no longer the main source of employment, even in the most rural of areas of the UK, the multiplier effects of a renaissance in farming are significant, as is the enrichment of the local environment. In Northern Ireland, for example, the Department of Agriculture and Rural Development suggests a whole range of options, under five key headings:

- Specialist crops and livestock. The stress here is to develop a product that has a distinctive niche market, usually at the top end of the price range, e.g. dairy goats, worm breeding, biomass, game birds, dairy sheep.
- Tourism and leisure. Farmhouses are large by modern standards and, because of changes in farming practices in recent years, farms often have redundant outbuildings – which could be converted into tourist accommodation (B&B, self-catering), riding centres or 'put and take' fisheries.
- Adding value to farm produce, e.g. farmhouse cheese, farm shops.
- Manufacturing and crafts, e.g. cake decorating.
- Services, e.g. boarding kennels, horse livery and equine sports.

Case study: The Eden Project

The Eden Project, which opened in 2001, is situated close to St Austell in Cornwall, in a rural and relatively poor area. It had cost £80 m to build and subsequent building work has raised the total capital investment to over £120 m, made up of £51 m of Millennium Commission funds, £39 m of public funds, £20 m of bank loans and £13 m from revenues.

▲ **Figure 3:** The Eden Project.

It is hidden inside a 60-metre deep, 15-hectare former china clay pit, which is surrounded by a dramatic horticultural landscape. Since its opening it has welcomed 5 million visitors, vastly exceeding all expectations.

The sheer scale of Eden as an ongoing environmental project and tourist attraction has naturally made an impact on the local community. In an area with high unemployment, it has been largely welcomed, offering thousands of jobs directly – and indirectly, through the multiplier effect. There has, however, been some anger locally over certain issues. The admission prices, for example, are considered too high in an area which is so poor. Another complaint is the traffic congestion in the area, due to the sheer number of visitors. Although Eden attempts to draw at least 20% of its visitors from transport other than cars – and it is possible to arrive by train and then bus, or by bicycle – there is still a massive increase in traffic levels, in a county with no motorways and very few dual carriageways.

As a 'project' as well as tourist attraction, Eden is a long-term venture. The idea behind Eden is that it will be here for ever. The domes are maintenance-free for at least 25 years, time enough for the ecosystems to mature into climax vegetation. Plants are bred in the Eden nursery, and an endangered plants breeding programme is also in place. Eden runs an educational programme aimed at schools and the general public. Training programmes are also run for local businesses. Eden plans to develop and evolve, so that, as they say in their literature, 'it will be bigger and better – mature but always fun'.

- Eden now directly employs around 400 people, year-round.
- 90% of employees live within a 30 km radius and 95% are from Cornwall.
- Eden's wage bill is more than £4 m a year, the vast majority of which is spent locally.
- Eden's strong 'buy local' policy means it spends 61% (nearly £5 m) of its purchasing budget in Cornwall, and 75% of the budget in the South West.
- 81% (£1.5 m) of the catering budget is spent with Cornish food and drink producers.
- 61% (£1.1 m) of the retail budget is spent buying Cornish retail goods.
- 55% (£2.2 m) of the general goods budget (ranging from paper clips to fire extinguishers) is spent with Cornish suppliers.
- 47 of Eden's top 60 suppliers who responded to a survey said they had taken on a total of 23 staff as a direct result of their contracts with Eden, which had boosted their turnover by £2.7 m.
- Visitor spend at Eden during the period was £16.3 m, made up of £7.8 m for admission fees and Friends' subscriptions; £4.4 m was spent on buying goods and £4.1 m was spent on buying refreshments.
- Although visitor numbers have fallen from their peak in 2002, they still comfortably exceed the planned 750,000 per year estimates.
- One of the biggest impacts is the extension of the tourist season for the whole region because what used to be 'out-of-season' visitors to the project also visit other local attractions.
- In total it is estimated that the project brings 5,500 jobs to the region, £177 m extra retail turnover and £81 m extra income.

▶ **Figure 4:** The location of the Eden Project and other Cornish attractions.

1. Land's End Family Adventure Park
2. The Minack Open Air Theatre
3. Geevor Tin Mine
4. St Michael's Mount
5. Paradise Park Wildlife Sanctuary
6. Trevarno Estate Gardens
7. Flambards Theme Park and Village
8. Goonhilly Earth Station Visitor Centre
9. Trebah Gardens
10. National Seal Sanctuary
11. Craft Trail
12. Pendennis Castle
13. The National Maritime Museum
14. Holywell Bay
15. Lappa Valley Steam Railway
16. Springfields Fun Park and Pony Centre
17. Dairyland Farm World
18. Shires Family Adventure Park
19. Trewithen
20. The Lost Gardens of Heligan
21. Charlestown Shipwreck & Heritage Centre
22. The Eden Project
23. Lanhydrock House
24. Bodmin & Wenford Railway
25. Tintagel Castle
26. Jamaica Inn
27. Killarney Springs

Case study: Kielder District heating system

► **Figure 5:** A woodchip burner in Kielder.

The remote forestry village of Kielder (population about 200) in Northumberland has set up a shared wood-fuelled heat network to heat private houses and communal buildings, including the youth hostel and visitor centre at Kielder Castle. Locally grown wood from Sitka spruce is chipped and stored by Forest Enterprise at a fuel store in the village, which is filled up about three to four times a year. The woodchip is fed into a boiler generating hot water which is piped to surrounding buildings, where 'heat exchanges' transfer the energy into domestic central heating and hot water systems. The local community company, Kielder Community Enterprise Ltd, then charges the householders. The woodchip fuel supply ensures that the local forestry jobs are secure and it contributes to the Kielder Regeneration Initiative, helping to ensure the future viability of the village. The scheme is one of the first of its kind in the UK and is particularly innovative in terms of using a local resource, adopting new technology and operating at a community level.

Rural enterprise schemes

Rural enterprise schemes involve the establishment of new and often innovative activities in rural areas. Very many of these schemes make claims as to their 'sustainability'. It is a fair criticism that the concept of sustainability has been bent in so many directions and used in so many ways as to become increasingly hard to assess. For example, in deeply rural Nevada mining companies use 'heap leaching' techniques to extract gold. Heap leaching involves the extraction of very large quantities of rock, which are crushed and then piled up onto enormous plastic sheets before being drizzled with a solution of toxic sodium cyanide that dissolves the gold as it seeps through the mountain of crushed rock. Heap leach mining is very popular with mining companies but it leaves a considerable environmental problem with open pits up to 500 metres deep and often 2 km wide. These are big because it takes so much rock to yield a few tonnes of gold. On average it takes 3 million tonnes of rock to yield 1 tonne of gold, each tonne yielding just 3. And yet despite the apparent environmental destruction the companies involved are keen to point out to a sometimes concerned public that they are committed to 'sustainable development'. One of the world's largest mining companies who are, amongst other enterprises, involved in heap leach mining in Nevada and many other locations define sustainable development in the following way:

> 'Our approach to sustainable development is embedded through all levels of our organisation from our Chief Executive and Chairman through to the day to day operations. We try to minimise the adverse effects of our activities and improve every aspect our performance. In addition, wherever we operate, we hold the health and safety of our employees and the environment to be a core value.
>
> We work as closely as possible with our host countries and communities, respecting their laws and customs and ensuring a fair share of benefits and opportunities.'

http://www.riotinto.com/ourapproach/sustainabledevelopment.asp

Such definitions do not match up especially well with the definitions of sustainable development that are in common circulation outside the world of corporate capitalism, the best known of which owes its origin to the Brundtland commission that reported back to the United Nations in 1987.

This famous definition is seldom quoted in full as the exhortation that 'the essential needs of the world's poor' should be accorded 'overriding priority' is a difficult challenge to meet.

'Sustainable development is development that meets the needs of the present without compromising the ability of future generations to meet their own needs. It contains within it two key concepts:

- the concept of 'needs', in particular the essential needs of the world's poor, to which overriding priority should be given; and
- the idea of limitations imposed by the state of technology and social organization on the environment's ability to meet present and future needs.'

In the context of rural enterprise schemes, whether they be gold mining in Nevada or less controversial projects, almost all are planned and 'sold' with sustainability as part of the message. You should be aware that this 'message' may need very careful analysis.

Measuring success

In order to measure the success (or failure) of a rural regeneration programme, it is important to identify those things that can be measured (using available statistics) and those that can be judged qualitatively (through photographs and oral histories).

▼ **Figure 6:** Lincolnshire and the other East Midlands counties.

There are six categories that can be measured:

- Skills and economic activity
- Capital, land and property
- Business
- Access to services
- Infrastructure
- Rural communities.

The data below is taken from an evaluation of Lincolnshire's recent history (www.lincse.org.uk/documents/Hidden%20Crisis-%20A%20Rural%20Strategy%20for%20Lincolnshire.doc). Lincolnshire is one of the most rural counties in England, and it has struggled to attract inward investment.

Figure 7 shows that average incomes in Lincolnshire are low compared with neighbouring counties.

	Self-employed				Employed				All taxpayers		
	Number		£000		Number		£000		Number	£000	
	000	%	Mean	Med	000	%	Mean	Med	000	Mean	Med
Northamptonshire	36	10.8	21.0	14.1	262	78.9	21.0	16.5	332	22.0	16.5
Leicestershire	38	12.3	19.0	12.4	241	77.7	20.2	16.0	310	21.5	16.2
Derbyshire	39	10.2	16.5	11.0	291	76.4	19.1	15.4	381	19.8	15.1
Nottinghamshire	39	10.3	17.5	10.9	283	74.9	18.8	15.4	378	19.6	15.0
Lincolnshire	41	12.3	18.4	11.9	247	74.4	17.8	15.0	332	18.9	14.9
East Midlands total	*222*	*10.6*	*18.2*	*11.8*	*1610*	*77.0*	*18.9*	*15.3*	*2090*	*19.8*	*15.2*
UK	3190	11.0	20.2	11.9	22000	76.1	20.5	15.9	28900	21.6	15.8
Notes: Med = Median. Some taxpayers are neither employed nor self-employed Source: Inland Revenue website, statistics section, Table 3.13.											

▲ Figure 7: East Midlands counties ranked by mean income of all taxpayers.

Figure 8 shows that no industries are doing well by comparison with neighbouring counties.

		Size of industry in Lincolnshire (2000)		
		Small	Average	Large
Growth rate of industry in Lincolnshire (1995–2000)	Slow	• Financial intermediation • Real estate, renting & business activities	• Transport, storage & communication • Other services	• Agriculture • Construction • Hotels & restaurants • Public admin.
	Average	• Mining & quarrying • Manufacturing	• Electricity, gas & water • Education	• Wholesale & retail • Health and social work
	Fast	None	None	None

▲ **Figure 8:** Size and growth rates of Lincolnshire industries compared with the regional average.

Figure 9 shows that qualification levels are low compared to the region and to England as a whole.

	England	East Midlands	Lincolnshire
No qualifications	28.9	31.6	32.8
Level 1	16.6	17.7	18.5
Level 2	19.4	18.8	20.0
Level 3	8.3	7.8	6.9
Level 4/5	19.9	16.6	14.2
Other qualifications/level unknown	6.9	7.4	7.7
All people	*100.0*	*100.0*	*100.0*

▲ **Figure 9:** Qualifications held by adults (%), Census 2001.

Access to services is difficult in Lincolnshire, as is shown by the situation in East Lindsey, the district which makes up about a third of the county, including nearly all the coast:

• East Lindsey has the highest percentage of people of retirement age or over and is in the top five districts in the country.
• It has the highest number of people with limiting long-term illnesses in the county, with 12% claiming sickness or disability-related benefits.
• Access to health issues was identified as being a problem for communities along the coastal strip in the Accessibility Planning Pilot Project, completed in spring 2004.
• A high proportion of the population have either no or very low levels of qualifications, with over a third having no recognised qualifications.
• East Lindsey has one of the highest proportions of the populations with poor basic numeracy and literacy skills.
• A high percentage of people perceive courses as being difficult to access.
• There are comparatively high levels of unemployment and long-term unemployment.
• Many jobs are seasonal and, as such, mask unemployment statistics.

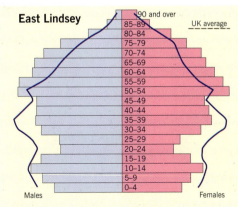
▲ **Figure 10:** The population pyramid for East Lindsey.

- Employers in the area have reported a high number of hard-to-fill vacancies due to skills shortages, yet East Lindsey is one of the areas least likely to provide training plans.
- The Mablethorpe Job Centre is scheduled for closure.   Source: Lincolnshire Development

East Lindsey's population is old and ageing. The population pyramid (Figure 10) reveals a very different structure from that of the country as a whole.

Taking it further

Your own local research should look at a wide range of secondary data as well as attempting to evaluate success through primary sources, such as oral histories and questionnaires.

Fieldwork

Aim:

To establish the success (or failure) or rural regeneration programmes.

Note: It would be sensible if this work were based in the same area as that carried out in Chapters 27 and 28, to assess need and to examine the details of these rebranding exercises.

1. Photographic evidence of before and after rebranding gathered directly and from the internet and other secondary sources.
2. Oral histories to establish how areas have changes over time and whether those changes are well regarded by local residents.
3. Questionnaires of visitors and residents to assess the strength and weaknesses of rebranding projects.
4. Data from www.imd.communities.gov.uk/ for both 2004 and 2007 (and beyond) to assess any changes in levels of rural deprivation caused by rural regeneration programmes.
5. Data about population changes in the local area to assess the impact of rural regeneration on the age structure of that population.

Risk assessment

This is a low-risk exercise, but you need to take special care when conducting interviews and taking photographs. Residents may not take kindly to too much discussion about 'deprivation' or the success or failure of regeneration projects, so keep to the point of the exercise.

Health and safety

Make sure that all fieldwork is conducted with at least one other person and make sure that a responsible adult knows where you are at all times. Take care when crossing roads.

Conclusion

You may very well find that the success or failure of the project(s) is hard to determine because you have a very wide variety of responses. All such enterprises can provoke hostility as well as support.

Evaluation

This work could be extended by looking at comparable regions with similar profiles in terms of population characteristics to see whether they have a different record of success.

Summary

Having studied this chapter you are now in a position make judgements about the success or failure of rural rebranding schemes. You can answer examination questions about the methods used to evaluate these schemes and offer examples of projects that have been more or less successful. You will be able to discuss these ideas and concepts and provide located examples of them:

- The variable success of rural rebranding schemes.
  - The various methods used to achieve that success.
  - How to evaluate the success of rural regeneration schemes.

MCQ

To try an exam question using what you have learned in this chapter, turn to page 280.

CHAPTER 30 How successful have urban areas been in rebranding themselves?

Key terms

Brownfield development
Cultural regeneration
Flagship schemes
Greenfield development
Top-down and bottom-up
  projects

Learning objectives

After studying this chapter, you will be able to discuss these ideas and concepts and provide located examples of them:
- The way to assess success or failure of urban regeneration programmes.
- The history of successes and failures in urban regeneration and rebranding schemes.
- The value of using sport to stimulate urban regeneration.

How to measure success

The success or failure of regeneration schemes is not at all easy to evaluate. At one level, key social indicators might show success. Figure 2 lists ten social and economic variables that could be assessed and measured in any attempt to identify successful cities.

▲ **Figure 1:** The National Centre for Popular Music in Sheffield. This 'flagship' rebranding project opened in March 1999 and closed in July 2000.

271

Factor	Always a sign of success?	How measured?
1. A growing population	Generally, growth is a 'good' thing but some cities can grow simply because in-migration from rural areas is rapid.	Numbers from census data, but be careful to look closely. The Super Output Area (SOA) data might reveal that some areas are growing as they 'gentrify', whilst others continue to decline. Look at the structure of the population too.
2. More jobs and better jobs	The key here is 'better' jobs. Rising employment in the city is the key and not rising employment in general with few 'city' jobs being created.	Data on employment categories. Look out for jobs in finance and sectors related to quaternary employment and 'knowledge-based' jobs.
3. A more educated population	There is a strong correlation between successful cities and high levels of educational attainment. The presence of universities is helpful here.	School scores can be measured using the league tables in the UK, and the educational levels of the population are available in the SOA database.
4. Rising income levels and falling levels of deprivation	Yes, but beware of the averages offered by some databases. If the gap between rich and poor is widening then an average rise might disguise this gap.	Per capita income figures at a local level and data about multiple deprivation is available for most countries.
5. Improving retail figures	Declining Central Business Districts (CBDs) lose their retail functions and the negative multiplier impacts, especially as flagship stores close.	Shop occupancy rates and retail turnover figures may be available. Photographic evidence and old Goad maps can be investigated to measure changes in a retail structure.
6. Improving property values	Property values will rise when demand for property rises.	Comparative studies can use sites such as http://www.nethouseprices.com/ and http://www.upmystreet.com/
7. A healthier population	Poorer societies are less healthy. Higher rates of smoking, alcoholism and drug-related illnesses are frequently found in 'failing' cities'.	Health data can be derived from the multiple deprivation database on http://www.communities.gov.uk/communities/neighbourhoodrenewal/deprivation/deprivation07/ Go to the interactive mapping link, find your area and then click on the 'health domain'.
8. A low crime rate	There is quite a strong correlation between crime rates and poverty, but this does not work across national boundaries.	Data is often hard to find, but look at newspaper reports of changes in both the frequency and pattern of crime in an urban area. This data can also be found on the multiple deprivation database (as above, but click on the 'crime domain').
9. A good cultural and sporting environment	The venues of top cultural 'acts' – from symphony orchestras to rock bands – often signifies 'success'. So too do sports teams. Declining cities often struggle to compete at the very top level. (There are exceptions, of course, such as Liverpool FC in the 1980s when the city was in rapid decline.)	By studying league tables and concert venues for leading artists. Trace the historical record of a football club from its 'glory' days to today. Compare the First Division in 1970 with the Premier League today, and map them.
10. Attractive and successful neighbourhoods	Sometimes it is easier to judge success in cities just by looking at them and photographing them. Cities in decline have lower incomes, both in terms of average incomes and city taxes. Lower tax income means less money available.	Photographic evidence and archive material can be compared.

▲ **Figure 2:** Measuring success.

Case study: Measuring success in Detroit

Detroit has had several attempts to regenerate and has undertaken several rebranding exercises. As with all large cities, change has been more or less continuous over its entire history, but self-conscious planning and rebranding is a much more recent phenomenon. The timeline for Detroit (see the table below) does not always make happy reading. The city plans are available on: /www.ci.detroit.mi.us/plandevl/advplanning/masterplan.htm.

Key terms

Flagship schemes are often the main schemes that are supposed to lead to further inward investment. They may take the form of a city centre redevelopment, a sports stadium or a major cultural initiative.

Period	Scheme	Success?
1950s	The 'Master Plan' for Detroit developed broad strips of industrial and commercial land use, surrounded by residential areas.	Growth did take place in a few limited areas, but general decline was evident as factories closed and the population fell.
1960s	Slum-clearance projects in largely black working-class areas of the city.	The affected communities were seldom involved in the process – and were often alienated by it. Major urban riots did not help the outsiders' view of the city. However, the city's music scene took off with the development of 'Motown'.
1970s	Larger projects were started, such as the 'model' projects in Layfayette, Coba Hall and the Convention Center.	These projects have lasted but they did not address Detroit's fundamental problem, and the 'white flight' to the suburbs accelerated.
1980s	The Renaissance Center (RenCen) – a flagship scheme – had been started in the previous decade but became the focus of a CBD redevelopment that tried to turn 'Motown' into a financial and business centre. An urban transport system – the People Mover – was built in 1987.	The project lost money and the RenCen was not fully occupied. The city continued to lose jobs and population. The People Mover is hardly used, and with most jobs now being outside the city, commuting is out of the city rather than in.
1990s	A new mayor set the tone by suggesting that self-initiatives were more important. General Motors have moved their HQ into the RenCen and major plans were launched for sports complexes and casinos in the city centre.	There were some signs of a deceleration in the decline, but no obvious evidence of regeneration.
2000s	Renewed efforts to rebrand and a switch of emphasis to leisure and tourism, including the Super Bowl of 2006 and super-casinos.	Higher international profile and development of a 'cool' image, but the substantial changes are yet to show up in the database of the city.

One person's view of the real problem

'I found it possible, when walking around most parts of Detroit's downtown, to imagine I was the only white person in the city. Occasionally another white person would pass by in a car, but I rarely encountered them on the street. Most people I passed viewed me with a curious glance and were invariably friendly and helpful when I talked to them. I have never experienced a city as segregated as this. One evening I went to see a Detroit Tigers baseball game at their new stadium Comerica Park. Built over several blocks of land in the heart of downtown, this huge stadium can seat over 60,000 people. On the night I went, there were more like 10,000 – the Tigers are struggling at the moment, plus it was only a friendly match. However I was immediately struck by the fact that the crowd was almost exclusively white. On game nights the numerous vacant lots in this portion of the downtown are flooded with the cars of whites from the suburbs, who go straight to the stadium, and leave directly afterwards.

The next evening I went down to Hart Plaza on the riverfront to join the large crowds enjoying the Annual Caribbean festival. Once again I was struck by the racial composition of the crowd – this time overwhelmingly black. I enjoyed the music, the stalls and the evening sunshine, before walking back to the hotel. I could count the number of white people I saw during the evening (excluding police) on one hand.'

Surely this is the city's crucial crisis, not the blocks of derelict skyscrapers.

Case study: Measuring success in Detroit *(continued)*

The history of Detroit suggests that some urban problems are not immediately soluble. The reasons are not hard to find:

• Globalisation has led to a fierce competition for inward investment between cities.

• That competition is international. Every dollar, yen or euro invested, for example in Detroit, is not invested in competitor cities.

• The demand for these funds outstrips their supply, so some places will not attract sufficient funds to do much more than slow down decline and improve lives in some areas.

• Globalisation has also led to a widening gap between rich and poor, making cities more polarised, with greater problems of urban deprivation.

• The better-off middle classes have the financial power to make the choice to leave cities and establish their own spaces outside the city boundaries.

▲ **Figure 3:** The MGM Grand Casino, which opened in downtown Detroit in October 2007. The new complex features almost a hectare of gambling space and a 17-storey luxury hotel with 400 rooms.

• Cities are thus also in competition with their own suburbs. Whilst Detroit has declined, the rural–urban fringe has prospered. Similar stories can be told of many old industrial cities.

• Thus the 'new' inner city facilities might be used by the more affluent suburban classes (as with the Detroit Tigers and the MGM Grand), but leakage means that the profits do not stay in the city.

Successful English cities

Urban renaissance needs to spread out beyond our city centres. Most of our city-centre population growth consists of young and single people. To draw families back to cities, we need to create beautiful and family-friendly suburbs too. Architects and planners have often neglected, or even derided, suburbs. They may lack the urban vitality and mix that many of us enjoy, but they provide a quieter, greener environment for families and can enhance the mix of housing that a city can offer. The best suburbs – linked to the city by good public transport – already offer a model for a different style of environmentally sustainable urban living. We need to bring all of them up to this standard, through intensification and new infrastructure.

(Richard Rogers, 'How to build intelligent suburbs', Guardian, 2 December 2006)

Since 1997 the dominant policy regarding English cities has been based on the views of Lord Rogers of Riverside, an architect (whose signature buildings include the Pompidou Centre in Paris and the Lloyds Building in London). Rogers led an Urban Task Force for the government which presented its findings in 1999. The report is very much the work of an architect, with a heavy emphasis on the built environment. The panel did not include any economists, nor do any appear to have been consulted. The report has a strong emphasis on the urban core, the need for density and the use of brownfield sites. It also argues that local people should be more heavily involved in creating a vision for their area.

In the first 75 years of the twentieth century, as urban planning developed, the dominant ideology of the discipline was to segregate urban functions into their own spaces. The New Towns built after the Second World War modelled in their turn on the earlier Garden Cities marked the 'high-water mark' of this paradigm. Retail and office functions were concentrated in the central area, an industrial zone created and discrete residential 'neighbourhoods' laid out around the centre; these residential neighbourhoods had very few services beyond a few low order shops and primary schools and were often divided one from another by quite wide areas of functionless open-space. The social impacts were neither predicted nor always recognised quickly but the CBDs became empty in the evenings and provided ideal sites for what subsequently became dubbed as anti-social behaviour. The neighbourhoods were largely characterless and provided very few foci in which local communities could come together and develop a sense of belonging, let alone loyalty to 'place'. Vocal critics such as the Canadian writer Jane Jacobs proved to be influential as a 'paradigm shift' took place in urban planning. Residents in local communities struggled to be heard when presenting their own critique of the planners and their grand schemes of social engineering which seemed to marginalise the poorest and neediest in society. Thus mixed usage, synergy, holistic communities and sustainable places replaced neighbourhood, zonation and segregation in the planners 'handbook'; at least on this side of the Atlantic.

Successful cities attract investment and display a range of economic and social characteristics that are positive. They need to demonstrate that not only have the key players a contemporary understanding of the needs of the community they serve but also the ability to listen to that community. The shift from the grand 'top-down' schemes of the mid twentieth century to the more locally rooted 'bottom-up' schemes can sometimes be seen as mere wordplay but there is, in almost all cases, more recognition today that local communities must be listened to.

Although cities are in competition they also cooperate, at least in the sharing of data, in their pursuit of 'success'. Thus 'benchmarking exercises' are carried out to help evaluate the way in which to measure success (www.compete-eu.org/benchmarking/benchmarking_databycity.asp).

The benchmarking data covers a number of themes thought to be significant measures of success:

- Connectivity
- Employment and unemployment
- Employment by sector
- Key employment sectors
- Gross value added
- Life expectancy
- Population
- Qualifications.

The English cities that have performed well are generally – although not exclusively – in the south of the country. This reflects the growth in the southern economy, stimulated by London's role as a global city.

Other partial success stories – in terms of value added – amongst cities that have invested heavily in urban rebranding include Manchester, Bristol and Newcastle. The role of developing 'cultural services' in the programme for regeneration is well known, but its success is not totally clear. At least 56 places in England now have 'cultural quarters' as part of their regeneration effort. This began with Sheffield in the 1990s and has spread since. There is enormous variety in these efforts and not all have been notably successful.

Examiners' tip

It is important to be aware of how average figures for cities can disguise local variations. Whilst the history of a city as a whole might look positive, there may be some of its SOAs that are multiply deprived – and perhaps getting worse.

Examiners' tip

Remember that success is a relative idea. We measure our city's success in terms of how other cities are performing. If they are performing even more badly, then perhaps our problems are not as severe as we thought. And vice versa.

In Sheffield, for example, the National Centre for Popular Music was planned to cost £6 m and attract 600,000 visitors a year, with a considerable multiplier impact on a city not generally regarded as an 'event' place. In fact the building cost £15 m and visitor numbers totalled 65,000 in the first 6 months – well below the predicted 300,000. It then became a night-club and was later sold to Sheffield Hallam university for a mere £1.5 m. Creditors lost 90% of what they had invested and, in the view of one commentator, the centre was 'an unmitigated disaster'. In rebranding, failures of this type do a good deal of damage to the reputation of a city. Two lessons stand out: that predictions are often unreasonably optimistic, and that optimism is occasionally deliberate in order to raise funds. The second risk is particularly high when planners who spend money do not have to bear the costs of failure.

In spite of this, some success has been achieved in Sheffield, in addressing the major social issue that faced this deindustrialising steel city. Its unemployment problems were well publicised in the 1997 film, *The Full Monty*, but since those days Sheffield's unemployment has fallen (although it is still above the UK average), whilst the record on income, employment and city-based work have improved only gradually.

▲ **Figure 4:** Canary Wharf, with buildings rising to 50 storeys.

Case study: Canary Wharf in London – a success story?

In the nineteenth century, Canary Wharf was one of the wharves in the West India Docks, at the heart of London's vast network of docks. It was the place in which goods from the Canary Islands were unloaded and then distributed to the many industries that grew around the docks. 'Docklands' thrived until the 1960s, despite being badly damaged during the Second World War, but then the move towards containerisation (which involved larger ships which could not come up river as far as London) meant that all the old docks became progressively redundant, and the last one closed in 1980. This had a significant multiplier effect on the surrounding area and, in total, around 150,000 jobs were lost in Docklands between 1967 and 1977.

Redevelopment began in 1981, with the formation of the London Docklands Development Corporation and the Docklands Enterprise Zone, one of the first public–private partnerships of the modern era. The initial aim was to attract light industry to the area, in the manner that light industry had moved to West London areas such as Park Royal, earlier in the century. However, the City of London's deregulatory 'Big Bang' in 1986 led to a rapid growth in demand for large open-plan offices that were hard to find in the cramped City of London. Following the example of New York (where Citibank had made a successful move from Wall Street to Manhattan's midtown), Credit Suisse, First Boston and Morgan Stanley agreed to take space in a new tower block in Canary Wharf. Foreign banks, insurance companies and related high-end tertiary and quaternary employers were all competing for space as London expanded its role as a 'global' city – and the new development at Canary Wharf flourished. But construction was not straightforward, and there was much local opposition. Many residents thought that they would not benefit from such a development, and the construction company, Olympia & York, went bankrupt in 1992 as part of the general property recession of the early 1990s.

Ultimately, however, few can doubt that Canary Wharf – and Docklands as a whole – has been anything other than a success. Today the area has 33 office blocks, with 90,000 people working in over 1.3 million m² of office space, generating its own very significant multiplier effect. It has allowed the massive expansion of London as a financial centre, raising average wages and producing significant amounts of tax revenue for the government.

Two lessons stand out:

- First, it will always be easier to revitalise an area that adjoins a prosperous place with considerable potential for expansion.
- Second, although many people from the local area are now employed in the financial sector, it would be wrong to claim that prospects for those who lost their jobs in the docks have been transformed.

Case study: Failure in Newcastle?

The Scotswood and Benwell area of Newcastle, known as the 'West End', has seen many attempts at regeneration since the Second World War. Some of its low-quality Victorian housing was cleared and replaced by council estates in the 1960s and 1970s. But as Newcastle deindustrialised, a combination of very low skill levels, few local jobs, low incomes and poor public transport meant that there was a sense in which the West End became a world of its own. The 2001 census showed that 13,759 people live in Scotswood and Benwell – 5% of the city's population; 45% of this population has no qualifications, 61% of households have no access to a car and unemployment is nearly 70% higher than the Newcastle average. There are approximately 6,900 properties in the Scotswood and Benwell area, of which

▲ **Figure 5:** Housing development in Benwell.

between 6,000 are 6,500 are occupied. The rest are vacant – or awaiting demolition under previously agreed clearance programmes.

The West End's problems are not the result of neglect by the authorities. In 2003, when the government announced £73 m for the 'Newcastle and Gateshead Housing Market Renewal Pathfinder', whose prime focus is the West End, Professor Fred Robinson wrote: 'So, here we go again. Another new regeneration programme is to be targeted on the West End of Newcastle'.

The long line of policy initiatives included Urban Aid in the 1960s, Estate Action and Inner City Partnerships in the 1970s, City Challenge and Enterprise Zones in the 1980s, the Single Regeneration Budget in the 1990s, and New Deal for Communities and the Housing Market Renewal Pathfinder funding in the 2000s. The New Deal for Communities alone is expected to spend £55 m.

Many of those people who could leave, have left – the population has fallen by a third in 2 years. In the words of one West End resident: 'There's been no regeneration, just lots of demolition and people moving out'. There are frequent complaints that although local residents have been 'consulted', they have ultimately been ignored, as top-down policies seek to clear away old housing – and probably the old residents – and 'gentrify' areas. This leads to a new incoming class of residents to replace the older residents, who simply have to go elsewhere.

In 2007 the Council launched its newest approach to regenerating the West End. This involved 'growing' the prosperity of the city centre westward, with the launch of the Discovery Quarter, the UK's first Housing Expo and an Academy.

The council has also announced plans (with partners One NorthEast and Newcastle University) for a world-beating Science City development, on the former Scottish & Newcastle Brewery site, with pioneering research links to Newcastle General Hospital.

As the data from www.imd.communities.gov.uk/InformationDisplay.aspx show (see Figure 6), after many years of urban regeneration policies, Benwell and other areas of Newcastle's West End are still amongst the most deprived areas in the country, albeit with a very uneven pattern of deprivation.

It is not clear whether all this urban policy in the area has been a failure or merely insufficient, but no one could claim it as a success.

Key terms

Top-down approaches to regeneration involve planners applying schemes to areas of the city with limited consultation in the affected areas. By contrast, bottom-up approaches grow out of the publicly expressed needs of local communities.

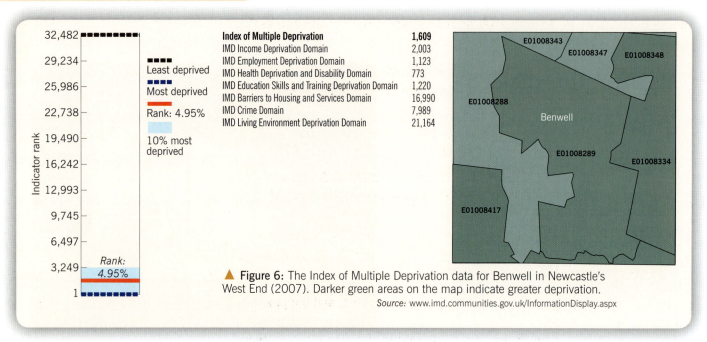

Index of Multiple Deprivation	1,609
IMD Income Deprivation Domain	2,003
IMD Employment Deprivation Domain	1,123
IMD Health Deprivation and Disability Domain	773
IMD Education Skills and Training Deprivation Domain	1,220
IMD Barriers to Housing and Services Domain	16,990
IMD Crime Domain	7,989
IMD Living Environment Deprivation Domain	21,164

▲ **Figure 6:** The Index of Multiple Deprivation data for Benwell in Newcastle's West End (2007). Darker green areas on the map indicate greater deprivation.

Source: www.imd.communities.gov.uk/InformationDisplay.aspx

Examiners' tip

Remember that there are always winners and losers from urban regeneration and rebranding schemes, even the 'unsuccessful' ones.

The costs of the Olympics

London's Olympic bid has been sold to the nation on the basis that the Games will add hugely to the regeneration of a depressed region of East London and that the long-term benefits will outweigh the costs. Opponents argue that this does not allow for the possibility that the huge spend involved might have been better spent on other regenerative projects. They also claim that the recent history of the Games (see table) is not altogether encouraging.

Date	Location	Costs and benefits
2012	London	Cost so far (March 2008) about $18bn The initial estimate, back in 2002, was £2bn (about $4bn).
2008	Beijing	Cost $35bn (March 2008) – TV rights $1.7bn Very expensive and eventual profitability is doubtful.
2004	Athens	Cost $7bn – TV rights $1.5bn Loss-making. Crumbling venues lying empty, all promises of regeneration just a distant memory. The stadium has only opened once since the Games – on the first anniversary, to admit visitors to look around.
2000	Sydney	Cost $2.25bn – TV rights $1.3bn Needed a government loan and profitability was marginal. Follow-up tourist boost was spoilt by 9/11, and overall profitability is debatable.
1996	Atlanta	Cost $991m – TV rights $898m The 'privatised' Olympics that were profitable for a few but did the city little good – and generated very little follow-on income.
1992	Barcelona	Cost $9.1bn – TV rights $636m City only got $3bn revenue from $10bn investment, but tourist numbers almost doubled long-term, thanks to increased prestige. Olympic zone, however, now tatty.
1988	Seoul	Cost: $3.1bn – TV rights $400m Verdict: Modest ($30m) operating profit, but South Korea's economy grew by 12% in games year. Unparalleled political and economic showcase.
1984	Los Angeles	Cost $483m – TV rights $287m Verdict: The first profitable Olympics since 1932, LA's $1.4bn profit made it the template for the commercialisation of the Games. They were run along strictly business lines – even the stadium was recycled from 1932.

▲ **Figure 7:** A financial history of the Olympics.

In a story published in November 2002, before the London bid was successful, the following claim was made:

> The British Government have been told they would not lose money by hosting the 2012 Olympics in London – and could even make a small profit.
>
> Consultants Ove Arup are expected to tell Parliament in a report published on Friday that hosting the Games would cost under £2bn.
>
> That prompted the British Olympic Association (BOA) to claim that 'guaranteed incomes and benefits' would outstrip the £2bn London would have to shell out.

(http://news.bbc.co.uk/sport1/hi/front_page/2381115.stm)

Some have offered the following assessment of how Olympics can be funded to meet the very high costs:

- The Barcelona Model, in which the whole country is taxed, and the proceeds invested in the host city.
- The Athens Model, in which the whole of Europe is taxed, and the proceeds invested in the host city.
- The Montreal Model (1976), in which the host city is taxed, and goes spectacularly bankrupt.

Fieldwork

Aim:
To establish the success (or failure) of an urban regeneration programme.
Note: It would be sensible if this work was based in the area used earlier in this Unit to assess need and to examine the details of a rebranding programme.

1. Photographic evidence of before and after rebranding, gathered directly and from the internet and other secondary sources.
2. Oral histories to establish how areas have changed over time and whether those changes are well regarded by local residents.
3. Questionnaires of visitors and residents to assess the strength and weaknesses of rebranding projects.
4. Data from www.imd.communities.gov.uk for both 2004 and 2007 (and beyond) to assess any changes in levels of urban deprivation caused by regeneration programmes.
5. Data about population changes in the local area to assess the impact of urban regeneration on the age structure of that population.

Risk assessment
This is a low-risk exercise, but you need to take special care when conducting interviews and taking photographs. Residents may not take kindly to too much discussion about 'deprivation' or the success or failure of regeneration projects, so keep to the point of the exercise.

Health and safety
Make sure that all fieldwork is conducted with at least one other person and make sure that a responsible adult knows where you are at all times. Take care when crossing roads.

Conclusion
You may very well find that the success or failure of the project is hard to determine because you have a very wide variety of responses. All such enterprises can provoke hostility as well as support.

Evaluation
This work could be extended by looking at comparable regions with similar profiles in terms of population characteristics to see whether they have a different record of success.

Summary

Having read this chapter you are now able to appreciate how difficult urban regeneration can be and how its success or failure can be measured. The case studies of Detroit, Newcastle and Canary Wharf hold important lessons about urban rebranding, and you will be able to discuss these ideas and concepts and provide located examples of them:

- The way to assess success or failure of urban regeneration programmes.
  - The history of successes and failures in urban regeneration and rebranding schemes.
  - The value of using sport to stimulate urban regeneration.

MCQ

Exam practice

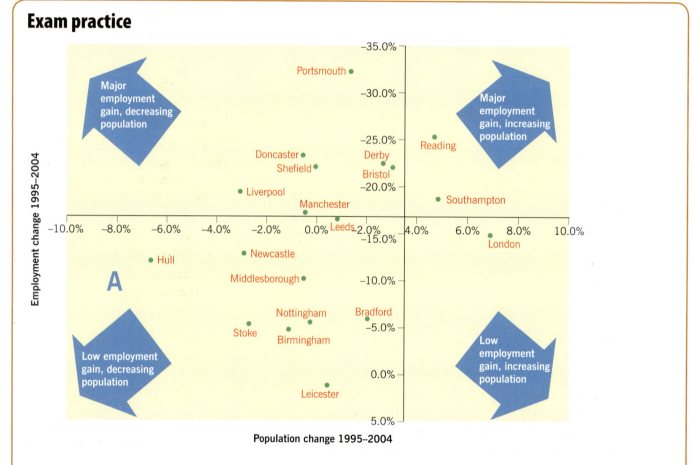

Population change 1995–2004

Study the figure.

(a) Describe and suggest reasons for the distribution of the cities with the worst performing economies as shown in quadrant A. [10]

(b) Using your research experience suggest how the two criteria (decreasing population and low employment gain) used by the Centre for Cities would suggest a need for rebranding. What primary fieldwork would you carry out to provide evidence of a need to rebrand? [15]

(c) With reference to examples of urban areas you have investigated examine some of the rebranding strategies used to attract work, people and visitors. [10]

Exam guidance and advice

The AS Geography assessment consists of two examinations, Unit 1 and Unit 2. Very importantly, the content of the Units is different, as is the style of assessment. This is summarised in the table below.

Unit	% of AS	Exam length	Content	Rubric	Exam format and skills
1 - Global Challenges	60%	1 ½ hours	Wide ranging global study of World at risk (hazards and climate change) and Going global (globalisation and migration)	Section A=65 marks Section B=25 marks	Section A: short, structured resource-based questions. All questions are compulsory. Tests your knowledge and understanding across the whole Unit. Section B: Resource-based extended writing on your choice of question from a choice of four (climate change, hazards, globalisation and migration)
2 - Geographical Investigations	40%	1 hour	Geographical research into the physical environment (either extreme weather or crowded coasts) and the human environment (rebranding places or unequal spaces).	Section A=35 marks (physical environment) Section B=35 marks (human environment)	In both sections, extended writing to show your knowledge and understanding of secondary research, primary fieldwork and GIS, for your two chosen options. Each option will have one compulsory question so you choose one question from Section A and one from Section B.

Unit 1

Think of the Unit 1 exam paper as a letter T (as shown, right). In both Section A and Section B, we are testing your knowledge and understanding of the work you have learnt (Assessment Objective 1 [AO1]) and how you can apply this to new situations, such as a new resource (Assessment Objective 2 [AO2]).

Section A

Important points to note are that:

- The 65 marks for Section A will be split more or less equally across the six questions. Each question will be worth 10 to 12 marks.
- The six questions will be split more or less equally across the 'World at risk' and 'Going global' topics.
- Most questions will focus on a global/international scale.
- The questions will be focused on assessing the range of content from the left-hand column of the specification.

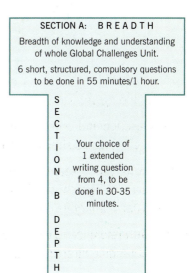

SECTION A: BREADTH

Breadth of knowledge and understanding of whole Global Challenges Unit.

6 short, structured, compulsory questions to be done in 55 minutes/1 hour.

SECTION B DEPTH

Your choice of 1 extended writing question from 4, to be done in 30-35 minutes.

A typical Section A question is shown in the table below.

Question 1, Section A			
1a	1b	1c	1d
1-2 marks	1-2 marks	2-3 marks	4-5 marks
Extracting information from a simple resource (a map, diagram, photo or graph)	A multiple choice question, such as identifying the correct definition of a key term	A follow-up question requiring simple explanation, such as 'suggest two reasons'	A slightly more extended final question asking for broad explanations
Total marks for each Section A question will be in the range of 10 to 12			

Timing in Section A is absolutely vital, as you have about 1 hour to cover 65 marks, therefore you are working to at least a mark per minute.

Section A will be marked by point marking, so as a general rule, if a question is worth 4 marks, you should make four clear points.

Section B

In Section B, you will need to make a choice of attempting one question from a choice of four. The questions will cover four topic areas: hazards, climate change/ global warming, migration and cities, and globalisation

Choice is always difficult when you are working at speed. Think about which topics you are most confident on, and examine the resources that go with the questions carefully.

Each Section B question will consist of two parts. Part (a) of the question is the smaller, worth 10 marks, and this will be linked to a resource (figure). This is likely to be a more complex resource than those you encountered in Section A. The resource, which could be a graph, map, table, etc., will need to be used in your answer to the part (a) question.

The part (b) of the question does not refer to a resource. This part is longer – 15 marks – and is a piece of extended writing. It will need to be completed in 15 to 20 minutes and most students would write about two sides.

Questions will be more open and allow you to discuss the question in more depth. It will be up to you to ensure that your answer is structured (organised and clearly set out), is supported by examples to back up your points and uses correct geographical terminology.

Some part (b) questions will refer to compulsory case studies, such as the Philippines, Arctic, Eastern European Migration in the EU and climate change impacts in Africa. These questions will require detailed case study knowledge and understanding. More open questions, not referring to compulsory case studies, will require shorter examples – perhaps three to four sentences.

It is important to realise that Section B is levels marked. Which level you obtain depends on the quality of your answer. This means the quality of geographical content, but also your Quality of Written Communication (QWC). This is assessed in Section B, but not in Section A. The table on the next page illustrates the differences between levels.

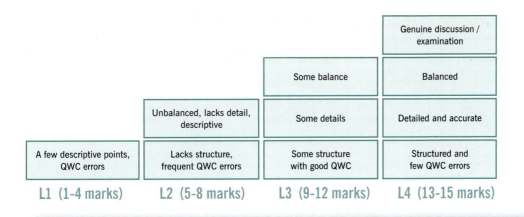

			Genuine discussion / examination
		Some balance	Balanced
	Unbalanced, lacks detail, descriptive	Some details	Detailed and accurate
A few descriptive points, QWC errors	Lacks structure, frequent QWC errors	Some structure with good QWC	Structured and few QWC errors
L1 (1-4 marks)	**L2 (5-8 marks)**	**L3 (9-12 marks)**	**L4 (13-15 marks)**

Case studies

Compulsory

In this specification, there are six compulsory case studies that you will need to study and learn in detail (maps, diagrams, key statistics). The compulsory case studies are:

• Multiple Hazard Hotspots – the Philippines and California
• Global Warming impacts – the Arctic and Africa
• Migration flows – Eastern Europeans to the UK and UK to Southern Europe

Advisable

As well as the compulsory case studies, you will also need smaller case studies and examples to ensure you have sufficient depth to answer the Section B questions. Some suggestions would be:

• Contrasting TNCs
• Contrasting world cities and megacities
• Example of climate adaptation and mitigation strategies.

Taking it further

For a list of the case studies featured in the Student Book, read 'Knowing your case studies' on your Student CD-ROM.

Unit 2

Unit 2 is designed to test your knowledge, understanding and skills linked to your primary fieldwork and your secondary research (books, articles, websites, databases) on your chosen option topics.

Read the specification and identify for your chosen options all of the fieldwork and research tasks you should have carried out. For some, you may not have had a chance to visit first hand (i.e. fieldwork), but, for most, you should have carried out primary data collection.

In the exam you will need to identify the questions that relate to your chosen options (one physical, one human). If, for example, you have studied crowded coasts and rebranding places do not attempt the questions on extreme weather and unequal spaces. In the exam, when a 'red mist' of stress and panic descends some students make bad choices! Do not be tempted by a colourful resource or seemingly 'nice' question on an option you have not studied!

Each of the four questions on the Unit 2 exam paper has a similar structure. Each question has three components and the order of these components may be different in different exam series.

1. Analysing a resource – usually 10 marks

The resource could be a photograph of a re-imaged city centre, map of coastal change, weather chart or census data comparing two locations. GIS maps and other digital images are a possibility, as are a set of fieldwork results.

The question will focus on describing and analysing the resource, with some explanation. This is a data-response question, where you combine information from the resource with your own knowledge and understanding. This type of question will not directly ask you to refer to your own fieldwork and research, but you can discuss it if you want.

2. Describing and explaining your fieldwork and research – usually 15 marks

There will always be a question which asks you directly about the fieldwork and research (note, both primary and secondary data sources) you have carried out. This question could focus on any part of the fieldwork and research investigation process, as shown in the table.

Taking it further

For advice on preparing your fieldwork for exams for Unit 2, read 'Getting your fieldwork and research exam-ready' on your Student CD-ROM.

Before you go	Designing an inquiry into a topic, identifying research sources and designing fieldwork methods
Out and about	Collecting data and researching sources; being aware of the limitations of data and its collection
Working with the results	Analysing and interpreting results; in the exam, you could be given some results to analyse, including results of statistical tests such as Spearman's Rank
What does it mean?	Evaluating results and coming to conclusions based on your research and fieldwork

Mark schemes for these questions could be said to be 'fieldwork and research first'. In other words, you need to focus on your own personal fieldwork and research before going into the exam. The depth and detail you can go into about your own work will be crucial to gaining a good mark. This question carries 15 to 35 marks so it is crucial to get it right.

3. Examining, problems, issues and management options – usually 10 marks

A third question will ask you to focus more on the topic content you were taught in class. This will be a more open question using command words such as 'explain' or 'examine'.

As with the two parts above, the writing style is extended. Some questions will allow you to use your fieldwork and research, but you will not be directly asked to use it. As a general rule, the more you can use you own fieldwork and research examples the more detailed and realistic your answers will tend to be.

You have 1 hour to complete the two questions. Be very careful to spend equal time on the human option question and the physical option question. Each 35-mark question = 30 minutes. Be careful to examine the weighting of the sub-parts of questions: the 15-mark question requires more time to be spent answering it than the 10-mark sub-parts.

QWC is assessed in each part of the Unit 2 exam so make sure you learn key terms and write in a clear, formal style.

INDEX